William C. Guenther
Professor of Statistics
University of Wyoming

Concepts of
Statistical
Inference

McGraw-Hill Book Company
New York   St. Louis
San Francisco   Toronto
London   Sydney

CONCEPTS OF STATISTICAL INFERENCE

Library of Congress Catalog Card Number 64-8276

25093

II

To Lee Ann

Preface

This book was written for a general one-semester (or one-quarter) introductory course in statistics. The primary objective has been to acquaint the student with the ideas and language of statistical inference without unduly slanting the examples and problems toward any particular field of application. Since so many new concepts have to be mastered, a minimum of emphasis has been placed upon computing, algebraic details, and complicated statistical methods.

The main features of the book are as follows:

1 Special emphasis is placed upon selecting the correct model and investigating the reasonableness of the conditions under which the model is derived.
2 A number of tables and graphs are presented; some of them appear for the first time in an elementary textbook. The state of statistical tables has been greatly improved over the past few years, and this book incorporates a number of the advances. Some calculations, such as those yielding power, were formerly very difficult but are now quite simple with the use of new graphs. Consequently, a more sophisticated approach to standard statistical problems can be taken.
3 Numerous worked examples are included which are written out in detail to show the student how to attack similar problems in the Exercises and in his practical application of statistical inference.

4   The Exercise sections contain problems pertaining to a wide variety of applications of statistical inference. Answers to the odd-numbered problems in Chapters 1 to 4 and selected sets of problems in Chapters 5 to 8 are given in the rear of the book, in greater detail than is usual where the problem seems to require this detail.   Those Exercises for which answers are given are marked by a diamond symbol   ◆   in the Exercise sections.

5   To assist the student with the organization and assimilation of Chapters 5 to 8, a summary has been provided at the end of each of these chapters.

No previous statistical experience has been assumed. A working knowledge of high-school algebra should provide sufficient mathematical background.   It is, however, a good idea to precede a course taught from this book with a semester of college mathematics, mainly for the experience and maturity to be gained from it.

In a class meeting three times a week, it may be difficult to cover every section of the eight chapters.   If material has to be omitted, it is recommended that the choice be some combination of the following: Section 6-6, Section 6-7, all or part of Chapter 7, all or part of Chapter 8.   Chapters 7 and 8 are in no way dependent upon one another.

Logically this course can be followed by a number of special-topics or methods courses.   Some of these include analysis of variance, regression and correlation, sampling, time series, nonparametric statistics, quality control, and methods applicable to some special field.

At the University of Wyoming this course has been taught with large lecture sections (preferably handled by an experienced staff member) meeting three times a week and small laboratory or problem sections (taught by graduate students) meeting twice a week. Although this system may not be ideal, it does provide a satisfactory method of handling a great many students, provided the laboratory sections are not too large.

I am indebted to Sir Ronald A. Fisher, F.R.S., Cambridge, and Dr. Frank Yates, F.R.S., Rothamsted, and to Messrs. Oliver and Boyd Ltd., Edinburgh, for permission to reprint parts of Table No. III from their book, "Statistical Tables for Biological, Agricultural, and Medical Research."   Also, I want to acknowledge my appreciation to Prentice-Hall, Inc., for permission to reproduce Section 1-15 and Exercises 1.3, 1.5, 1.9, 1.12, 1.13, 1.14, 1.17, and 1.27 of my book, "Analysis of Variance," 1964, and to the other authors and publishers whose names appear with the tables and graphs of Appendix D.

WILLIAM C. GUENTHER

Contents

Introduction

Many authors have defined statistics as a field of endeavor in which data are collected and analyzed for the purpose of drawing conclusions. The statement, although true, does not give the beginning student much appreciation for the subject. It is, however, very difficult to describe a field as comprehensive as statistics in a single sentence or paragraph.

The above definition as applied to the modern concept of statistics implies a number of things. First, the data that are collected are a sample or part of a much larger body of data (which it may or may not be possible to collect in its entirety) called the population. Second, the purpose of drawing the sample is to make some inference or draw some conclusion about the population. Third, inferences drawn are usually accompanied by statements which indicate the amount of confidence the statistician has in the results. To make such statements requires some knowledge of probability and what we shall call probability models. Fourth, the type of experiment which particularly lends itself to statistical analysis is one which yields different results when repeated under essentially the same conditions. Classic examples of such experiments are coin and dice throwing, but the results produced by subjecting human beings, animals, or other objects to the same environmental conditions yield this type of data.

As we have indicated, probability is a fundamental tool in statistical inference; consequently, our first objective will be to gain some understanding of that subject. With only an elementary knowledge of probability we can construct some highly useful probability models which will be used later to characterize the behavior of statistical experiments.

This is intended to be an introductory course in statistics. It is not expected that the student will be a statistician even if he receives a top grade. Some reasonable objectives for the course are:

1 To introduce students to the language and philosophy of statisticians.
2 To acquaint students with the types of problems that lend themselves to statistical solution.
3 To present enough basic statistical technique that the student can work some standard-type problems.
4 To enable the student to read and understand the summarized results of statistical experiments performed by others. He may never have to perform an experiment on his own, but he might have to read about the work of others in journals.
5 To interest some students in further study of statistics.

CHAPTER ONE

Probability

1-1 INTRODUCTION

Probability has become a very important field of study with many applications reaching outside the realm of statistics. Applied probability problems arise frequently in modern industries. As students of statistics, we are interested in probability primarily because it is essential that we have some understanding of the subject before we proceed to a discussion of statistical inference.

One might consider probability as a measure of likelihood so constructed that it ranges from 0 to 1. If an event is impossible, the weight or measure 0 is assigned to it. On the other hand, an event that is certain to happen is assigned weight 1. In between these extremes, weights are so chosen that the more likely an event, the

3

higher its probability. The weights that are assigned may depend upon prior knowledge of the situation, experimental evidence, or just plain intuition. For example, if a coin is tossed a large number of times, it is reasonable to expect about the same number of heads and tails unless the coin is unbalanced or the tossing procedure is biased. It would seem sensible, therefore, to associate the weight $\frac{1}{2}$ with the head when discussing coin-tossing probabilities. We cannot prove that this is the correct number to use; nevertheless, it seems plausible.

In the coin example it is implied that the figure $\frac{1}{2}$ is associated with long-run behavior. Thus when we say that the probability of a head is $\frac{1}{2}$, we do not mean that 1 out of every 2 tosses results in a head; we mean, rather, that in the long run we expect heads to show about half the time.

1-2 DEFINITIONS OF PROBABILITY

Suppose that we have a well-balanced (or symmetric) die with six sides numbered from 1 to 6. We may feel that any one of the sides is as likely to show as any other when the die is rolled. If our assumption is true, then it is quite likely that we would associate a probability of $\frac{1}{6}$ with each of the six faces. Consideration of examples of this type led to this, the classical, definition of probability:

CLASSICAL DEFINITION *If an experiment can produce n differ-* (1-1)
ent mutually <u>exclusive results all of which are equally likely</u>, and if f of these results are considered favorable, then the probability of a favorable result is f/n.

Two events are mutually exclusive if the occurrence of one prevents the occurrence of the other. The appearance of a 1 and a 2 on a single throw of die is impossible. A 1 can appear and a 2 can appear, but not both together. Thus the outcomes 1 and 2 are mutually exclusive events.

Let E stand for the event "getting a 4 or a 5 on the throw of a die." To compute the probability that E happens, which we shall denote by $\Pr(E)$, consider a 4 and 5 as favorable results. Thus $f = 2$, $n = 6$, and $\Pr(E) = \frac{2}{6}$ by the definition.

One objection to the classical definition is that it contains the phrase "equally likely," as yet undefined. Attempts to define it usually lead to the use of phrases such as "equally probable," and critics point out that this involves circular reasoning. The objection is not serious,

underlined sections are the key words to this def.

4

however, since almost everyone has an intuitive feeling of what is meant. We might be hard-pressed to define "time," yet we use the word frequently with little or no confusion. It is possible that, owing to inexperience, we might label events as equally likely when actually they are not.

A practical objection to the classical definition is that it depends upon a priori analysis. When calculating probabilities associated with a true die, no difficulty arises. Suppose one has a crude homemade wooden die cut in some odd shape with six numbered sides which are not "equally likely." What is the probability of a 1? The classical definition offers no assistance. This type of situation has led to the following definition:

RELATIVE FREQUENCY DEFINITION *Suppose that an experi-*   (1-2)
ment is performed n times with f successes. Assume that the relative frequency f/n approaches a limit as n increases. (Experience indicates that this is the case in most practical situations.) Then the probability of a success is

$$\lim_{n \to \infty} \frac{f}{n}$$

Of course, we can never obtain the probability as given by this limit. The best we can do is to make an estimate based upon a large n. From a practical point of view the definition is somewhat awkward. It does, however, demonstrate the long-run concept of probability.

For our next definition of probability, we need the notion of *sample space*. To illustrate this concept, consider tossing a coin twice. The possible outcomes can be denoted by HH, HT, TH, and TT, where the first letter indicates the result of the first toss and the second letter the result of the second toss. A number of pictorial representations are possible; one of them appears in Fig. 1-1. That is, each of the four outcomes can be represented as a point in space. These will be called *sample points,* and the set or collection S of all sample points represent- ing the possible outcomes will be called the sample space. The oval- shaped curve around the four points in Fig. 1-1 serves no purpose other than to indicate that the sample space is contained therein.

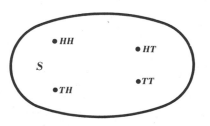

Figure 1-1 A sample-space repre- sentation containing the four pos- sible outcomes of two tosses of a coin.

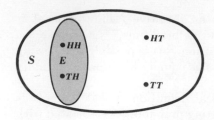

Figure 1-2   A sample space and an event.   The event E, a subset of sample space S, represents the outcome "head on the second toss."

Any subset E of the sample space is called an *event*.   The small oval in Fig. 1-2 is drawn around HH and TH, a subset of S.   The event E represents the outcome resulting in a head on the second toss.   If two events have no points in common, they are said to be mutually exclusive.   Let E' represent the result "tail on the second toss."   Then E and E' are mutually exclusive.

Now assign to each point of S a weight w_i subject to

(a) $w_i \geqq 0$

(b) $w_1 + w_2 + \cdots = \Sigma w_i = 1$ (1-3)

All (1-3) implies is that the weights are positive numbers between 0 and 1 inclusive and that the sum of the weights is equal to 1.   The capital sigma is a standard mathematical notation for sum.   Obviously it is easier to write the abbreviation Σw_i for the sum than to write it out in its entirety, particularly if the number of terms is large.   In the coin example, only four points comprise the sample space and it is reasonable to assign weights of $\frac{1}{4}$ to each.   We now make the following definition:

MATHEMATICAL DEFINITION   *The probability $Pr(E)$ of any*   (1-4) *event E is the sum of the weights of all sample points in E.*

There are many problems in which the sample space consists of a finite number n of points for which it is reasonable to assign equal weights $1/n$ to each.   When this situation is encountered, definition (1-4) can be modified to read:

MODIFIED MATHEMATICAL DEFINITION   *The probability $Pr(E)$*   (1-5) *that event E will occur is the ratio of the number of sample points in E to the total number of sample points in S.   That is,*

$$Pr(E) = \frac{n(E)}{n}$$

where $n(E)$ is the number of sample points in E.

Finally, we note that since it is possible for E to contain only one point, each weight is itself a probability.

6

Although (1-4) is well adapted to proving mathematical theorems, it is of no assistance in determining the weights. To use (1-5), we must recognize from consideration of the problem at hand that equal weights are reasonable. The definition, however, does not help us in this recognition process. Consequently we have to depend upon experience and intuition.

EXAMPLE 1-1

Four slips of paper numbered 1, 2, 3, 4 are placed in a hat and one slip is drawn out. What is the sample space? What weights would you assign to the sample points? Suppose the number is recorded, the slip replaced, and another number drawn. Now what answers would you give?

Solution

When one number is drawn, the sample space is composed of four points which we could number 1, 2, 3, 4. If the slips are the same size so that each has an equal opportunity of being selected, the weights $\frac{1}{4}, \frac{1}{4}, \frac{1}{4}, \frac{1}{4}$ are reasonable. When two slips are drawn as described, the sample space contains 16 points which could be designated

1, 1	2, 1	3, 1	4, 1
1, 2	2, 2	3, 2	4, 2
1, 3	2, 3	3, 3	4, 3
1, 4	2, 4	3, 4	4, 4

where the first number is the result of the first draw and the second is the result of the second draw. If the slips are well mixed after each draw, it is reasonable to assign a weight of $\frac{1}{16}$ to each point.

EXERCISES

1-1   An ordinary coin is tossed three times. What is the sample space? What weights would you assign to the points of the sample space? What is the probability that two out of three times the result is heads?

1-2   Suppose that an ordinary coin is tossed until a head appears. What is the sample space?

1-3   From an urn containing four white and two red balls, one ball is drawn. What is the sample space? What weights seem reasonable for the sample points? What is the probability of drawing a red ball?

1-4   A symmetric die is rolled once. What is the sample space? Assign weights to the sample points.

1-5   A symmetric die is rolled twice. What is the sample space?
      Assign weights to the sample points. What is the probability
      of rolling a total of 7 on the two rolls?

1-6   A card is selected from a deck of 52 cards. Describe the sample
      space and assign weights to the sample points. What is the
      probability that the card is a heart?

1-7   Three sprinters A, B, and C race against each other frequently;
      they have won 60, 30, and 10 per cent of the races, respectively.
      For tomorrow's race, what is the sample space? What weights
      would you assign to the sample points? What is the probability
      that A loses?

1-8   Based upon very extensive study, the records of an insurance
      company reveal that the population of the United States can be
      classified according to ages as follows: under 20, 35 per cent;
      20 to 35, 25 per cent; 35 to 50, 20 per cent; 50 to 65, 15 per cent;
      and over 65, 5 per cent. Suppose that you could select an indi-
      vidual in such a way that everyone in the United States has an
      equal chance of being chosen. Using the above information,
      describe a sample space for the selected individual's age and
      assign weights to the sample points. What is the probability
      that the individual is over 35?

1-9   A shipment of paint contains 2,000 gallon cans of which 800 are
      white, 500 are yellow, 300 are red, 300 are green, and 100 are
      blue. During transit, the cans are accidentally submerged in
      water and all labels are lost. Upon arrival the cans are placed
      upon a platform and one is selected and opened. Regarding
      color of the selected can, what is the sample space? What
      weights would be assigned to the various sample points? What
      is the probability that the selected can contains red, white, or
      blue paint?

1-10 Suppose the weather bureau classifies each day according to
      wind condition as windy or calm, according to rainfall as moist
      or dry, and according to temperature as above normal, normal,
      below normal. What sample space is needed to characterize a
      day? How might you assign weights to the sample points?

1-3 THE ADDITION AND MULTIPLICATION THEOREMS

In many probability problems it is convenient to regard an event as
resulting from two or more simpler events. In Example 1-1 the event
2, 3 from the sample space with 16 points arises from the event 2 with
sample space 1, 2, 3, 4 on the first draw and from the event 3 with

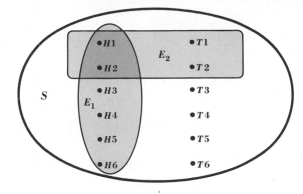

Figure 1-3 Sample space for coin and die thrown simultaneously. E_1 is the event "head"; E_2 is the event "1 or 2."

sample space 1, 2, 3, 4 on the second draw. It is often easier to evaluate the probability of an event by first finding the probabilities of simpler events and then using theorems to compute the probability of the more complicated situation.

Suppose that we throw an ordinary coin and a symmetric die simultaneously. Let E_1 represent the occurrence of a head on the coin and E_2 represent the occurrence of a 1 or a 2 on the die. The 12-point sample space S and events E_1 and E_2 are pictured in Fig. 1-3. The oval includes points with attribute E_1, the rectangle points with attribute E_2. Points with both attributes E_1 and E_2 are within both the rectangle and the oval. Let E_1E_2 denote the event that both E_1 and E_2 happen and let $E_1 + E_2$ denote the event that either E_1 or E_2 (or both) happens. It seems reasonable to give each of the 12 points a weight $\frac{1}{12}$. With this assignment we see by using definition (1-4) that

$$\Pr(E_1E_2) = \frac{1}{12} + \frac{1}{12} = \frac{2}{12} \quad \text{both will happen } \therefore \frac{2}{12}$$
$$\Pr(E_1 + E_2) = 8(\frac{1}{12}) = \frac{8}{12} \quad \text{either will happen or both}$$

We can also write

$$\Pr(E_1 + E_2) = 6(\frac{1}{12}) + 4(\frac{1}{12}) - 2(\frac{1}{12})$$
$$= \Pr(E_1) + \Pr(E_2) - \Pr(E_1E_2) \quad \text{* addition formula know} \tag{1-6}$$

The reasoning behind (1-6) is simple. We add the weights of the points in regions E_1 and E_2 and subtract the weights in E_1E_2 because they have been added to the sum twice. Formula (1-6) is called the *addition theorem*. An important special case arises when E_1 and E_2 are mutually exclusive so that E_1E_2 contains no points. Since there are no weights to add up, $\Pr(E_1E_2) = 0$ and (1-6) reduces to

$$\Pr(E_1 + E_2) = \Pr(E_1) + \Pr(E_2) \tag{1-7}$$

If E_1, E_2, E_3, . . . are mutually exclusive events, then the generaliza-

9

tion of (1-7) yields

$$Pr(E_1 + E_2 + E_3 + \cdots) = Pr(E_1) + Pr(E_2)$$
$$+ Pr(E_3) + \cdots \quad (1\text{-}8)$$

We note that if $E_1 + E_2 + \cdots + E_n = S$ so that n mutually exclusive events exhaust all possibilities, then

$$Pr(E_1 + \cdots + E_n) = Pr(E_1) + \cdots + P(E_n)$$
$$= Pr(S)$$
$$= 1$$

To illustrate (1-8), we can use the coin-die example. Let E_1 denote the event H5 or H6, E_2 the event T1, T2, or T3, and E_3 the event H1. Referring to Fig. 1-4, we see that $Pr(E_1) = \frac{2}{12}$, $Pr(E_2) = \frac{3}{12}$, $Pr(E_3) = \frac{1}{12}$ and

$$Pr(E_1 + E_2 + E_3) = Pr(E_1) + Pr(E_2) + Pr(E_3)$$
$$= \frac{2}{12} + \frac{3}{12} + \frac{1}{12} = \frac{6}{12}$$

In the coin-die example of Fig. 1-3 $Pr(E_1E_2)$ is computed from the definition. Since this is not always the most convenient method, we next develop a formula that is useful for this type of calculation. Suppose we know that E_1 is certain to occur and we want to compute the probability that E_2 will occur subject to this condition. Denote this probability by $Pr(E_2|E_1)$ and call it the probability that E_2 happens given E_1 has already happened. This is known as a *conditional probability*. To take a specific situation, consider the E_1 and E_2 in Fig. 1-3. If we assume that E_1 is certain to happen, E_1 now plays the role of S in the preceding examples and the number of points in E_2 is reduced from four to two, yielding Fig. 1-5. New weights must be selected, and $\frac{1}{6}$ for each point seems reasonable. Consequently, $Pr(E_2|E_1) = \frac{2}{6}$.

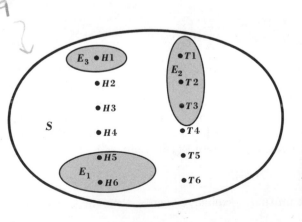

Figure 1-4 *Three mutually exclusive events resulting from the simultaneous tossing of a coin and a die.*

10

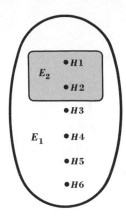

Figure 1-5   A conditional event.   If it is assumed that E_1 is certain to happen, the sample space is reduced to E_1 and $Pr(E_2|E_1) = \frac{2}{6}$.

This could also be found by using Fig. 1-3 and noting that

$$Pr(E_2|E_1) = \frac{\frac{2}{12}}{\frac{6}{12}} = \frac{2}{6}$$

$$= \frac{Pr(E_1E_2)}{Pr(E_1)} \tag{1-9}$$

Actually, all (1-9) implies is that the situation of Fig. 1-5 can be obtained from Fig. 1-3 by reassigning weights so that the weights are still in the same ratio and still sum to 1.   This is easily accomplished by dividing the original weights by the sum of the original weights in E_1, or $Pr(E_1)$.   In our example $Pr(E_1) = \frac{6}{12} = \frac{1}{2}$, so the new weights can be obtained by dividing the old ones by $\frac{1}{2}$ (or multiplying them by 2).   Another way to write (1-9) is

$$Pr(E_1E_2) = Pr(E_1)Pr(E_2|E_1) \qquad \text{MULTIPLICATION THEOREM} \tag{1-10}$$

Formula (1-10) is called the *multiplication theorem*.   The generalization of (1-10) yields

$$Pr(E_1E_2E_3 \cdots E_n)$$
$$= Pr(E_1)Pr(E_2|E_1)Pr(E_3|E_1E_2) \cdots Pr(E_n|E_1 \cdots E_{n-1}) \tag{1-11}$$

In the coin-die example we note that $Pr(E_2|E_1) = \frac{2}{6} = \frac{4}{12} = Pr(E_2)$. In this case (1-10) reduces to

$$Pr(E_1E_2) = Pr(E_1)Pr(E_2) \tag{1-12}$$

and E_1 and E_2 are said to be *independent*.   It is not surprising that E_2 does not depend upon E_1 if we consider the physical aspects of the experiment.   The result on the die does not influence the result for the coin, and vice versa.   Since E_1 represents the occurrence of a head on the coin and E_2 the occurrence of a 1 or 2 on the die, $Pr(E_1)$ does not depend upon E_2 and $Pr(E_2)$ does not depend upon E_1.   If events

11

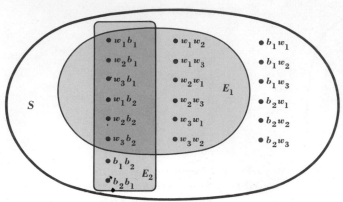

*Figure 1-6   Sample space with dependent events. E_1
is the event "white ball on first draw"; E_2 is the event
"black ball on second draw."*

$E_1, E_2, \ldots, E_n$ are independent of one another, then (1-11) becomes

$$\Pr(E_1 \cdots E_n) = \Pr(E_1)\Pr(E_2) \cdots \Pr(E_n) \tag{1-13}$$

It is usually easy to recognize independence of events, as we have
recognized it above, by considering the physical features of the experiment.   For example, if a die is rolled 10 times, the result on any one
roll in no way affects the result on any other roll and the 10 rolls constitute a series of 10 independent events.   In general, if any event in a
series of events in no way influences the outcome of any other event in
the series, the events are independent.   Examples in which events are
independent even though they do not appear to be so at first glance
have been constructed.

     If $\Pr(E_2|E_1) \neq \Pr(E_2)$, the events E_1 and E_2 are said to be *depend-
ent.*   Let us consider an example illustrating dependent events.   Suppose that from an urn containing three white balls and two black balls
two draws are to be made.   Let E_1 be the event "getting a white ball
on the first draw" and E_2 be the event "getting a black ball on the
second draw."   Assume that the two draws are made successively
without replacement.   Let w_1, w_2, w_3 represent the three white balls
and b_1, b_2 represent the black ones.   The sample space is composed of
the 20 points in Fig. 1-6.   The first letter and subscript denote the
outcome of the first draw and the second letter and subscript the result
of the second draw.   Suppose that we assign a weight of $\frac{1}{20}$ to each
point, which is a reasonable choice if the balls are selected without
looking.   By definition (1-4) we have

$$\Pr(E_1) = 12(\tfrac{1}{20}) \qquad \Pr(E_2) = 8(\tfrac{1}{20})$$
$$\Pr(E_1E_2) = 6(\tfrac{1}{20}) \qquad \Pr(E_1 + E_2) = 14(\tfrac{1}{20})$$

12

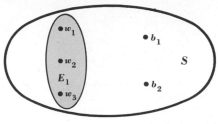

Figure 1-7 Sample space for first draw. E_1 is the event "white ball is drawn."

If we consider the two draws individually, the sample space for the first draw consists of the five points of Fig. 1-7. If each point is assigned a weight of $\frac{1}{5}$, then $\Pr(E_1) = \frac{3}{5}$. Given that E_1 has happened and, renaming the two remaining white balls W_1, W_2, the sample space for the second draw consists of the four points of Fig. 1-8. Assigning a weight of $\frac{1}{4}$ to each point yields $\Pr(E_2|E_1) = \frac{2}{4}$. Consequently, by the multiplication theorem,

$$\Pr(E_1E_2) = \Pr(E_1)\Pr(E_2|E_1) = \frac{3}{5}\left(\frac{2}{4}\right) = \frac{6}{20}$$

which is the result obtained by using only definition (1-4). To compute $\Pr(E_2)$ by using the theorems, we observe that E_2 can happen in two ways, that is, by drawing a white first and a black second or a black first and a black second. The first order of drawing yields event E_1E_2. Let $\bar{E}_1$ be the event getting a black ball on the first draw (or, what is the same thing, "not getting a white ball") so that the second order of drawing can be designated $\bar{E}_1E_2$. Now

$$\Pr(\bar{E}_1E_2) = \Pr(\bar{E}_1)\Pr(E_2|\bar{E}_1)$$

From Fig. 1-7 $\Pr(\bar{E}_1) = \frac{2}{5}$. Given that the first draw is black, the sample space for the second draw consists of the four points in Fig. 1-9 (renaming the remaining black ball B_1). Again using the weight $\frac{1}{4}$ for each point, we get $\Pr(E_2|\bar{E}_1) = \frac{1}{4}$. Thus

$$\Pr(\bar{E}_1E_2) = \left(\frac{2}{5}\right)\left(\frac{1}{4}\right) = \frac{2}{20}$$

Since a black ball can appear on the second draw preceded by either a white or a black but not both, E_1E_2 and $\bar{E}_1E_2$ are mutually exclusive

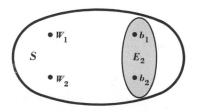

Figure 1-8 Sample space for second draw given first draw is white. E_2 is the event "black ball is drawn."

13

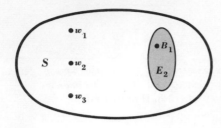

Figure 1-9 Sample space for second draw given first draw is black. E_2 is the event "black ball is drawn."

and by the addition theorem

$$\Pr(E_2) = \Pr(E_1 E_2) + \Pr(\bar{E}_1 E_2)$$
$$= \tfrac{6}{20} + \tfrac{2}{20} = \tfrac{8}{20}$$

Finally,

$$\Pr(E_1 + E_2) = \Pr(E_1) + \Pr(E_2) - \Pr(E_1 E_2)$$
$$= \tfrac{3}{5} + \tfrac{8}{20} - \tfrac{6}{20} = \tfrac{14}{20}$$

For this example it may seem that it is simpler to use the definition than the theorems. With only 20 sample points this may be true. If the urn contains 35 white and 15 black balls, then the sample space contains 2,450 points and it would be extremely tedious to draw the counterpart of Fig. 1-6. However, the theorems provide expressions for probabilities rather quickly. It is, of course, not necessary to draw a picture of the sample space every time for simple situations like those of Figs. 1-7 to 1-9.

EXAMPLE 1-2

A symmetric die is thrown twice. What is the probability of getting a 2 and a 3 in that order? In any order?

Solution

The throws are independent, and the sample space for each throw consists of 6 points, each with associated weight $\tfrac{1}{6}$. Consequently, the probability of rolling a 2 the first time is $\tfrac{1}{6}$, the probability of rolling a 3 the second time is $\tfrac{1}{6}$, and by (1-12) the probability of rolling a 2 and then a 3 is $(\tfrac{1}{6})(\tfrac{1}{6}) = \tfrac{1}{36}$. The argument and answer are the same for rolling a 3 and then a 2. Since the two orders are mutually exclusive, the probability of rolling a 2 and a 3 in either order is $\tfrac{1}{36} + \tfrac{1}{36} = \tfrac{2}{36}$.

EXAMPLE 1-3

If a die is thrown twice, what is the probability of getting at least one 2?

14

Solution

Any one of three mutually exclusive events will yield at least one 2. Designate these by $2X$, $X2$, 22, where X stands for anything but a 2, the first symbol indicates the result of the first throw, and the second symbol indicates the result of the second. We have, by using the multiplication theorem for independent events,

$$\Pr(2X) = \Pr(2)\Pr(X) = (\tfrac{1}{6})(\tfrac{5}{6}) = \tfrac{5}{36}$$
$$\Pr(X2) = \Pr(X)\Pr(2) = (\tfrac{5}{6})(\tfrac{1}{6}) = \tfrac{5}{36}$$
$$\Pr(22) = \Pr(2)\Pr(2) = (\tfrac{1}{6})(\tfrac{1}{6}) = \tfrac{1}{36}$$

Then by the addition theorem for mutually exclusive events

$$\Pr(2X + X2 + 22) = \Pr(2X) + \Pr(X2) + \Pr(22)$$
$$= \tfrac{5}{36} + \tfrac{5}{36} + \tfrac{1}{36} = \tfrac{11}{36}$$

EXAMPLE 1-4

Two cards are dealt from an ordinary deck. What is the probability that at least one is a heart?

Solution

At least one heart is drawn if the result is either HX, XH, or HH, where X stands for a spade, diamond, or club. On the first draw there are 52 sample points, each with weight $\tfrac{1}{52}$. On the second draw with 51 remaining cards there are 51 sample points, each with weight $\tfrac{1}{51}$. We have, by using the multiplication theorem for dependent events,

$$\Pr(HX) = \Pr(H)\Pr(X|H) = (\tfrac{13}{52})(\tfrac{39}{51}) = \tfrac{1}{4}(\tfrac{39}{51})$$
$$\Pr(XH) = \Pr(X)\Pr(H|X) = (\tfrac{39}{52})(\tfrac{13}{51}) = \tfrac{1}{4}(\tfrac{39}{51})$$
$$\Pr(HH) = \Pr(H)\Pr(H|H) = (\tfrac{13}{52})(\tfrac{12}{51}) = \tfrac{1}{4}(\tfrac{12}{51})$$

$$\frac{13}{52} = \frac{1}{4}$$

Then by the addition theorem for mutually exclusive events

$$\Pr(H) = \Pr(HX + XH + HH) = \Pr(HX) + \Pr(XH) + \Pr(HH)$$
$$= \tfrac{1}{4}(\tfrac{39}{51}) + \tfrac{1}{4}(\tfrac{39}{51}) + \tfrac{1}{4}(\tfrac{12}{51})$$
$$= \tfrac{15}{34}$$

EXAMPLE 1-5

For the situation of Example 1-4, what is the probability of drawing a heart or a spade?

Solution

From Example 1-4, the probability of drawing at least one heart is $\tfrac{15}{34}$. Similarly, the probability of drawing at least one spade is $\tfrac{15}{34}$. To obtain the probability of one or the other, we must use (1-6), since the two events are not mutually exclusive. Thus we need the probability of drawing both a heart and a spade, which is

$$\Pr(HS) + \Pr(SH) = {}^{13}\!/_{52}({}^{13}\!/_{51}) + {}^{13}\!/_{52}({}^{13}\!/_{51}) = {}^{13}\!/_{102}$$

Hence, the probability of drawing a heart or a spade is

$${}^{15}\!/_{34} + {}^{15}\!/_{34} - {}^{13}\!/_{102} = {}^{77}\!/_{102}$$

Alternate Solution

Let E_1 be the event "drawing a heart or a spade" and $\bar{E}_1$ be the event "not drawing a heart or a spade (that is, drawing clubs and diamonds)." Obviously $\Pr(E_1) + \Pr(\bar{E}_1) = 1$, since one or the other must happen. Hence, $\Pr(E_1) = 1 - \Pr(\bar{E}_1)$. If $\bar{E}_1$ is to happen, then a club or diamond must be drawn each time. On the first draw 26 of the 52 sample points are clubs or diamonds. A club or a diamond having been drawn, 25 of the remaining 51 cards are clubs or diamonds. Using equal weights each time, the multiplication theorem for dependent events yields for the probability of a club or a diamond on two successive draws $({}^{26}\!/_{52})({}^{25}\!/_{51}) = {}^{25}\!/_{102}$. Thus

$$\Pr(E_1) = 1 - ({}^{25}\!/_{102}) = {}^{77}\!/_{102}$$

as before.

EXERCISES

Use the addition and multiplication theorems in preference to the definition.

◆ 1-11 A coin is tossed three times. What is the probability that two out of three times the result is heads?

1-12 Two dice are rolled. What is the probability that the total on the two dice is 6?

◆ 1-13 Two cards are dealt from a deck. What is the probability that one is an ace and one a king?

1-14 An urn contains six red and four black balls. Two balls are drawn out in succession without replacement. What is the probability that the first is red, the second black? What is the probability of getting a red ball and a black ball in either order? What is the probability of drawing a white ball? If five balls are drawn out, what is the probability that at least one is red?

◆ 1-15 A die is rolled until a 6 appears. What is the probability that exactly four rolls are required?

1-16 Three cards are dealt from a deck. What is the probability that two are red and one is black?

1-17 Suppose it is known that three hunters, say, A, B, and C, can kill a pheasant on $\frac{1}{2}$, $\frac{2}{3}$, and $\frac{3}{4}$ of their shots, respectively. What is the probability that they can kill a bird if all three shoot at it?

1-18 A hat contains 100 slips of paper numbered from 1 to 100. Three are drawn out successively without replacement. What is the probability that two of the numbers are larger than 90?

1-19 Weather bureau records for the city of Laramie indicate that 30 per cent of the days are cloudy, 50 per cent are windy, and 10 per cent are both cloudy and windy. What is the probability that a day is either cloudy or windy?

1-20 A company has two cars which it keeps available to its employees for business purposes. One of the cars is in use 70 per cent of the time and the other 80 per cent of the time during business hours. If a car is needed immediately, what is the probability that either is available? Assume that the cars are used independently of one another.

1-4 PERMUTATIONS AND COMBINATIONS

We have seen how it is sometimes simpler to compute probabilities by using the addition and multiplication theorems rather than the definition. In this section we shall discuss some counting formulas that can be used to simplify the calculation of probabilities, especially in cases where enumeration is excessive. The counting formulas can be used either with or without the theorems.

Suppose that there are three highway routes between towns A and B and two routes between towns B and C. Then there is a total of six possible routes from A to C traveling through B. With each of the three routes for the first lap, there are two choices for the second lap, giving the total of six. This illustrates a fundamental principle of counting: If a first thing can be done in n_1 ways after which a second thing can be done in n_2 ways, then the two things can be done in $n_1 n_2$ ways. The truth of the principle is readily demonstrated by making a list of the ways the two things can be done. For example, using the numbering of Fig. 1-10, the routes are 1–4, 2–4, 3–4, 1–5, 2–5, 3–5. The principle is readily extended to r things. If the first thing can be done in n_1 ways, after which a second thing can be done in n_2 ways, . . . , after which an rth thing can be done in n_r ways, then all r things can be done in $n_1 n_2 \cdots n_r$ ways.

Consider three things that we shall call A, B, and C. They can be

Figure 1-10   Highway routes and fundamental counting principle.

arranged in six ways if we use all three.   The arrangements, called permutations, are

$$ABC, \ ACB, \ BAC, \ BCA, \ CAB, \ CBA$$

We would like to have a formula for counting the number of permutations of n things using all n at a time.   The counting principle provides the answer.   The first thing can be chosen from any of the total of n, after which the second thing can be selected from any of the remaining $n - 1$.   Consequently, the first two places in the permutation can be chosen in $n(n - 1)$ ways.   With each choice for the first two things, the third can be chosen in $n - 2$ ways.   By continuing this line of reasoning, we find that the number of permutations of n things taken n at a time is

$$_nP_n = n(n - 1)(n - 2) \cdots (3)(2)(1) = n! \tag{1-14}$$

where the symbol $n!$ is called n factorial.   When $n = 3$, $3! = 3 \cdot 2 \cdot 1 = 6$, agreeing with the result obtained by enumeration.   Sometimes we wish to count the number of permutations of n things taken r at a time, where r is less than n.   With the three letters A, B, and C the permutations taken two at a time are

$$AB, \ AC, \ BA, \ BC, \ CA, \ CB$$

We proceed as before, but since there are only r positions to fill in the permutation, the product replacing (1-14) contains only r numbers. The number of permutations of n things taken r at a time is

$$\begin{aligned}_nP_r &= n(n - 1) \cdots [n - (r - 1)] \\ &= n(n - 1) \cdots (n - r + 1)\end{aligned} \tag{1-15}$$

Multiplying and dividing the right-hand side of (1-15) by $(n - r)!$ results in the more convenient form

$$_nP_r = \frac{n!}{(n - r)!} \tag{1-16}$$

If $r = n$, (1-16) reduces to (1-14), since $0!$ is defined to be 1.

18

EXAMPLE 1-6

Use formula (1-16) to obtain the number of permutations of 10 things taken 3 at a time.

Solution

$n = 10, r = 3, n - r = 7$, and

$$_{10}P_3 = \frac{10!}{7!} = \frac{10 \cdot 9 \cdot 8 \cdot 7 \cdot 6 \cdot 5 \cdot 4 \cdot 3 \cdot 2 \cdot 1}{7 \cdot 6 \cdot 5 \cdot 4 \cdot 3 \cdot 2 \cdot 1} = 10 \cdot 9 \cdot 8 = 720$$

It is probably just as easy to argue directly as we did when deriving this formula. We immediately get $10 \cdot 9 \cdot 8 = 720$ choices.

Next, suppose that we want to count the number of permutations of n things taken n at a time but that not all n things are distinguishable. To take a simple example, consider the permutations of the letters of the word "book." Four different letters yield $4! = 24$ different permutations. However, this is too large a number, since some of the permutations look exactly alike because the o's are indistinguishable. To clarify this point, assume that the o's have subscripts (denote them o_1 and o_2) so that we can tell them apart. Then bo_1o_2k and bo_2o_1k are different permutations; but if the subscripts are dropped, both look exactly alike. Let P be the number of distinguishable permutations. If for each of the P permutations, subscripts are added to the o's and the o's are permuted, then the total number of permutations of n distinct things taken n at a time is obtained. In other words, this total is $2!P$. But we already know that the total is $4!$, so consequently $2!P = 4!$, or $P = (4!)/(2!)$. The argument can be readily generalized. Let n_1 things be alike, n_2 alike, . . . , n_k alike such that $n_1 + n_2 + \cdots + n_k = n$. Then the number of distinct permutations P gives rise to $Pn_1!n_2! \cdots n_k!$ permutations if subscripts are added to the like things and each of the like things is permuted in all possible ways. But this product must be the same as the total number of permutations of n things taken n at a time, which is $n!$. Hence

$$Pn_1! \cdots n_k! = n! \text{ or}$$
$$P = \frac{n!}{n_1!n_2! \cdots n_k!} \tag{1-17}$$

EXAMPLE 1-7

Count the number of distinct permutations which can be constructed from the word "Mississippi."

Solution

The $n = 11$ letters are composed of $n_1 = 1$ m, $n_2 = 4$ i's, $n_3 = 4$ s's, $n_4 = 2$ p's. Thus

$$P = \frac{11!}{1!4!4!2!} = \frac{11 \cdot 10 \cdot 9 \cdot 8 \cdot 7 \cdot 6 \cdot 5 \cdot 4 \cdot 3 \cdot 2 \cdot 1}{1 \cdot 4 \cdot 3 \cdot 2 \cdot 1 \cdot 4 \cdot 3 \cdot 2 \cdot 1 \cdot 2 \cdot 1}$$
$$= 11 \cdot 10 \cdot 9 \cdot 7 \cdot 5 = 34,650$$

In some counting problems order is not important. For example, we may want to know the number of five-card hands which can be constructed from an ordinary deck. A hand dealt A K Q J 10 of hearts is the same as one with K Q J 10 A or one with Q J 10 A K of hearts. Consequently, many permutations lead to the same hand or combination of cards. By *combination*, we mean an unordered grouping of things. A formula for the number of combinations of n things taken r at a time can be obtained by counting the number of permutations two ways. We already know from (1-16) that the number of permutations of n things taken r at a time is $n!/(n - r)!$. Let $\binom{n}{r}$ denote the number of combinations of n things taken r at a time. Another procedure for constructing all permutations of n things taken r at a time would be to write down all $\binom{n}{r}$ combinations and then permute all r letters of each. This yields $\binom{n}{r} r!$ permutations, which must equal $n!/(n - r)!$. Consequently,

$$\binom{n}{r} = \frac{n!}{r!(n - r)!} \tag{1-18}$$

EXAMPLE 1-8

How many 5-card hands can be constructed from a deck of 52 cards?

Solution

The answer is the number of combinations of 52 things taken 5 at a time or

$$\binom{52}{5} = \frac{52!}{5!47!} = \frac{52 \cdot 51 \cdot 50 \cdot 49 \cdot 48}{1 \cdot 2 \cdot 3 \cdot 4 \cdot 5} = 2,598,960$$

EXAMPLE 1-9

What is the probability that a 5-card poker hand contains 3 aces?

Solution

The total number of sample points is $\binom{52}{5}$ from Example 1-8. If a hand is dealt fairly, then an equal weight of $1/\binom{52}{5}$ for each point is reasonable. We need to count the number of points that correspond to 3 aces. Now 3 aces can be chosen in $\binom{4}{3} = 4$ ways. With each choice, the hand can be filled out by choosing 2 cards from the remaining 48 non-aces in $\binom{48}{2}$ ways. Then the total number of hands containing 3 aces is $\binom{4}{3}\binom{48}{2}$, and the probability of such a hand is

$$\frac{\binom{4}{3}\binom{48}{2}}{\binom{52}{5}} = \frac{94}{54,145} = .0017$$

EXERCISES

1-21 In how many ways can five people be seated in a row? Suppose that three are men and two are women and that their positions are determined by drawing numbers out of a hat. What is the probability that men occupy the end positions?

1-22 How many distinct permutations can be formed from the letters AAABBCCCC? What would be the answer if the letters were all different?

1-23 Eight men are available to form a basketball team. How many ways can the team be formed if each man can play any of the five positions? If five men are to be chosen from the eight, how many ways can this be done?

1-24 Suppose that of the eight men available in Exercise 1-23, three are over 6 feet tall. Assuming that height is not considered in picking the team, what is the probability that all three are on the starting five?

1-25 In how many ways can a five-card hand be constructed so that it contains two aces and two kings?

1-26 How many different sets of answers are possible for a 10-question true-false examination? *1024* $2\ 10^{\text{Power}}$

1-27 How many distinct permutations can be made from the word "statistics"?

1-28 A hat contains 25 slips of paper numbered 1 to 25. If three are drawn without replacement, what is the probability that all three are less than 10?

We have encountered a number of experiments which may produce different results even though they can be repeated under the same conditions. Experiments of this type are often called *random experiments*. Our examples have included dice throwing, coin tossing, drawing numbers from a hat, drawing balls from an urn, and dealing hands of cards. A variable quantity whose value is determined by the outcome of a random experiment is called a *random variable*.

Let us consider some simple examples of random variables. If a single die is thrown and the number of spots showing is x, then x is a random variable that can take on the values 1, 2, 3, 4, 5, 6. In addition, x^2, $x + 1$, or any other function of x is a random variable. If two dice are thrown, then the random variable that we would most likely consider is the sum of the spots, say, y. The random variable y can assume any of the values 2, 3, . . . , 12. Other examples are the number of heads showing in ten tosses of a coin, the number of aces in a five-card hand, and the number of white balls obtained if three balls are drawn from an urn.

We shall not use a special notation for random variables. However, there are two in common use. Some writers use capital letters, reserving small letters for particular assumed values of the variables. Unfortunately, some well-known random variables have traditionally been identified by small letters. Other writers use boldface instead of ordinary type. The latter system has more disadvantages than the former. In some printing styles boldface is very difficult to distinguish, and the contrast is not well adapted to blackboard technique. Although one notation or the other is desirable in more theoretical writing, lack of one does not provide a serious handicap.

A table listing all possible values that a random variable can take on together with the associated probabilities is called a *probability distribution*. The probability distribution for the outcome x of a single balanced die is given in Table 1-1. We note that the sum of all probabilities in a probability distribution is 1. Frequently we shall find it convenient to use a formula instead of this table. The same informa-

Table 1-1 Probability distribution for a single die

x	1	2	3	4	5	6
$\Pr(x)$	$\frac{1}{6}$	$\frac{1}{6}$	$\frac{1}{6}$	$\frac{1}{6}$	$\frac{1}{6}$	$\frac{1}{6}$

Table 1-2   Cumulative distribution for a die

r	1	2	3	4	5	6
$F(r)$	$\frac{1}{6}$	$\frac{2}{6}$	$\frac{3}{6}$	$\frac{4}{6}$	$\frac{5}{6}$	1

tion is provided by

$$\Pr(x) = f(x) = \tfrac{1}{6} \qquad x = 1, 2, 3, 4, 5, 6$$

A formula, or function $f(x)$, from which probabilities associated with various values of the random variable can be obtained is called a *probability function* or *frequency function*. As we shall see, many important probability functions are tabulated, but quite often in another form.   Usually tables contain

$$F(r) = \sum_{x \leqq r} f(x) = \Pr(x \leqq r) \tag{1-19}$$

which is known as the *cumulative distribution* or *distribution function*. Table 1-2 gives the cumulative distribution for the random variable x of Table 1-1.   Thus, for example,

$$F(3) = f(1) + f(2) + f(3) = \tfrac{1}{6} + \tfrac{1}{6} + \tfrac{1}{6} = \tfrac{3}{6}$$

Another important concept in probability theory which had its origin in gambling is *expected value*.   As a simple illustration, suppose that 100 tickets are sold at \$1.00 each to raffle off a watch worth \$80.00. Since one ticket is worth \$80.00 and the other 99 will pay off nothing, the average or expected value of a ticket is

$$\frac{\$80 + \$0 + \cdots + \$0}{100} = \$80 \left(\frac{1}{100}\right) + \$0 \left(\frac{1}{100}\right)$$
$$+ \cdots + \$0 \left(\frac{1}{100}\right)$$
$$= \$.80$$

If one participated in many such raffles, in the long run one would expect to get about 80 cents back for each dollar invested.   In general, we define expected value as follows: If a random variable x has possible outcomes $x_1, x_2, \ldots, x_k$ occurring with probabilities $f(x_1), f(x_2), \ldots, f(x_k)$, respectively, then the *expected value* of x is

$$E(x) = x_1 f(x_1) + x_2 f(x_2) + \cdots + x_k f(x_k)$$
$$= \sum_{i=1}^{k} x_i f(x_i) \tag{1-20}$$

For the raffle example we could classify the outcomes in terms of the amount to be won. Thus $x_1 = \$80 - \$1 = \$79$ if the winning ticket is held and $x_2 = -\$1$ if a losing ticket is held. Since it is reasonable to assign a weight of $1/100$ to the drawing of each ticket, $f(x_1) = 1/100$, $f(x_2) = 99/100$, and the expected or average winning per ticket is

$$\$79(1/100) + (-\$1)(99/100) = -\$.20$$

The Greek letter mu is often used to denote the expected or average value of a random variable. Hence, we shall frequently write μ instead of $E(x)$.

Definition (1-20) can be readily extended to a situation in which a random variable has an infinite number of outcomes which can be put into one-to-one correspondence with the positive integers (such as in Exercise 1-2). Merely replace the k above the summation sign by infinity. That is, $E(x)$ will be the sum of an infinite number of terms, and its evaluation may be a fairly difficult mathematical problem.

EXAMPLE 1-10

Suppose that the probability function for a random variable x is $f(x) = x/10$, $x = 1, 2, 3, 4$. List the values which would be included in the probability distribution, list all the values of the cumulative distribution, and find the expected value of x.

Solution

$f(1) = 1/10, f(2) = 2/10, f(3) = 3/10, f(4)\ 4 = 4/10$
$F(1) = 1/10$
$F(2) = 1/10 + 2/10 = 3/10$
$F(3) = 1/10 + 2/10 + 3/10 = 6/10$
$F(4) = 1/10 + 2/10 + 3/10 + 4/10 = 1$

The expected value of x is

$$E(x) = 1(1/10) + 2(2/10) + 3(3/10) + 4(4/10) = 3$$

EXAMPLE 1-11

A gambling game that was played at small-town celebrations a few years back was known as "chuckaluck." The player bets an amount, say, \$1, on a number from 1 to 6. To be specific, let us take 2. Then a cage containing two dice is spun. If two 2's appear, the player gets his dollar back with two additional dollars. If only a single 2 appears, the player receives one dollar in addition to having his bet returned. If no 2's appear, the house wins. Find the probability distribution of the number of 2's and the player's expected winnings for a single play.

24

Solution

In Example 1-3 we found that the probability of getting one 2 is $^{10}\!/_{36}$ and the probability of getting two 2's is $^{1}\!/_{36}$. By subtraction, the probability of getting no 2's is $1 - {^{10}\!/_{36}} - {^{1}\!/_{36}} = {^{25}\!/_{36}}$. Letting $x =$ the number of 2's, the probability distribution of x is

x	0	1	2
$f(x)$	$^{25}\!/_{36}$	$^{10}\!/_{36}$	$^{1}\!/_{36}$

Let $y =$ the player's winnings. The probability distribution of y is

y	$-\$1$	$\$1$	$\$2$
$g(y)$	$^{25}\!/_{36}$	$^{10}\!/_{36}$	$^{1}\!/_{36}$

and the expected value of y is

$$E(y) = (-\$1)^{25}\!/_{36} + (\$1)^{10}\!/_{36} + (\$2)^{1}\!/_{36} = -\$13/36 = -\$.36$$

In other words, if the game is played a large number of times, the player would expect to lose on the average about 36 cents for each play. For most games played in gambling casinos, this figure is about 2 to 4 cents on the dollar.

EXERCISES

1-29 Find the probability distribution for the number of heads appearing when two coins are tossed. What is the expected number of heads?

1-30 Find the probability distribution for the number of heads appearing when three coins are tossed. What is the expected number of heads?

1-31 Two symmetric dice are thrown. Let $x =$ the sum of the spots. Find the probability distribution of x, the cumulative distribution, and the expected value of x.

1-32 The probability function of a random variable x is $f(x) = x/21$, $x = 1, 2, 3, 4, 5, 6$. Make a table of the distribution function and find the expected value of x.

1-33 Suppose that the chuckaluck game of Example 1-11 is changed by increasing each of the winning payoffs by $1. Now what is the expected value of y?

1-34 A hat contains 10 slips of paper numbered 1 to 10. One number is to be drawn. Let x denote the number. Find the probability distribution of x and the expected value of x.

1-35 A four-answer multiple-choice examination with five questions is taken by a student who guesses at each answer. Suppose that the probabilities of getting 0, 1, 2, 3, 4, 5 correct answers are 1/1024, 15/1024, 90/1024, 270/1024, 405/1024, 243/1024. What is the expected number of correct answers?

1-36 Suppose that in families with four children the probabilities of having 0, 1, 2, 3, 4 boys are respectively 1/16, 4/16, 6/16, 4/16, 1/16. Find the expected number of boys in a family of four children.

1-37 A blindfolded individual is given four different brands of cigarettes to smoke, told the names of the brands, and asked to identify each. Suppose that if the individual possesses no discriminatory ability, the probabilities of making 0, 1, 2, 3, 4 correct identifications are respectively 9/24, 8/24, 6/24, 0, 1/24. What is the expected number of correct identifications for such an individual?

1-6 CONTINUOUS RANDOM VARIABLES

Our discussion in the preceding sections of this chapter has been concerned entirely with what we call discrete probabilities. The sample space for every situation has been either a finite number of points or an infinite number which is countable. The latter case arises in Exercise 1-2 when a coin is tossed until a head appears. Though the sample space consists of an infinite number of points identified by H, TH, TTH, · · · , these can be counted by identifying H with 1, TH with 2, TTH with 3, etc. In other words the points of the sample space can be put into a one-to-one correspondence with the positive integers. A sample space which includes only a finite number of points or an infinite number which is countable is called a *discrete sample space*. A random variable associated with a discrete sample space is known as a *discrete random variable*. In many of the problems involving discrete random variables, the variable can assume only nonnegative integer values. That is, quantities such as the number of heads appearing in ten throws, the sum of spots on two dice, the number of white balls drawn from an urn, and the number of aces in a five-card hand can take on only values 0, 1, 2, etc.

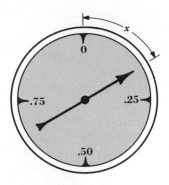

Figure 1-11   A balanced pointer.

In many interesting statistical problems the random variable under consideration can take on any value within an interval (or perhaps several intervals). A random variable of this type is called a *continuous random variable*. Let us turn to a simple example. Consider the spinner pictured in Fig. 1-11 with the outside scale labeled uniformly from 0 to 1. Assume that it is perfectly balanced, that is, as likely to stop one place as another if spun. Let x denote the distance on the circular scale from 0 to the arrow end of the spinner. Suppose that E_1 is the event that x is between .50 and .75. Our intuition tells us that .25 would be a good choice for $\Pr(E_1)$, the probability that E_1 happens. We would like to construct a method of assigning weights to an event E which is harmonious with our notions of probability, particularly definition (1-4). In this example it is easy. We define

$\Pr(E) = \Pr(x$ belongs to an interval or several intervals comprising $E)$
$\qquad = $ length of E

We note that the probability $\Pr(E)$ satisfies the conditions

(a) $\Pr(E) \geqq 0$ *for any E*
(b) $\Pr(S) = 1$ $\qquad\qquad\qquad\qquad\qquad\qquad\qquad\qquad$ (1-21)

where S is the entire sample space, that is, the whole interval $0 \leqq x < 1$, which roughly correspond to (1-3). If the interval E has no length, then $\Pr(E) = 0$. Hence the probability that x takes on any specific value, say, $x = .50$, is 0, a fact which is true for any continuous random variable.

We can also regard the $\Pr(E)$ of the spinner example as the area above the horizontal axis and under the curve

$f(x) = 1 \qquad 0 \leqq x < 1$
$\quad\ \ = 0 \qquad$ elsewhere

between the end points of the interval defining E. Thus if E is the interval $.50 < x < .75$, the area under the curve between .50 and .75 is .25 (see Fig. 1-12).

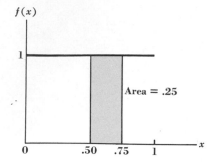

Figure 1-12 Probability interpreted as area under a curve.

The function $f(x)$ is called a density function and has the properties:

(a) *It is nonnegative.*

(b) *The total area under the curve is 1.* (1-22)

Any function $f(x)$ having properties (1-22) can be used as a density function, and areas under $f(x)$ within intervals can be interpreted as probabilities. It is easy to construct density functions. Any nonnegative $f(x)$ can be used if the area under the curve is finite. If the area is C instead of 1, construct a new $f(x)$ by dividing the old one by C. Constructing density functions which give realistic probabilities for real-life problems is not so easy and is a chore which usually requires a joint effort by the mathematical statistician and the experimental scientist. The evaluation of areas under most important density functions is a difficult numerical problem. Fortunately, tables that make the evaluation easy in cases that we shall consider are available.

The preceding discussion suggests that we could make the following definition of probability in the continuous case:

Let $f(x)$ be a density function with the properties (1-22) and E (1-23)
be an interval or several intervals in the sample space S. Then
$Pr(E)$ is the area under $f(x)$ over E.

In comparing the continuous situation with the discrete we have observed that (1) intervals are used instead of sample points, (2) weights are associated with intervals instead of with points, (3) probabilities are evaluated by finding areas under curves rather than by summing weights.

Several important density functions will be discussed in the next chapter. At that time we shall consider the tables that enable us to compute the probabilities.

CHAPTER TWO

Probability Models

2-1 INTRODUCTION

The calculation of probabilities is an essential step in statistical inference.   One of the big problems facing the experimenter is the selection
of a model to describe the behavior of his data.   When used in a
probabilistic sense, the term "model" usually refers to a mathematical
statement or formula used in studying the results of an experiment or
predicting the behavior of future repetitions of the experiment.   However, it would not be inconsistent with the dictionary definition of the
word to use "model" to mean the assumptions that are necessary to
derive the formula.   Either interpretation will be satisfactory for our
purposes, although we shall usually have the former in mind.

The objective of this chapter is to investigate some of the more important probability models. Some will apply to discrete random variables, others to continuous random variables. In the simpler situations we shall start with a set of assumptions that characterize a large class of experiments and actually derive the formula that is used to compute probabilities. Numerical calculations will be relatively simple because extensive tables are available. For the beginning student it is more important to learn to associate the correct model with the situation at hand than to memorize formulas.

2-2 BINOMIAL PROBABILITY MODEL

There are several reasons for beginning our study of probability models with the binomial. First, the model can be used to compute probabilities associated with a number of commonly occurring situations. Second, the model formula is easy to derive, requiring the use of only elementary probability concepts which have already been covered in Chap. 1. Third, it is a straightforward task to investigate the reasonableness of the assumptions required for the derivation of the model formula. Finally, the necessary computations are very simple, since extensive tables of the binomial distribution are available.

Consider a series of events or experiments which have the following properties:

(a) *The result of each experiment can be classified into one of two categories: success and failure.*
(b) *The probability, p, of a success is the same for each experiment.*   (2-1)
(c) *Each experiment is independent of all the others.*
(d) *The experiment is performed a fixed number of times, say, n.*

These conditions appear to be satisfied when a true die is rolled 10 times, regarding a 1 or a 2 as a success and using $\frac{1}{3}$ for the value of p. Now suppose we would like to know the probability of obtaining exactly four successes. One way to achieve the result is SSSSFFFFFF, where S and F denote success and failure. That is, we could be successful the first four times and fail the last six times. The probability that this happens is

$$(\tfrac{1}{3})(\tfrac{1}{3})(\tfrac{1}{3})(\tfrac{1}{3})(\tfrac{2}{3})(\tfrac{2}{3})(\tfrac{2}{3})(\tfrac{2}{3})(\tfrac{2}{3})(\tfrac{2}{3}) = (\tfrac{1}{3})^4(\tfrac{2}{3})^6$$

a result obtained by using the multiplication theorem for independent events and the fact that $p = \frac{1}{3}$ on each roll. Obviously, there are lots of other orders of successes and failures which will yield exactly

30

four successes (for example, SSSFSFFFFF). The probability of obtaining each of these orders is $(\frac{1}{3})^4(\frac{2}{3})^6$. Further, the orders are mutually exclusive, since the occurrence of one specified order excludes the occurrence of any other order. Then, by the addition theorem the probability of 4 successes in 10 trials is a multiple of $(\frac{1}{3})^4(\frac{2}{3})^6$, the multiplier being the number of ways 10 things taken 10 at a time can be permuted if 4 are alike and 6 are alike. We know this latter number is $\dfrac{10!}{4!6!} = \dbinom{10}{4}$. Consequently,

$$\Pr(4 \text{ successes in } 10 \text{ trials}) = \binom{10}{4}\left(\frac{1}{3}\right)^4\left(\frac{2}{3}\right)^6$$

We now generalize the above discussion to yield a formula for the probability of x successes in n trials. One way to achieve these successes is

$$\underbrace{S \cdots S}_{x \text{ times}} \underbrace{F \cdots F}_{n - x \text{ times}}$$

that is, be successful x times, then fail $n - x$ times. By the multiplication theorem, the probability that this happens is

$$\underbrace{pp \cdots p}_{x \text{ times}} \underbrace{q \cdots q}_{n - x \text{ times}} = p^x q^{n-x}$$

where $q = 1 - p$. There are lots of other orders which yield x successes and $n - x$ failures, all mutually exclusive, the probability associated with each being $p^x q^{n-x}$. Hence, by the addition theorem, the probability we seek is the total number of orders multiplied by $p^x q^{n-x}$. Since this number is the number of permutations of n things taken n at a time when x are alike and $n - x$ are alike, which is

$$\frac{n!}{x!(n - x)!} = \binom{n}{x}$$

we obtain the formula

$$b(x;n,p) = \binom{n}{x} p^x q^{n-x} \tag{2-2}$$

for the probability of x successes in n trials of an experiment which succeeds with probability p. The random variable x can take on any of the values 0, 1, 2, . . . , n. The name "binomial" arises from the fact that $b(x;n,p)$ is a term in the expansion of the binomial $(q + p)^n$.

In most interesting binomial-type problems we need a sum of terms rather than individual terms.   Appendix D-1 gives values of

$$B(r;n,p) = \sum_{x=0}^{r} b(x;n,p)$$
$$= b(0;n,p) + b(1;n,p) + \cdots + b(r;n,p)$$
$$= \Pr(r \text{ or fewer successes in } n \text{ trials}) \qquad (2\text{-}3)$$

for some values of p and n.   Several extensive tables of binomial sums have been published.   The largest of these are [1] and [8].†   The Harvard table gives right-hand sums $[\Pr(x \geq r)$ instead of $\Pr(x \leq r)]$ to five decimal places for $n = 1(1)50(2)100(10)200(20)500(50)1{,}000$ and $p = .01(.01).50, \frac{1}{16}, \frac{1}{12}, \frac{1}{8}, \frac{1}{6}, \frac{3}{16}, \frac{1}{3}, \frac{3}{8}, \frac{5}{12}, \frac{7}{16}$.   This notation means that the table entries are given for $n = 1, 2, 3, \ldots, 49,$ 50, 52, 54, ... 98, 100, 110, ... , 190, 200, 220, ... , 480, 500, 550, ... , 950, 1,000 and $p = .01, .02, \ldots .49, .50$ plus the nine fractional values.   The Ordnance Corps table also gives right-hand sums to seven decimal places for $n = 1(1)150$ and $p = .01(.01).50$. Several smaller tables are found in [4], [5], and [7].   Tables of this type are easily duplicated on modern high-speed computing equipment. Now we turn our attention to some examples.

EXAMPLE 2-1

If an ordinary die is thrown four times, what is the probability that exactly two 6's occur?

Solution

First we check conditions (2-1).

(a)   Each throw results in a 6 or not a 6.
(b)   For each throw $p = \frac{1}{6}$ remains constant as the probability of a success.
(c)   Successive throws are independent.
(d)   The die is thrown four times.

Hence the binomial model seems appropriate for this situation with $n = 4$, $x = 2$ and

$$b\left(2;4,\frac{1}{6}\right) = \binom{4}{2}\left(\frac{1}{6}\right)^2\left(\frac{5}{6}\right)^2 = \frac{150}{1296}$$

EXAMPLE 2-2

In Example 2-1, what is the probability of two or fewer 6's?

† Numbers in brackets are those of references listed at the end of the chapter.

Solution

By two or fewer 6's we mean zero, one, or two 6's. We get

$$\Pr(\text{no 6's}) = \binom{4}{0}\left(\frac{1}{6}\right)^0\left(\frac{5}{6}\right)^4 = \frac{625}{1296}$$

$$\Pr(\text{one 6}) = \binom{4}{1}\left(\frac{1}{6}\right)^1\left(\frac{5}{6}\right)^3 = \frac{500}{1296}$$

$$\Pr(\text{two 6's}) = \binom{4}{2}\left(\frac{1}{6}\right)^2\left(\frac{5}{6}\right)^2 = \frac{150}{1296}$$

Since the three events are mutually exclusive, the probabilities are added together:

$$\Pr(\text{two or fewer 6's}) = \Pr(x \leq 2)$$
$$= \frac{625}{1296} + \frac{500}{1296} + \frac{150}{1296}$$
$$= \frac{1275}{1296}$$

EXAMPLE 2-3

In a 10-question true-false examination, what is the probability of getting 70 per cent or better correct by guessing?   Exactly 7 out of 10 correct?

Solution

Check conditions (2-1).

(*a*)   Assuming each question is answered, it is right or wrong.
(*b*)   For each question the probability of a correct guess is $p = \frac{1}{2}$.
(*c*)   Successive questions are independent if each gives no information about the correctness of any of the others.   A good examination should be so constructed.
(*d*)   There are 10 questions.

Hence the binomial model with $n = 10$, $p = \frac{1}{2}$ seems to be appropriate.   We want the probability of 7, 8, 9, or 10 correct.   This is

$$\sum_{x=7}^{10} b(x;10,\tfrac{1}{2}) = 1 - \sum_{x=0}^{6} b(x;10,\tfrac{1}{2})$$
$$= 1 - .82812 \quad \textit{from Appendix D-1}$$
$$= .17188$$

The probability of getting exactly seven correct is

$$\sum_{x=0}^{7} b(x;10,\tfrac{1}{2}) - \sum_{x=0}^{6} b(x;10,\tfrac{1}{2})$$
$$= .94531 - .82812 \quad \textit{from Appendix D-1}$$
$$= .11719$$

EXAMPLE 2-4

In a 20-question, 5-answer multiple-choice examination, what is the probability of getting 6 or more correct by guessing?

Solution

We observe that

(a) Assuming all questions are answered, each is right or wrong.

(b) For each question the probability of a correct guess is $p = \frac{1}{5}$.

(c) When each answer is a guess, presumably the result of any question does not influence the answer to any other question. In many multiple-choice examinations there would be real doubt whether the independence condition is satisfied.

(d) The examination contains 20 questions.

Thus the binomial model with $n = 20$, $p = \frac{1}{5} = .20$ seems to be a reasonable one to characterize the situation. We want

$$\Pr(6 \text{ correct}) + \cdots + \Pr(20 \text{ correct})$$
$$= \sum_{x=6}^{20} b(x;20,.20)$$
$$= 1 - \sum_{x=0}^{5} b(x;20,.20)$$
$$= 1 - .80421 \quad \textit{from Appendix D-1}$$
$$= .19579$$

EXAMPLE 2-5

It is estimated that 90 per cent of a potato crop is good, the remainder having rotten centers that cannot be detected unless the potatoes are cut open. What is the probability of getting 20 or less good ones in a sack of 25 potatoes?

Solution

It is not unreasonable to assume

(a) The potato can be classified as good or bad.

(b) The probability of getting a good potato remains approximately $p = .90$ from trial to trial, since the crop consists of a very large number of potatoes.

(c) Potatoes are independently good or bad.

(d) In addition, the number of trials is a fixed number.

Thus we can use the binomial model with $n = 25$, $p = .90$ to compute an answer. We need

$$\sum_{x=0}^{20} b(x;25,.90)$$

Since the tables give p's only up to .50, the latter sum cannot be read directly from the tables. However, since getting 20 or fewer good ones is the same as getting 5 or more bad ones, it is apparent that

$$\sum_{x=0}^{20} b(x;25,.90) = \sum_{x=5}^{25} b(x;25,.10)$$
$$= 1 - \sum_{x=0}^{4} b(x;25,.10)$$
$$= 1 - .90201 \qquad \textit{from Appendix D-1}$$
$$= .09799$$

Thus when $p > \frac{1}{2}$, interchange the roles of p and q, success and failure.

In Examples 2-3 to 2-5 there is some room to doubt that the assumptions (2-1) are satisfied. This is not an uncommon state of affairs in probability problems. One often encounters situations in which the conditions needed to derive the probability model are not fulfilled. When this happens, the model may still give probabilities that are sufficiently close to the actual probabilities for practical purposes. Some further experience with the particular type of problem under consideration is then necessary to verify the adequacy of the model.

In Example 2-5 we encountered a p larger than $\frac{1}{2}$ and found that the roles of both p and q and success and failure had to be interchanged to enter the tables. It is easy to write down a general formula for this situation. To evaluate

$$\Pr(x \leq r) = \sum_{x=0}^{r} b(x;n,p) = B(r;n,p)$$

we observe that the probability of r or fewer successes is the same as the probability of $n - r$ or more failures. Consequently

$$B(r;n,p) = \sum_{x=n-r}^{n} b(x;n,q)$$
$$= 1 - \sum_{x=0}^{n-r-1} b(x;n,q)$$
$$= 1 - B(n - r - 1;n,q) \qquad (2\text{-}4)$$

Perhaps it is easier to go through the above procedure each time than to remember and use (2-4).

EXERCISES

Use Appendix D-1 to evaluate probabilities in the following problems. Comment upon the reasonableness of the binomial assumptions.

2-1 A well-known baseball player has a lifetime batting average of .300.   If he comes to bat five times in his next game, what is the probability that he will get three hits?   More than two hits?

2-2 A four-answer multiple-choice examination has 100 questions. Assuming that a student only guesses and answers every question, what is the probability that he gets 30 or more correct? Suppose that the instructor decides that no grade (number correct) will be passing unless the probability of getting or exceeding that grade by guessing is less than .01.   What is the minimum passing grade?

2-3 A missile manufacturer claims that his missiles are 90 per cent effective.   The Air Force checks the stock by firing 10 missiles and obtains 5 successes.   What is the probability of obtaining 5 or fewer successes if $p = .9$?   What conclusion is one apt to draw?

2-4 Suppose that 25 voters are chosen independently of one another and asked if they favor a certain proposal.   If 40 per cent of the voters favor the proposal, what is the probability that a majority of the 25 voters chosen will favor the proposal?

2-5 Suppose that you believe that you can hit a bull's-eye with a dart one time in ten.   If this is the case, compute the probability of scoring 15 or more bull's-eyes in 100 throws.   What is the probability of obtaining exactly 15 bull's-eyes?

2-6 It is known that 25 per cent of all rabbits inoculated with a serum containing a certain disease germ will contract the disease. If 20 rabbits are inoculated, what is the probability that at least 3 get positive reactions?

2-7 Weather bureau records in a certain locality show that 40 per cent of the days in April are cloudy.   Find the probability that, during the first 20 days of next April, at most 5 days will be cloudy.

2-8 In order to select its beer tasters, a brewery gives an applicant a tasting examination.   The applicant is presented with four glasses, one of which contains ale and three of which contain beer, and he is asked to identify the one containing ale.   If the procedure is repeated 10 times and the brewery requires 7 or more correct answers for a satisfactory score, what is the probability that an applicant will pass the test if he cannot discriminate and only guesses each time?   Suppose that the applicant does possess discriminatory ability and has a certain probability p of making a correct choice on each trial. What is the smallest value of p of those given in Appendix D-1 that will guarantee the applicant at least a probability of .85 of passing the test?

◆ 2-9 The standard cure for tuberculosis is successful 30 per cent of the time. A new cure is tried on a group of 50 patients and is successful in 29 cases. What conclusion is one apt to draw and why?

2-3 THE NEGATIVE BINOMIAL PROBABILITY MODEL

Consider a series of events or experiments having the following properties:

(a) *The result of each experiment can be classified into one of two categories: success and failure.*
(b) *The probability p of a success is the same for each experiment.* (2-5)
(c) *Each experiment is independent of all the others.*
(d) *The experiment is repeated a variable number of times until a fixed number of successes is obtained.*

Only (d) differs from assumptions (2-1), which were used to obtain an expression for the probability of x successes in n trials. Now we shall derive a formula for the probability that N repetitions of the experiment are required to achieve c successes.

As an illustration, suppose that we continue to roll a die and regard a 1 or 2 as a success, so that $p = \frac{1}{3}$, until $c = 4$ successes have occurred and we would like to know the probability that $N = 10$ trials are required. One way to achieve the desired result is SSSFFFFFFS, that is, succeed the first three times, fail the next six, and then succeed. Obviously, the last trial must be a success or four successes would have been achieved sooner. By the multiplication theorem, the probability of the above sequence is $(\frac{1}{3})^4(\frac{2}{3})^6$. Once more many other sequences, all mutually exclusive with probability of occurrence $(\frac{1}{3})^4(\frac{2}{3})^6$, yield the desired result. Hence, again we need to count the number of ways S's and F's can be permuted. Since the last letter must be an S, only the remaining 9 letters can be rearranged, the number of rearrangements being $\frac{9!}{3!6!} = \binom{9}{3}$. Consequently,

$$\text{Pr(10 trials are required to achieve 4 successes)} = \binom{9}{3}\left(\frac{1}{3}\right)^4\left(\frac{2}{3}\right)^6$$

The preceding argument is easily generalized. One way to achieve c successes in exactly N trials is

$$\underbrace{\text{S} \cdots \text{S}}_{c\,-\,1\text{ times}} \underbrace{\text{F} \cdots \text{F}}_{N\,-\,c\text{ times}} \text{S}$$

that is, be successful $c - 1$ times, fail the next $N - c$ times, and succeed the last time. By the multiplication theorem, the probability that this happens is

$$\underbrace{p \cdots p}_{c\,-\,1\text{ times}} \underbrace{q \cdots q}_{N\,-\,c\text{ times}} p = p^c q^{N-c}$$

Next we count all the mutually exclusive orders which yield the cth success on the Nth trial. Since the last letter in every sequence must be an S, this leaves $c - 1$ of the S's and $N - c$ F's for forming permutations. The number that can be constructed is

$$\frac{(N - 1)!}{(c - 1)!(N - c)!} = \binom{N - 1}{c - 1}$$

the total number of ways to permute $N - 1$ things taken $N - 1$ at a time if $c - 1$ are alike and $N - c$ are alike. By using the addition theorem, we obtain the formula

$$b^*(N;c,p) = \binom{N - 1}{c - 1} p^c q^{N-c} \tag{2-6}$$

for the probability that the cth success occurs on the Nth trial. The random variable N can take on any of the values $c, c + 1, c + 2, \ldots$. The name *negative binomial* arises from the fact that $b^*(N;c,p)$ is a term in the expansion of $p^c(1 - q)^{-c}$.

Negative binomial probabilities can be evaluated from an ordinary binomial table. It is known that

$$B^*(r;c,p) = \sum_{N=c}^{r} \binom{N - 1}{c - 1} p^c q^{N-c} = \sum_{x=c}^{r} \binom{r}{x} p^x q^{r-x}$$

$$= 1 - \sum_{x=0}^{c-1} \binom{r}{x} p^x q^{r-x}$$

$$= 1 - B(c - 1;r,p) \tag{2-7}$$

Thus a left-hand sum of negative binomial probabilities is equal to a right-hand sum of ordinary binomial probabilities.

EXAMPLE 2-6

A student takes a five-answer multiple-choice examination orally. He continues to answer questions until he gets five correct answers. What is the probability that he gets them on or before the twenty-fifth question if he guesses at each answer?

Solution

The reasonableness of assumptions (*a*) to (*c*) of (2-5) was discussed in Example 2-4. Also, (*d*) is satisfied, since the number of questions required to achieve five successes is a random variable. Thus we use the negative binomial model with $c = 5$, $r = 25$, $p = \frac{1}{5}$. We have

$$B^*\left(25;5,\frac{1}{5}\right) = \sum_{N=5}^{25} \binom{N-1}{4}\left(\frac{1}{5}\right)^5\left(\frac{4}{5}\right)^{N-5} \quad \text{or} \quad \sum_{N=5}^{25} b^*\left(N;5,\frac{1}{5}\right)$$

$$= \sum_{x=5}^{25} \binom{25}{x}\left(\frac{1}{5}\right)^x\left(\frac{4}{5}\right)^{25-x} \quad \text{or} \quad \sum_{x=5}^{25} b\left(x;25,\frac{1}{5}\right)$$

$$= 1 - \sum_{x=0}^{4} \binom{25}{x}\left(\frac{1}{5}\right)^x\left(\frac{4}{5}\right)^{25-x}$$

$$= 1 - B\left(4;25,\frac{1}{5}\right)$$

$$= 1 - .42067 \qquad \text{\textit{from Appendix D-1}}$$

$$= .57933$$

EXAMPLE 2-7

Consider again the potato crop of Example 2-5. Suppose that a cook needs 20 good potatoes for a meal, so he selects potatoes at random, cuts them open, and throws away the bad. What is the probability that he must cut open more than 25 potatoes?

Solution

The assumptions (*a*) to (*c*) of (2-5) have already been discussed in Example 2-5. Since the number of successes is a fixed quantity, the negative binomial with $c = 20$, $p = .9$ is appropriate. We need

$$\sum_{N=26}^{\infty} \binom{N-1}{19}(.9)^{20}(.1)^{N-20} = 1 - \sum_{N=20}^{25} \binom{N-1}{19}(.9)^{20}(.1)^{N-20}$$

$$= 1 - \sum_{x=20}^{25} \binom{25}{x}(.9)^x(.1)^{25-x}$$

$$= \sum_{x=0}^{19} \binom{25}{x}(.9)^x(.1)^{25-x}$$

$$= \sum_{x=6}^{25} \binom{25}{x}(.1)^x(.9)^{25-x}$$

$$= 1 - \sum_{x=0}^{5} \binom{25}{x}(.1)^x(.9)^{25-x}$$

$$= 1 - .96660 \qquad \text{\textit{from Appendix D-1}}$$

$$= .03340$$

This result could also be obtained as follows:

$$\begin{aligned}
\Pr(N \geq 26) &= 1 - \Pr(N \leq 25) \\
&= 1 - B^*(25;20,.9) \\
&= 1 - [1 - B(19;25,.9)] \qquad by \ (2\text{-}7) \\
&= B(19;25,.9) \\
&= 1 - B(25 - 19 - 1;25,.1) \qquad by \ (2\text{-}4) \\
&= 1 - .96660 \qquad from \ Appendix \ D\text{-}1 \\
&= .03340
\end{aligned}$$

EXAMPLE 2-8

To determine who pays for coffee, three people each toss a coin and the odd man pays.   If the coins all show heads or all show tails, they are tossed again.   What is the probability that a decision is reached in five tosses or fewer?

Solution

A decision is reached on any trial if the result is two heads and a tail or two tails and a head.   To compute the probability of these events, the binomial is appropriate since

(a)   Each coin will show either a head or a tail.
(b)   The probability of resulting in a head is $\frac{1}{2}$ for each coin.
(c)   The three coins are tossed independently of one another.
(d)   Exactly three coins are tossed in each case.

Thus $n = 3$, $p = \frac{1}{2}$, and

$$\Pr(2 \text{ heads, 1 tail}) = \binom{3}{2}\left(\frac{1}{2}\right)^2\left(\frac{1}{2}\right) = \frac{3}{8}$$

$$\Pr(1 \text{ head, 2 tails}) = \binom{3}{1}\left(\frac{1}{2}\right)\left(\frac{1}{2}\right)^2 = \frac{3}{8}$$

and the probability of a decision is $\frac{3}{8} + \frac{3}{8} = .75$.
   Next each set of tosses is characterized by these facts:

(a)   A decision is reached or not reached with each set.
(b)   The probability of a decision is .75 for all sets.
(c)   The result of each set is independent of the result for any other set.
(d)   A variable number of sets is required to produce 1 decision.

Thus the negative binomial with $c = 1$, $p = .75$ is appropriate to determine the probability needed to answer the original question.   We have

$$\begin{aligned}
\Pr(N \leq 5) &= B^*(5;1,.75) \\
&= 1 - B(0;5,.75) \qquad by\ (2\text{-}7) \\
&= 1 - [1 - B(4;5,.25)] \qquad by\ (2\text{-}4) \\
&= B(4;5,.25) \\
&= .99902 \qquad by\ Appendix\ D\text{-}1
\end{aligned}$$

In summary we note that the binomial and the negative binomial are derived under almost the same set of conditions. In the first case the number of trials n is fixed and the number of successes x is a random variable. In the second case the number of successes c is fixed and the number of trials N is a random variable. As previously noted, x can be only one of the $n+1$ values $0, 1, 2, \ldots, n$, whereas the set of values available for N is infinitely large, containing all integers c or larger.

EXERCISES

Use Appendix D-1 to evaluate probabilities in the following problems. Comment upon the reasonableness of the negative binomial assumptions.

2-10 A well-known baseball player has a lifetime batting average of .300. He needs 32 more hits to up his lifetime total to 3,000. What is the probability that 100 or fewer times at bat are required for him to achieve his goal?

2-11 A student takes a four-answer multiple-choice examination orally. He continues to answer questions until he gets 10 correct answers. What is the probability that more than 25 questions are required if he guesses at each answer?

2-12 A missile manufacturer claims that his missiles are 90 per cent effective. The Air Force checks the stock by firing until 4 successes are obtained, and 11 trials are required. What is the probability that 11 or more trials are required if $p = .9$? What conclusion is one apt to draw?

2-13 Suppose that it is estimated that 40 per cent of a certain large group are strong supporters of a project and willing to volunteer their services if asked. The remaining 60 per cent will decline to volunteer. In order to get five people for a committee, members of the group are contacted one at a time until the committee is complete. Twenty-one contacts are required. If the 40 per cent figure is correct, what is the probability that 21 or more contacts are required? Are you inclined to believe the 40 per cent figure?

2-14 A scientist needs three diseased rabbits for an experiment. He has 20 rabbits available and inoculates them one at a time with a serum containing the disease germ, quitting if and when he gets 3 positive reactions. If the probability is .25 that a rabbit can contract the disease from the serum, what is the probability that the scientist is able to get 3 diseased rabbits from 20?

2-15 To determine who buys the coffee, four people toss one coin each. This is repeated until someone has a result different from the other three. What is the probability that a decision is reached in five or fewer repetitions?

2-4 THE MULTINOMIAL PROBABILITY MODEL

A fairly obvious generalization of the binomial yields the multinomial probability model. Consider a series of events or experiments with the following properties:

(a) *The result of each experiment can be classified into one of k categories C_1, C_2, . . . , C_k.*

(b) *The probabilities of falling into these categories are p_1, p_2, . . . , p_k in each experiment.* (2-8)

(c) *Each experiment is independent of all the others.*

(d) *The experiment is performed a fixed number of times, say, n.*

Thus, if $k = 2$, conditions (2-8) are the same as (2-1). We note that $p_1 + p_2 + \cdots + p_k = 1$, since the result of each experiment must fall into one of the k categories. To illustrate a series of events satisfying the above conditions, suppose that an unbiased die is to be rolled 10 times. Let C_1 be the outcome 1 or 2, C_2 be the outcome 3, 4, or 5, and C_3 be the outcome 6. Thus it is reasonable to take $p_1 = \frac{2}{6}$, $p_2 = \frac{3}{6}$, $p_3 = \frac{1}{6}$. We might like to know the probability that three of the rolls fall in category 1, five in category 2, and two in category 3. One order of outcomes that will yield this result is $C_1C_1C_1C_2C_2C_2C_2C_2C_3C_3$. By the multiplication theorem for independent events, the probability of this sequence is

$$(\tfrac{2}{6})(\tfrac{2}{6})(\tfrac{2}{6})(\tfrac{3}{6})(\tfrac{3}{6})(\tfrac{3}{6})(\tfrac{3}{6})(\tfrac{3}{6})(\tfrac{1}{6})(\tfrac{1}{6}) = (\tfrac{2}{6})^3(\tfrac{3}{6})^5(\tfrac{1}{6})^2$$

The number of mutually exclusive sequences, all having the same probability of occurrence, is $10!/3!5!2!$, the number of ways to permute

10 things taken 10 at a time if 3 are alike, 5 are alike, and 2 are alike. Using the addition theorem, we get for the probability

$$\frac{10!}{3!\,5!\,2!} \left(\frac{2}{6}\right)^3 \left(\frac{3}{6}\right)^5 \left(\frac{1}{6}\right)^2 = \frac{35}{432} = .081$$

We now generalize the above discussion to yield a formula for the probability of obtaining x_1 outcomes in category 1, x_2 outcomes in category 2, . . . , x_k outcomes in category k, where

$$x_1 + x_2 + \cdots + x_n = n$$

One order that produces the result is

$$\underbrace{C_1 \cdots C_1}_{x_1 \text{ times}} \underbrace{C_2 \cdots C_2}_{x_2 \text{ times}} \cdots \underbrace{C_k \cdots C_k}_{x_k \text{ times}}$$

By the multiplication theorem, the probability that this happens is

$$\underbrace{p_1 \cdots p_1}_{x_1 \text{ times}} \underbrace{p_2 \cdots p_2}_{x_2 \text{ times}} \cdots \underbrace{p_k \cdots p_k}_{x_k \text{ times}} = (p_1)^{x_1}(p_2)^{x_2} \cdots (p_k)^{x_k}$$

The total number of orders that produce the result is

$$\frac{n!}{x_1!\,x_2! \cdots x_k!}$$

the number of ways to permute n things taken all n at a time when x_1 are alike, x_2 are alike, . . . , x_k are alike. Since all the orders of outcomes have the same probability of occurrence and are mutually exclusive, we get the formula

$$f(x_1, x_2, \ldots , x_k; p_1, p_2, \ldots , p_k, n) = \frac{n!}{x_1! \cdots x_k!} (p_1)^{x_1} \cdots (p_k)^{x_k}$$

$$(2\text{-}9)$$

for the multinomial probability model. The x's can each take on any of the values 0, 1, 2, . . . , n, subject to the restriction that $x_1 + x_2 + \cdots + x_n = n$. The name "multinomial" arises from the fact that $f(x_1, x_2, \ldots , x_k; p_1, p_2, \ldots , p_k, n)$ is a term in the expansion of $(p_1 + p_2 + \cdots + p_k)^n$.

The computation of (2-9) can become a tedious chore, especially if n is very large. Tabulation would be cumbersome because of the variety of choices possible for the p's, k, and n. Fortunately, in many statistical situations where multinomial probabilities are encountered satisfactory approximations are available.

EXAMPLE 2-9

If a die is rolled five times, what is the probability that the results are a 1, a 2, and three other numbers?

Solution

First we check conditions (2-8).

(*a*) Each throw is a 1, a 2, or not a 1 or 2.
(*b*) The probabilities $p_1 = \frac{1}{6}$, $p_2 = \frac{1}{6}$, $p_3 = \frac{4}{6}$ remain constant for each throw.
(*c*) Successive throws are independent.
(*d*) The die is rolled five times, a fixed number.

Hence the multinomial model seems to be appropriate. Here $x_1 = 1$, $x_2 = 1$, $x_3 = 3$, and the probability of a 1, a 2, and three other numbers is

$$\frac{5!}{1!1!3!}\left(\frac{1}{6}\right)\left(\frac{1}{6}\right)\left(\frac{4}{6}\right)^3 = \frac{40}{243}$$

EXERCISES

Comment on the reasonableness of the multinomial assumptions in each of the following; then solve the problem.

2-16 A card is drawn from an ordinary deck of 52 cards. The result is recorded, the card is replaced in the deck, and the deck is shuffled. This is repeated 13 times. What is the probability of obtaining 5 spades and 3 hearts in the 13 selections?

◆ 2-17 In a large university it has been determined that 20 per cent live in fraternities or sororities, 30 per cent live in dormitories, and 50 per cent live in private homes. If a committee of five is selected, each person being chosen independently of the others, what is the probability that the committee has one person from a dormitory, one from a private home, and three persons from fraternities or sororities? What is the probability it contains three or more from fraternities and sororities?

2-18 Suppose that national records reveal that twice as many accidents occur on Saturday and Sunday as on other days of the week. That is, the probability of a Saturday accident is $\frac{2}{9}$, the probability of a Sunday accident is $\frac{2}{9}$, and the probability that an accident occurs on each of the other days of the week is $\frac{1}{9}$. From records, 50 accidents are selected independently of one another. The distribution of accidents according to the days of the week is

Sun.	Mon.	Tues.	Wed.	Thurs.	Fri.	Sat.
10	8	2	7	6	3	14

Write down, but do not attempt to evaluate, an expression for computing the probability of getting this particular distribution.

2-5 THE UNIFORM PROBABILITY MODEL

Suppose that an experiment can terminate in n mutually exclusive ways, all equally likely. The behavior of a true die on a single throw is an example of this kind of experiment. Any one of the six sides is as likely to show as any other. A more practical situation is created by writing k numbers, one each on k slips of paper of equal size; placing the numbers in a hat or box; mixing the slips well; and then drawing one.

For the die, the probability associated with each outcome is $\frac{1}{6}$. A formula or probability model for the situation is

$$f(x;6) = \frac{1}{6} \qquad x = 1, 2, 3, 4, 5, 6$$

Similarly, the model formula for the slips of paper is

$$f(x;k) = \frac{1}{k} \qquad x = x_1, x_2, \ldots, x_k \qquad (2\text{-}10)$$

where $x_1, x_2, \ldots, x_k$ are the k numbers. Thus $f(x;k)$ is the probability that x takes on any one specified value. Formula (2-10) will be called the *uniform probability model*. An important statistical application of the uniform probability model arises when we seek a random sample from a finite population. In statistics the word *population* is used to refer to the set of all conceivable observations (or measurements of some characteristic) which might be made under a given set of conditions. Examples are the ages of all people in a certain city, the weights of all horses in Kentucky, and the scores of all incoming freshmen at the University of Wyoming on entrance examinations. Used in a broader sense, a population may be a set or collection of objects or individuals for which we have no measurable characteristic in mind.

With time, patience, and cooperation we could eventually write down all the items in each of the above populations. When this is possible, the term *finite* is used to characterize the population. In many situations the set of observations is infinite. In studying the behavior of a die, we would probably regard the population as being the infinite set of outcomes which could be obtained from all conceivable throws made with the die in its present condition. It is obviously impossible to write down this set of observations. A *sample* is a subset or part of a population. The weights of 10 horses in Kentucky, the scores of 25 incoming freshmen, and the results of 100 throws of the die are samples.

Finally, consider the meaning of the word "random." If a population is finite, then a sample chosen in a manner which gives every sample of the same size an equal chance of being selected is called a *random sample*. In the infinite case a sample is random if each observation (*a*) comes from the same population and (*b*) is drawn independently of all the other observations. Conditions (*a*) and (*b*) seem reasonable for the 100 throws of a die. The outcome of any one throw in no way influences the outcome of any other. Thus we see that we might regard a population as a list (actual or imagined) of all possible outcomes of a random experiment. Hence it is not unreasonable to attempt to associate a probability distribution with the totality of observations which form a population. As we have mentioned previously, it can be a difficult problem to select a probability distribution which adequately characterizes a real-life situation.

Next let us consider how to use the uniform probability model in drawing a random sample from a finite population. Suppose that a population consists of seven individuals designated by 1, 2, 3, 4, 5, 6, 7. We want to select at random three individuals. To do this, we can place seven numbers in a hat and draw one number at a time without replacement until we have drawn out three slips. On all three draws, the probabilities associated with each outcome are uniform with $f(x;7) = \frac{1}{7}$ on the first draw, $f(x;6) = \frac{1}{6}$ on the second, and $f(x;5) = \frac{1}{5}$ on the third. We have yet to demonstrate that the probability of drawing any sample is the same as the probability of drawing any other. Suppose we draw 3, 5, 6. We can do this by getting 3, 5, or 6 on the first draw followed by drawing one of the two remaining numbers the second time and then drawing the remaining number the third time. The probabilities are respectively $\frac{3}{7}$, $\frac{2}{6}$, $\frac{1}{5}$, and by the multiplication theorem the probability of drawing this sample is

$(\frac{3}{7})(\frac{2}{6})(\frac{1}{5}) = 3!4!/7! = 1/\binom{7}{3}$. The argument is the same for each

of $\binom{7}{3}$ possible samples, so that the probability of drawing each is

$1/\binom{7}{3}$. Consequently, the procedure has produced a random sample.

The discussion is easily generalized to a population of N individuals and a sample of size n. On each selection the distribution is uniform. The probability that one of a specified set of n individuals is drawn the first time is n/N; the probability that one of the remaining $n - 1$ is selected the second time is $\dfrac{n-1}{N-1}$; . . . ; the probability

46

that the one remaining at the time of the last draw is then selected is $1/[N - (n - 1)]$. Consequently, the probability of drawing any specified set of n individuals is

$$\frac{n}{N} \frac{n-1}{N-1} \cdots \frac{1}{N-n+1} = \frac{n!(N-n)!}{N!} = \frac{1}{\binom{N}{n}}$$

No matter which set of n is selected, the probability of drawing the sample is $1/\binom{N}{n}$ for any one of the $\binom{N}{n}$ possible samples. That is, the distribution of samples is itself uniform with

$$f(x;k) = \frac{1}{\binom{N}{n}}, x = S_1, S_2, \ldots, S_k$$

where $k = \binom{N}{n}$ and $S_1, S_2, \ldots, S_k$ are the k possible samples. Here the variable x is n-dimensional, since each sample contains n values.

Fortunately, tables that make it unnecessary to draw numbers from a hat in order to obtain a random sample are available. The Rand Corporation has published a table [6] containing 1 million random digits. A small part of this table appears in Appendix D-2. One could construct such a table by using the hat procedure with the numbers $0, 1, \ldots, 8, 9$. After each draw the number would be recorded and replaced before the next draw. Thus the probability model for any one of the drawing results is

$$f(x;10) = \tfrac{1}{10} \qquad x = 0, 1, \ldots, 8, 9$$

so that each of the 10 integers is supposed to occur about 10 per cent of the time. From these numbers we can get a random observation from any uniform distribution. Suppose we want a random number between 1 and 57, inclusive. We select a page, put our finger some place on that page, and start reading numbers made up of two digits, proceeding down a column until we find one that is 57 or less. For example, suppose the first five such numbers below our finger are 92, 35, 49, 49, 16. Then our random selection is 35. If we desire a random sample of size 3, then we use 35, 49, 16, the first three numbers less than or equal to 57, ignoring a number already drawn. Similarly, if we want a random sample of size 50 from the numbers 284 to 3786, we use four columns and select the first 50 numbers between 0284 and 3786, inclusive, disregarding duplicates. When the bottom of the page is reached, we start at the top with the next column of four digits.

The Rand publication includes suggestions for use of the table. For example, a procedure superior to the one given above for selecting the starting position is outlined.   To use it, we select a seven-digit number by the previously described method.   Suppose that it is 4705457. Use the first five digits to locate a row (rows are numbered from 00000 to 19999).   Since we have 47054, which is out of the range, we reduce the first digit to a 0 (to a 1 if the first digit is odd) and use row 07054. The last two numbers, 57 in the example, are used to locate the column (there are 50 columns for each line).   Whenever the number exceeds 50, we subtract 50 from it to determine the row number.   Thus we begin in column 7 of line 07054.   Since Appendix D-2 contains only 200 rows, a five-digit number will suffice for locating the starting point. After using a five-digit number for this purpose, it is advisable to draw a line through it so that a different one will be used next time.

EXAMPLE 2-10

Draw a random sample of size 5 from the numbers 1, 2, . . . , 353.

Solution

Suppose that we use the five-digit number in the upper right-hand corner of the first page of Appendix D-2 to determine our starting point.   Since this number is 74945, we shall begin in row 149 with column 45.   The first three-digit number is then 293.   Below 293 we find 542, 838, 304, etc.   Our sample is 293, 304, 79, 84, 275.

EXERCISES

2-19   Suppose that your class contains 80 students numbered 1 to 80. Select a random sample of size 10 by using Appendix D-2.   Use the five-digit number in the upper left-hand corner of the first page of the table to determine the starting point.

2-20   Show that the first number selected in Exercise 2-19 comes from a uniform distribution with $f(x;80) = \frac{1}{80}$, $x = 1, 2, . . . , 80$.

2-6   THE HYPERGEOMETRIC PROBABILITY MODEL

Let us suppose that a sack of fruit contains six apples and four oranges. We may be interested to know the probability of getting two apples and three oranges if we were to draw five pieces of fruit from the sack one at a time without looking.   Knowing how to count combinations makes the problem fairly easy.   The total number of ways the drawing can be accomplished is $\binom{10}{5}$, the number of combinations of 10 things taken 5 at a time. Since 2 apples can be selected from 6 in $\binom{6}{2}$ ways and, with each of these selections, 3 oranges can be picked from 4 in $\binom{4}{3}$ ways, the total number of ways to draw 2 apples and 3 oranges is $\binom{6}{2}\binom{4}{3}$. Consequently, if each of the $\binom{10}{5}$ sample points is given equal weight, the definition of probability (1-4) yields

$$\frac{\binom{6}{2}\binom{4}{3}}{\binom{10}{5}} = \frac{\dfrac{6!}{2!4!}\dfrac{4!}{3!1!}}{\dfrac{10!}{5!5!}} = \frac{5}{21}$$

as our answer.

Before attempting to generalize the preceding discussion, we note *properties or conditions* that the following conditions characterize the situation.

(a) *The result of each draw can be classified into one of two categories, say, success (apples) and failure (oranges).*
(b) *The probability of a success changes on each draw.*
(c) *Successive draws are dependent.*
(d) *The drawing is repeated a fixed number of times.*   (2-11)

The fact that drawings are made without replacement changes (b) and (c) from the binomial situation. Obviously, if an apple is drawn the first time, the probability of drawing an apple the second time is reduced from an original $\frac{6}{10}$ to $\frac{5}{9}$. Since the outcome of any draw after the first is affected by what has happened on preceding draws, the drawings are dependent events. If the apple or orange is replaced after every draw and the fruit is mixed before the next draw, then the probability of a success remains constant, drawings are independent, and the binomial model is the appropriate one to use.

In general, the hypergeometric probability model is appropriate when *when else*

(a) *The drawing is made from N items.*
(b) *A random sample of size n is selected.*
(c) *k of the N items have some characteristic (for example, they may be defective).*   (2-12)

and we desire the probability of obtaining x defectives in the n draws. The three numbers N, n, and k are fixed, and x is a random variable.

The total number of ways to draw the n items is $\binom{N}{n}$. To obtain exactly x defectives implies that $n - x$ nondefective items must be drawn from a total of $N - k$ available. The total number of ways to get exactly x defectives and $n - x$ nondefectives is $\binom{k}{x}\binom{N-k}{n-x}$. Consequently, if each of the $\binom{N}{n}$ points is assigned equal weight, definition (1-4) yields for the probability that x of the n items are defective

$$p(N,n,k,x) = \left\{ \frac{\binom{k}{x}\binom{N-k}{n-x}}{\binom{N}{n}} \right\} \qquad (2\text{-}13)$$

In the apple-orange illustration we can make the identification $N = 10$, $n = 5$, $k = 6$, $x = 2$. In this case the possible choices for x are 1, 2, 3, 4, 5, or $n - (N - k) \leq x \leq n$ (we have to draw at least one apple). The alternative identification $N = 10$, $n = 5$, $k = 4$, $x = 3$ would work just as well if an orange were regarded as a defective. Now we see that the choices for x are 0, 1, 2, 3, 4, or $0 \leq x \leq k$. Thus x can be no smaller than the larger of the two numbers 0 and $n - (N - k)$, and it can be no larger than the smaller of k and n.

Appendix D-3 gives values of $p(N,n,k,x)$ and

$$P(N,n,k,r) = \sum_{x=\max[0,n-(N-k)]}^{r} p(N,n,k,x) = \Pr(x \leq r) \qquad (2\text{-}14)$$

for $N = 10$. An extensive table is found in [2], where both $p(N,n,k,x)$ and $P(N,n,k,r)$ are given to six decimal places for $N = 1(1)50(10)100$. In addition, some values are given for $N = 1000(100)2000$. A table for $N = 1(1)20$ is found in [5]. In order to enter Appendix D-3, it may be necessary to use the relationships

$$p(N,n,k,x) = p(N,k,n,x) \qquad \text{and} \qquad P(N,n,k,r) = P(N,k,n,r)$$

That is, n and k can be interchanged.

EXAMPLE 2-11

What is the probability of drawing two or fewer apples from a sack containing six apples and four oranges if five pieces of fruit are included in the draw?

Solution

The preceding discussion has indicated that the hypergeometric model is appropriate. We have already identified $N = 10$, $n = 5$, $k = 6$.

50

Now we want

$$\Pr(x \leq 2) = \Pr(1 \leq x \leq 2) = P(10,5,6,2)$$
$$= P(10,6,5,2)$$
$$= .261905 \qquad \textit{from Appendix D-3}$$

Without the table we compute

$$\frac{\binom{6}{1}\binom{4}{4}}{\binom{10}{5}} + \frac{\binom{6}{2}\binom{4}{3}}{\binom{10}{5}} = \frac{1}{42} + \frac{5}{21} = \frac{11}{42} = .261905$$

EXAMPLE 2-12

Ten vegetable cans, all the same size, have lost their labels. It is known that five contain tomatoes and five contain corn. If five are selected at random, what is the probability that all contain tomatoes? What is the probability that three or more contain tomatoes?

Solution

(a) There are $N = 10$ items to draw from.
(b) The number of draws made is $n = 5$, made at random.
(c) $k = 5$ of the 10 cans are tomatoes.

Hence the hypergeometric model is appropriate and the probability that all five are tomatoes is

$$p(10,5,5,5) = \frac{\binom{5}{5}\binom{5}{0}}{\binom{10}{5}} = .003968 \qquad \textit{from Appendix D-3}$$

The probability of obtaining three or more cans of tomatoes is 1 minus the probability of drawing two or fewer. Thus we want

$$1 - P(10,5,5,2) = 1 - .500000 = .500000 \qquad \textit{from Appendix D-3}$$

We observed that the binomial model is not appropriate for a series of experiments satisfying conditions (2-12) because the probability of a success is not constant and successive draws are dependent. If N is large and n/N is small, then the probability of a success changes very little from draw to draw and events are practically independent. Consequently, one would expect that the binomial would give good approximations to hypergeometric probabilities in this situation. Thus if 3,000 out of 10,000 people in a community favor a proposal, the probability of selecting a person who favors the proposal is .3 or very nearly this figure, whether the person selected is the first or twentieth one. For a discussion of hypergeometric approximations see [2].

EXERCISES

In each case discuss the appropriateness of the hypergeometric model. Use Appendix D-3 when possible.

2-21 The names of five men and five women are written on slips of paper and placed in a hat. Four names are drawn. What is the probability that two are men and two are women?

2-22 A 5-card hand is dealt from a well shuffled deck of 52 cards. What is the probability that it contains three aces? What is the probability that three or more cards are aces?

2-23 From a crate of 100 oranges, some of which are frozen, 10 are selected at random. Suppose that it is necessary to cut open an orange to determine whether or not it is frozen. What is the probability that 7 or more oranges out of the 10 are frozen if the box contains 20 frozen oranges? Write down an expression that would yield the answer, but do not evaluate it. (From tables the answer is .000302.) What conclusion is one apt to draw if a sample of 10 contains 7 frozen oranges?

2-24 Approximate the probability in Exercise 2-23 by using the binomial model.

2-7 THE POISSON PROBABILITY MODEL

A model often used for random variables distributed over time or space is the Poisson probability model. Experience has shown that the Poisson is an excellent model to use for computing probabilities associated with the number of calls coming into a telephone switchboard during a fixed period of time. We may know that the board can handle up to 20 calls per minute without being overtaxed. If the probability of 21 or more calls is sufficiently small, the board will provide efficient service. If it is not, then perhaps more lines or operators are needed to provide a satisfactory standard of service. The Poisson model is used to compute the required probability. Some other random variables for which the Poisson has been used to evaluate probabilities are:

1 The number of automobile deaths per month in a large city
2 The number of bacteria in a given culture
3 The number of red blood cells in a specimen of blood
4 The number of meteorites located on an acre of desert land
5 The number of typing errors per page
6 The number of defects in a manufactured article
7 The number of atoms disintegrating per second from radioactive material
8 The number of buzz-bomb hits on a square mile of London in 1944
9 The number of calls an individual receives per day
10 The number of deaths from horse kick per year for each army corps in the Prussian Army over a period of 20 years

In each of the above situations the following assumptions seem reasonable:

(a) *Events which occur in one time interval (or region of space) are independent of those occurring in any other time interval (or region of space) no matter how the interval is selected.*
(b) *The probability that an event occurs is proportional to the length of the time interval (volume or area of space).*
(c) *The probability that two or more events occur in a very small time interval (or region of space) is so small that it can be neglected.*

(2-15)

By using the assumptions (2-15), it is possible to show that the probability that exactly x successes occur in a given time interval (given volume or area of space) is

$$p(x;\mu) = \frac{e^{-\mu}\mu^x}{x!} \qquad x = 0, 1, 2, \ldots \qquad \mu = d^t \qquad (2\text{-}16)$$

where $e = 2.71828 \cdots$ and μ is the average number of successes occurring in the given time interval. Appendix D-4 contains cumulative sums

$$P(r;\mu) = \sum_{x=0}^{r} p(x;\mu) = \Pr(x \leqq r) \qquad (2\text{-}17)$$

for some values of μ. A fairly extensive table has been published by Molina [3]. His table gives $P(r;\mu)$ to at least six decimal places for $\mu = .001(.001).010(.01).30(.1)15.0(1)100$.

It is not as easy as with some of the preceding models to convince oneself that the assumptions (2-15) of the Poisson case are reasonable.

Sometimes it is obvious that the independence condition is not satisfied. For example, we might be tempted to use the Poisson to compute the probability distribution of the number of corn borers found in a hill of corn. A little reflection reveals that events are not independent, since insects are usually hatched in batches. As we have previously mentioned, however, models sometimes give fairly accurate probabilities even though all the assumptions are not satisfied. To pass final judgment on the appropriateness of the model, the experimenter has to rely on accumulated experimental evidence and statistical techniques (such as the chi-square test which is discussed in Sec. 6-6).

EXAMPLE 2-13

If a person receives five calls on the average during a day, what is the probability that he will receive fewer than five calls tomorrow? Exactly five calls?

Solution

According to previous discussion, experience has shown that the Poisson probability model is appropriate for this situation. The average value $\mu = 5$ is given. Thus we need

$$P(4;5) = \sum_{x=0}^{4} p(x;5) = .44049 \qquad by \ Appendix \ D\text{-}4$$

to answer the first question. The probability of receiving exactly five calls is

$$
\begin{aligned}
P(5;5) - P(4;5) &= .61596 - .44049 \\
&= .17547 \qquad by \ Appendix \ D\text{-}4
\end{aligned}
$$

That is, the probability of receiving exactly five calls is equal to the probability of receiving five or fewer minus the probability of receiving four or fewer.

EXAMPLE 2-14

A secretary claims that she averages one error per page. A sample page is selected at random from some of her work, and five errors are counted. What is the probability of her making five or more errors on a page if her claim is correct?

Solution

Perhaps the errors made are not independent of one another. If one or two errors occurring relatively near each other disturb the secretary, she may be inclined to make more errors relatively soon. However, assuming that the Poisson is appropriate, the probability is

$$\sum_{x=5}^{\infty} p(x;1) = 1 - \sum_{x=0}^{4} p(x;1) = 1 - P(4;1)$$
$$= 1 - .99634$$
$$= .00366$$

In view of the small probability we might be inclined to conclude one of the following:

1 The Poisson model is correct and a near miracle has occurred.
2 The model is correct but the wrong average value μ has been used.
3 The model is incorrect.

Probably (2) is the most plausible.

Besides being a probability model in its own right, the Poisson is sometimes used to approximate binomial probabilities when n is large and p is close to 0 or 1. Of course, it would make no sense to approximate a binomial sum which can be read directly from tables. The individual terms of the binomial are replaced with the corresponding terms from the Poisson with $\mu = np$.

EXAMPLE 2-15

A life insurance company has found that the probability is .00001 that a person in the 40 to 50 age bracket dies during a year period from a certain rare disease. If the company has 100,000 policyholders in this group, what is the probability that they must pay off more than four claims because of death from this cause?

Solution

The binomial model is not unreasonable since

(a) A person either dies from the disease or he does not.
(b) The records give $p = .00001$, constant for each person.
(c) Presumably, whether a person dies from the disease in no way affects what happens to another person in the group.
(d) The number of trials is $n = 100,000$.

Thus, the probability of more than four claims is

$$\sum_{x=5}^{100,000} \binom{100,000}{x} (.00001)^x (.99999)^{100,000-x}$$

Since $\mu = np = 100,000(.00001) = 1$, this is approximated by

$$\sum_{x=5}^{100,000} p(x;1) = 1 - P(4;1)$$

Appendix D-4 yields $P(4;1) = .99634$, so that $1 - P(4;1) = .00366$.

___

EXERCISES   *use D-4 table*

Comment upon the reasonableness of the Poisson model where necessary.

◆ 2-25 A city has, on the average, five traffic deaths per month. What is the probability that this average is exceeded in any given month? $P([X>5]) = 1 - P([X\leq5])$

$\lambda = \leq 5$
$\mu = 5$

2-26 If a typist makes two errors per page on the average, what is the probability of her typing a page with no errors? With one error? $P([X\geq20]) = 1 - P([X<20])$

◆ 2-27 A taxicab company has, on the average, 10 flat tires per week. During the past week they had 20. Assuming the Poisson model is appropriate, what is the probability of having 20 or more flats during a week? Would you suspect foul play? *Yes*

$\mu = 10$
$\lambda = <20 = 19$

2-28 An automobile insurance company has found that the probability of paying off on any given policy during a year is .001. What is the probability that the company has to pay 15 or more claims next year if it holds 10,000 policies?

◆ 2-29 An intercontinental ballistic missile has 10,000 parts. The probability that each part does not fail during a flight is .99995, and parts work independently of one another. The failure of any one part can make the flight a failure. What is the probability of a successful flight?

2-8 THE STANDARD NORMAL DISTRIBUTION

The models which we have discussed in Secs. 2-2 to 2-7 are discrete probability models. Each is used to compute probabilities associated with a particular type of discrete random variable. Now we turn to some important continuous probability models which will be used frequently in subsequent chapters. Whenever the models are used, the necessary assumptions will be listed. Although our main objective in this section will be to learn to evaluate probabilities for continuous

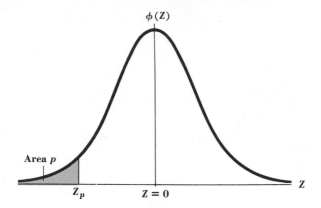

*Figure 2-1   Standard normal curve showing
tabled entry p.   The total area under the curve
is 1.*

probability models, one application of the standard normal will be given.

The density function for the standard normal distribution is

$$\phi(Z) = \frac{1}{\sqrt{2\pi}} \, e^{-Z^2/2} \tag{2-18}$$

where $e = 2.71828 \cdots$ and $\pi = 3.14159 \cdots$.   For our purposes it is not necessary to memorize (2-18).   It is, however, useful to know some geometric properties of the graph of $\phi(Z)$.   The standard normal curve is pictured in Fig. 2-1.   The curve approaches, but never touches, the horizontal axis.   The random variable Z can take on any value between $-\infty$ and $+\infty$.   However, the tables reveal that practically all of the area is between -3 and $+3$, so that the probability that Z is less than -3 or greater than $+3$ is very small.   The curve is symmetrical about the vertical axis through $Z = 0$.   In other words, the curve to the right of the vertical axis is exactly the same as the curve to the left of it.   Since the total area under a density function is 1, the area on each side of the vertical axis is $\frac{1}{2}$.   Because of the symmetry it is necessary to tabulate only areas on one side of the vertical axis.   However, to make the use of Appendix D-5 a little easier, entries are given for both positive and negative values of Z_p.

Appendix D-5 contains values of p such that

$$\Pr(Z < Z_p) = p \tag{2-19}$$

This means that the probability of obtaining a Z smaller than some specified Z_p is equal to p.   The geometrical relationship between

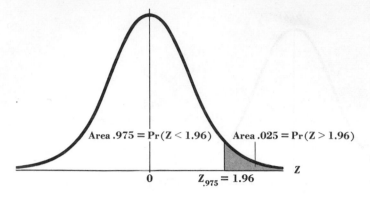

Figure 2-2   Standard normal curve showing $Pr(Z < 1.96)$
and $Pr(Z > 1.96)$ *as areas (Example 2-16).*

Z_p and p is illustrated in Fig. 2-1.   As an example, suppose we want to know the probability that Z is less than -1.12, that is, $Pr(Z < -1.12)$.   Proceed down the left-hand column of the first page of Appendix D-5 to $Z_p = -1.10$, then across the row to the column under .02.   We find $p = .1314$, so that $Pr(Z < -1.12) = .1314$.

EXAMPLE 2-16

Find the probability that Z is less than 1.96.

Solution

We look on the second page of Appendix D-5 opposite the row 1.9 and under the column .06.   The table yields $Pr(Z < 1.96) = .97500$.   We note that $Pr(Z < 1.96) + Pr(Z > 1.96) = 1$, since $Z < 1.96$ and $Z > 1.96$ are mutually exclusive events one of which must happen. Consequently, $Pr(Z > 1.96) = .02500$ by subtraction.   These area relationships are indicated in Fig. 2-2.

EXAMPLE 2-17

Find the probability that Z is between -1.12 and 1.96.

Solution

We seek the shaded area pictured in Fig. 2-3.   Since the events $Z < -1.12$ and $-1.12 < Z < 1.96$ are mutually exclusive,

$$Pr(Z < -1.12) + Pr(-1.12 < Z < 1.96) = Pr(Z < -1.96)$$

58

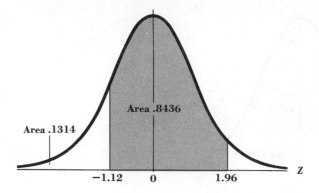

Figure 2-3   Standard normal curve showing
Pr(−1.12 < Z < 1.96) as an area (Example 2-17).

In other words

$$Pr(-1.12 < Z < 1.96) = Pr(Z < 1.96) - Pr(Z < -1.12)$$
$$= .9750 - .1314$$
$$= .8436$$

It is geometrically obvious that the shaded area is obtained by sub-traction.

EXAMPLE 2-18

Find $Z_{.95}$.

Solution

We want to find the value of Z which exceeds .95 of the area under the curve as indicated in Fig. 2-4.   From Appendix D-5 we find

$$Pr(Z < 1.64) = .9495 \qquad Pr(Z < 1.65) = .9505$$

Since .95 is halfway between .9405 and .9505, we use $Z_{.95} = 1.645$.

EXAMPLE 2-19

Find a value of Z, say, Z_0, such that $Pr(-Z_0 < Z < Z_0) = .95$.

Solution

We seek the shaded area in Fig. 2-5.   Since the curve is symmetrical, the area is .025 under each tail.   Hence the area below Z_0 is .975 and $Z_0 = Z_{.975} = 1.96$ from Example 2-16.

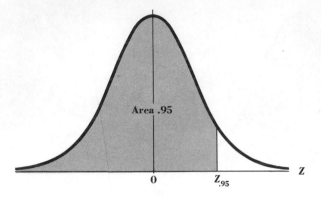

Figure 2-4 Standard normal curve showing $Z_{.95}$ (*Example 2-18*).

The standard normal can be used to approximate binomial probabilities. If a random variable x has a binomial distribution with given values of n and p, then

$$Z' = \frac{x - np}{\sqrt{npq}} \tag{2-20}$$

has approximately a standard normal distribution. Let us consider an illustration.

Figure 2-5 Standard normal curve showing Z_0 *such that $Pr(-Z_0 < Z < Z_0) = .95$ (Example 2-19*).

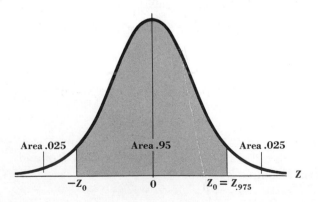

EXAMPLE 2-20

A die is thrown 1,000 times.   What is the probability that 170 or more 6's occur?

Solution

We have already discussed the adequacy of the binomial model in Example 2-1 for throwing a die a fixed number of times.   Here $n = 1,000$, $p = \frac{1}{6}$, $q = \frac{5}{6}$, and the exact probability is

$$\Pr(170 \leq x \leq 1,000) = \sum_{x=170}^{1,000} \binom{1,000}{x}\left(\frac{1}{6}\right)^{x}\left(\frac{5}{6}\right)^{1,000-x}$$
$$= .40158$$

from the Harvard University table.   To use the approximation, convert 170 and 1,000 to Z' units.   That is,

$$\frac{170 - 1,000(\frac{1}{6})}{\sqrt{1,000(\frac{1}{6})(\frac{5}{6})}} = .283 \qquad \frac{1,000 - 1,000(\frac{1}{6})}{\sqrt{1,000(\frac{1}{6})(\frac{5}{6})}} = 70.7$$

Then

$$\begin{aligned}\Pr(170 \leq x \leq 1,000) &\cong \Pr(.283 < Z < 70.7)\\ &= \Pr(Z < 70.7) - \Pr(Z < .283)\\ &= 1 - \Pr(Z < .283)\end{aligned}$$

From Appendix D-5

$$\Pr(Z < .28) = .6103 \qquad \Pr(Z < .29) = .6141$$

Thus, to two decimal places $\Pr(Z < .283) = .61$ and

$$\Pr(170 \leq x \leq 1000) \cong .39$$

Naturally, it would be ridiculous to go through the calculations in Example 2-20 to get an approximate answer when one correct to five decimal places is available in a table.   By going through them, however, we demonstrated that the approximation is fairly good.   The above approximation would most likely be used when (1) n is larger than 1,000, so that the range of the Harvard table is exceeded, and (2) p is between .05 and .95.   For smaller or larger p, the Poisson approximation demonstrated in Example 2-15 is apt to be better. The normal approximation is best when p is near $\frac{1}{2}$.   A slight improvement on the approximation is usually obtained by decreasing the lower limit and raising the upper of the binomial sum by $\frac{1}{2}$ before converting to Z' units (in Example 2-20 replace 170 by 169.5 and 1,000 by 1,000.5).   However, for $n > 1,000$ the improvement is very slight and rarely worthwhile in practical problems. In Example 2-20 the improved approximation yields a probability of .405.

EXERCISES

2-30   Use Appendix D-5 to find (a) $\Pr(Z < 1.37)$, (b) $\Pr(-.67 < Z < 1.37)$, (c) $\Pr(Z > 1.00)$, and (d) the probability that Z differs from 0 by at least 1.

◆ 2-31   Use Appendix D-5 to find (a) $Z_{.99}$, (b) $Z_{.90}$, (c) $Z_{.025}$, and (d) $Z_{.05}$.

2-32   Use Appendix D-5 to find Z_0, where $\Pr(-Z_0 < Z < Z_0) =$ (a) .90, (b) .98, (c) .99.

◆ 2-33   A die is thrown 2,880 times. What is the probability that the number of 6's is between 450 and 500, inclusive?

2-34   A coin is to be thrown 1,000 times. What is the probability of getting 490 or more heads? Approximate the answer and compare it to the exact result of .74667.

2-9   THE t, CHI-SQUARE, CHI-SQUARE DIVIDED BY DEGREES OF FREEDOM, AND F DISTRIBUTIONS

In this section we shall consider three other important continuous probability models. Since we shall have no use for the model formulas, they will not be given. Assumptions and applications are topics of later chapters. Our interest at this time is concentrated on graphs of the density functions and the use of the tables.

The t *distribution* is dependent upon a constant ν, called degrees of freedom, which is usually known in statistical applications. In most problems involving t, the degrees of freedom is an integer. Appendix D-6 contains entries for 38 different t distributions depending upon the choice of ν. To distinguish between the different distributions, we shall use the notation t_ν to denote a random variable having a t dis-

Figure 2-6   A typical t curve showing tabled entry $t_{\nu;p}$.

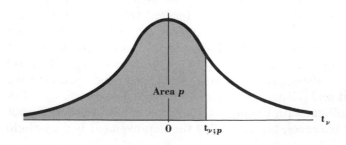

tribution with ν degrees of freedom.   A typical curve for a t-density function is given in Fig. 2-6.   Like the normal, it is symmetric about the vertical axis but has more area in the tails, less in the middle.   The larger the ν, the closer the curve resembles the normal distribution.   In fact, the bottom row of Appendix D-6 with $\nu = \infty$ gives entries that correspond to those found in Appendix D-5.

The entry in Appendix D-6 is the $t_{\nu;p}$ that makes

$$\Pr(t_\nu < t_{\nu;p}) = p \qquad (2\text{-}21)$$

for a given ν and p.   The geometrical relationship between p and $t_{\nu;p}$ is indicated in Fig. 2-6.   Since the curve is symmetrical, only p's larger than .50 need to be used in the table.

EXAMPLE 2-21

Find $t_{10;.975}$.

Solution

Under $p = .975$ and opposite $\nu = 10$ the table yields $t_{10;.975} = 2.228$. Thus $\Pr(t_{10} < 2.228) = .975$.   We note $t_{\infty;.975} = 1.96 = Z_{.975}$ as found in Example 2-16.

EXAMPLE 2-22

Find $t_{10;.025}$.

Solution

Since every t curve is symmetric about $t_\nu = 0$,

$$t_{10;.025} = -t_{10;.975} = -2.228$$

This relationship is illustrated in Fig. 2-7.   In general, $t_{\nu;1-p} = -t_{\nu;p}$.

Figure 2-7   Symmetry property of t curve.   The area under the curve and to the left of $t_{10;.025}$ is equal to the area to the right of $t_{10;.975}$.

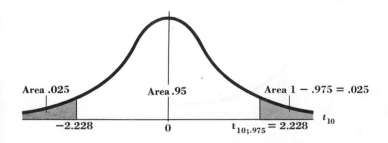

Area .025   Area .95   Area $1 - .975 = .025$

-2.228 0 $t_{10;.975} = 2.228$ t_{10}

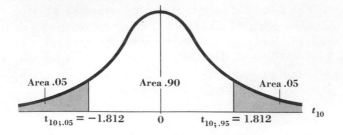

Figure 2-8 *t curve showing $t_{10;.95}$ and illustrating that $\Pr(-t_{10;.95} < t_{10} < t_{10;.95}) = .90$.*

EXAMPLE 2-23

Find the $t_{\nu;p}$ such that $\Pr(-t_{10;p} < t_{10} < t_{10;p}) = .90$.

Solution

The geometric situation is pictured in Fig. 2-8. Both tails must contain an area of .05. Hence, since 95 per cent of the area is below $t_{10;p}$, $p = .95$, $t_{10;.95} = 1.812$, $-t_{10;.95} = t_{10;.05} = -1.812$.

Since t_∞ has a standard normal distribution, it is often easier to find Z_p for a given p from the t table than from the normal table. For example, $Z_{.90} = t_{\infty;.90} = 1.282$, requiring no interpolation or guessing to determine the third decimal place.

The χ^2 *distribution*, like the t distribution, depends upon an integer-valued constant ν, again called degrees of freedom. Appendix D-7 contains entries for 37 different χ^2 distributions. We shall use χ^2_ν to denote a random variable having a χ^2 distribution with ν degrees of freedom. A typical curve for a χ^2 density function appears in Fig. 2-9.

Figure 2-9 *A typical χ^2 curve showing tabled entry $\chi^2_{\nu;p}$.*

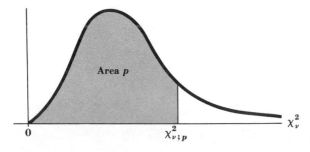

The χ_ν^2 variable cannot be negative, but it can take on any positive value. The entry in Appendix D-7 is the $\chi_{\nu;p}^2$ which makes

$$\Pr(\chi_\nu^2 < \chi_{\nu;p}^2) = p \tag{2-22}$$

EXAMPLE 2-24

Find $\chi_{10;.05}^2$ and $\chi_{10;.95}^2$.

Solution

Appendix D-7 yields $\chi_{10;.05}^2 = 3.94$ and $\chi_{10;.95}^2 = 18.31$. Thus

$$\Pr(\chi_{10}^2 < 3.94) = .05$$
$$\Pr(\chi_{10}^2 < 18.31) = .95, \text{ and } \Pr(3.94 < \chi_{10}^2 < 18.31) = .90.$$

Appendix D-8 gives the value of $\chi_{\nu;p}^2/\nu$ which makes

$$\Pr\left(\frac{\chi_\nu^2}{\nu} < \frac{\chi_{\nu;p}^2}{\nu}\right) = p \tag{2-23}$$

The random variable χ_ν^2/ν is called chi-square divided by degrees of freedom. Obviously, entries for chi-square can be converted to entries for chi-square divided by degrees of freedom, and vice versa. There are two reasons for including this latter table. First, entries approach 1 as ν gets large and interpolation is fairly easy for large degrees of freedom. Second, entries given to three significant figures require slightly less space, allowing more probability levels to be presented on each page.

EXAMPLE 2-25

Find $\chi_{10;.05}^2/10$ and $\chi_{10;.95}^2/10$ by using Appendix D-8.

Solution

It is easy to verify $\chi_{10;.05}^2/10 = .394$, $\chi_{10;.95}^2/10 = 1.83$ from the table. These are the same numbers one gets by dividing the results of Example 2-24 by 10.

The *F distribution* depends upon two integer-valued constants, ν_1 and ν_2, both of which are called degrees of freedom. We will use the notation F_{ν_1, ν_2} to denote a random variable having an F distribution

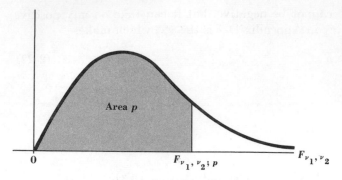

Figure 2-10   A typical F curve showing tabled entry
$F_{\nu_1, \nu_2; p}$.

with ν_1 and ν_2 degrees of freedom.   The entry in Appendix D-9 is
$F_{\nu_1, \nu_2; p}$, where

$$\Pr(F_{\nu_1, \nu_2} < F_{\nu_1, \nu_2; p}) = p \qquad (2\text{-}24)$$

A typical F-density function is shown in Fig. 2-10.   Like χ^2_ν, F_{ν_1, ν_2} cannot be negative but can take on any positive value.

EXAMPLE 2-26

Find $F_{10,5; .05}$ and $F_{10,5; .95}$.

Solution

Here $\nu_1 = 10$, $\nu_2 = 5$ and Appendix D-9 yields $F_{10,5; .05} = .301$,
$F_{10,5; .95} = 4.74$.   Obviously, $\Pr(.301 < F_{10,5} < 4.74) = .90$.

EXERCISES

◆ 2-35   Find (a) $t_{20; .99}$, (b) $t_{15; .05}$, (c) $t_{30; .50}$.
  2-36   Find $t_{20; p}$ so that it satisfies $\Pr(-t_{20; p} < t_{20} < t_{20; p}) = .95$.
◆ 2-37   Find (a) $\chi^2_{50; .01}$, (b) $\chi^2_{50; .99}$.
  2-38   Find (a) $\chi^2_{50; .01}/50$, (b) $\chi^2_{50; .99}/50$ from Appendix D-8.   Divide
          the answers for Exercise 2-37 by 50 and verify that the same
          results are obtained.
◆ 2-39   Find (a) $F_{5,10; .01}$, (b) $F_{5,10; .99}$, (c) $F_{40,40; .50}$.
  2-40   Use Appendix D-6 to find (a) $Z_{.99}$, (b) $Z_{.05}$, (c) the Z_p which
          makes $\Pr(-Z_p < Z < Z_p) = .99$.

REFERENCES

1 HARVARD UNIVERSITY COMPUTATION LABORATORY: "Tables of the Cumulative Binomial Probability Distribution," Harvard University Press, Cambridge, Mass., 1955.

2 LIEBERMAN, G. J., and D. B. OWEN: "Tables of the Hypergeometric Probability Distribution," Stanford University Press, Stanford, Calif., 1961.

3 MOLINA, E. C.: "Poisson's Exponential Binomial Limit," D. Van Nostrand Company, Inc., Princeton, N.J., 1949.

4 NATIONAL BUREAU OF STANDARDS: Tables of the Binomial Probability Distribution, *Applied Mathematics*, Series 6, 1950.

5 OWEN, D. B.: "Handbook of Statistical Tables," Addison-Wesley Publishing Company, Inc., Reading, Mass., 1962.

6 RAND CORPORATION: "A Million Random Digits with 100,000 Normal Deviates," The Free Press of Glencoe, New York, 1955.

7 ROMIG, H. G.: "50–100 Binomial Tables," John Wiley & Sons, Inc., New York, 1953.

8 U.S. ARMY ORDNANCE CORPS: Tables of Cumulative Binomial Probabilities, *Ordnance Corps Pamphlet ORDP20-1*, September, 1952.

CHAPTER THREE

Parameters, Statistics, and Sampling Distributions

3-1 INTRODUCTION

In the preceding chapter we computed probabilities associated with probability models. Before making any computations, we not only attempted to justify the use of the model but also had to identify certain constants. These constants are called *parameters*. For any given problem they are fixed numbers, but they may take on different values when another problem is considered. The parameters encountered in Chap. 2 were n and p with the binomial; c and p with the negative binomial; n, p_1, p_2, . . . , p_k with the multinomial; k with the uniform; N, n, and k with the hypergeometric; μ with the Poisson; ν with t and χ^2; and ν_1 and ν_2 with F. We shall define a *parameter* as a constant entering into the model formula.

For the probability problems of Chap. 2 all parameters were known. In many situations that arise this is not the case. Let us reconsider Example 2-5 concerning potatoes. We were given that $p = .90$ and $n = 25$. Knowing that 90 per cent of the population of potatoes were good, we were able to completely describe the behavior of the random variable x, the number of good potatoes in a sample of size 25. The probability model that enabled us to do this was

$$b(x;25,.90) = \binom{25}{x} (.90)^x (.10)^{25-x}$$

A random variable, such as x, that is associated with a sample is called a *statistic*. In a more practical situation we would not know p and it is quite likely that we would want to make some inference about it. Suppose that a potato wholesaler claims that his product is 90 per cent good. We might believe him, but it is possible that we would require some evidence to support his claim before we accepted it as the truth. In order to make a decision, suppose that we count the number of good potatoes in a random sample of size 25 and accept his statement unless too few good potatoes are found in the sample.

The number "too few" could be determined on a probability basis computed under the assumptions that the binomial model is correct (which we are willing to believe) and that $p = .90$ (about which we are undecided). In statistical language this procedure is called *testing a hypothesis*, and it will be considered in later chapters. As we shall use the terms, a *hypothesis* is an assumption concerning the parameters of a model formula and a *test* is a rule indicating when to reject the hypothesis. In the above example the hypothesis is $p = .90$. The test could be: Reject $p = .90$ if 19 or fewer good potatoes are in the sample of 25.

The potato example illustrates the main difference between probability and statistics. Probability theory enables us to derive distributions for statistics based on samples drawn from a specified population. A distribution associated with a statistic is called a *sampling distribution*. Statistics, on the other hand, uses the information known about sampling distributions to draw inferences concerning the population by examining the behavior of a sample.

In the potato example we may not be interested in testing a hypothesis about the proportion of good potatoes. We are stuck with the crop no matter what p happens to be. We may, however, want to estimate p from a random sample to make some sort of price adjustment. Two kinds of estimates are in common usage. The first, called a *point estimate*, yields one value, say, $\hat{p} = .81$, which is our best guess for the proportion of good potatoes. The second, called an *interval estimate*, specifies a range such as .76 to .85 which we think includes or captures the true but unknown p. This chapter will include some point estimates, but interval estimation will be discussed in conjunction with hypothesis testing.

The probability models encountered in Chap. 2 can all be regarded as sampling distributions. The binomial is the sampling distribution of the number of successes in n trials when the probability of a success remains constant and trials are independent. The negative binomial is the sampling distribution of the number of trials required to achieve c successes when the probability of a success is constant from trial to trial. The hypergeometric is the sampling distribution of the number of good items in a sample of size n drawn without replacement from a population of N items containing k good ones. The Poisson is the sampling distribution of the number of times an event happens in a given time interval (area or volume of space) given the average number of successes is μ and assuming the Poisson is a reasonable model. The normal, t, χ^2, and F are sampling distributions for statistics to be encountered in this and some of the following chapters.

3-2 THE MEAN AND MEDIAN AS MEASURES OF AVERAGE

It is easy to construct a number of practical situations in which one would like to know the average or expected value of a random variable. The chuckaluck game of Example 1-11 is an illustration. If the expected winnings per play are too low, the gambler will not play. A tomato juice cannery might like to know the average contents per can to see how it compares with the standard printed on the label. Even though the cannery tries to put 46 ounces in each can, the weight will vary from can to can because measurements are subject to inaccuracies. A wheat grower might like to know the average yield per acre for a new variety in order to decide whether to adopt the new variety. A smoker in fear of developing lung cancer would possibly like to know the average nicotine content per cigarette for some brand to compare it to a safe standard.

In general, the true population mean μ is unknown. Providing information about it is a statistical problem. One logical estimate to use in its place is called the *sample mean*. If $x_1, x_2, \ldots, x_n$ is a random sample from a population, then

$$\bar{x} = \frac{x_1 + x_2 + \cdots + x_n}{n} = \frac{1}{n} \sum_{i=1}^{n} x_i \tag{3-1}$$

is called the mean of the random sample or the sample mean.

70

The sample mean has two properties that make it a very desirable point estimate. First, it is unbiased. A statistic is said to be an *unbiased estimate* of a parameter if the average or expected value of the statistic is equal to the parameter. In other words, the sampling distribution of the random variable $\bar{x}$ has the same average value as the original population. We shall demonstrate this fact by a numerical example in Sec. 3-5. The second desirable feature is that the sample mean tends to be closer to μ than any other unbiased estimate based upon the same sample.

Another measure of average sometimes used is the median $\tilde{\mu}$. For a continuous random variable x, the median is the value below (or above) which lies 50 per cent of the area under the density function. For the standard normal $\tilde{\mu} = Z_{.50} = 0$, and for the t distribution $\tilde{\mu} = t_{\nu;.50} = 0$, since both curves are symmetric about the origin. Thus, in the notation of Secs. 2-8 and 2-9 for a continuous random variable x, $\tilde{\mu} = x_{.50}$. That is,

$$Pr(x < \tilde{\mu}) = .50 \tag{3-2}$$

In most statistical applications involving the median, it is assumed that the random variable is continuous. It is more difficult to define the median in the discrete case, and the definition will not be given here.

To estimate the median, a sample median $\tilde{x}$ is used. When the sample values have been arranged in increasing order of magnitude, the sample median is the middle value if the number of observations is odd and the average of the two middle values if the number of observations is even. Thus if the sample is 7, 2, 5, the sample median is 5; and if the sample is 7, 2, 5, 9, the sample median is $(5 + 7)/2 = 6$.

In statistical inference the mean is far more important than the median. The latter is sometimes used as a quick approximation to the former.

3-3 MEASURES OF VARIABILITY

In many problems that arise variability is a very important consideration. The manufacturing of machined parts furnishes a typical example. It is of little help to know that the average ½-inch nut fits the average ½-inch bolt. Unless most nuts fit on most bolts, the machining process is turning out a product that is too variable to be of much practical use. If the abilities of the members of a class vary widely, perhaps different teaching techniques will be used than if the class is fairly uniform. Fuses for hand grenades should have small variability in their burning times. If the grenade explodes in either too short or too long a time after the fuse is set, the user is apt to be a fatality.

In attempting to construct a measure of variability, it is likely that we would first consider $E(x - \mu)$ for the random variable. On the surface this seems like a perfectly respectable measure of variability to use. Unfortunately, $E(x - \mu) = 0$ for every random variable x. For the discrete case this follows immediately (the continuous case requires calculus), since

$$
\begin{aligned}
E(x - \mu) &= \sum_{i=1}^{k} (x_i - \mu)f(x_i) \\
&= \sum_{i=1}^{k} x_i f(x_i) - \mu \sum_{i=1}^{k} f(x_i) \\
&= \mu - \mu(1) = 0
\end{aligned}
$$

Consequently, $E(x - \mu)$ is worthless as a measure of anything.

The next logical choice for a measure of variability is the *mean or average deviation*. It is defined to be $E(|x - \mu|)$. Let us illustrate the concept with the random variable x whose probability distribution appears in Table 1-1. First, by definition

$$
\begin{aligned}
\mu &= 1(\tfrac{1}{6}) + 2(\tfrac{1}{6}) + 3(\tfrac{1}{6}) + 4(\tfrac{1}{6}) + 5(\tfrac{1}{6}) + 6(\tfrac{1}{6}) \\
&= {}^{21}\!/_{6} = 3.5
\end{aligned}
$$

Then we can construct Table 3-1. The vertical bars mean absolute value. That is, μ is subtracted from the value of x and the sign is discarded. The table yields $E(|x - \mu|) = 1.5$. The interpretation is that x will differ from μ by 1.5 units on the average. Mean deviation is rarely used, primarily because it does not have the nice mathematical

Table 3-1 *Calculation of mean deviation for die random variable*

x	$|x - \mu|$	$f(x)$	$|x - \mu|f(x)$
1	2.5	$\tfrac{1}{6}$	2.5/6
2	1.5	$\tfrac{1}{6}$	1.5/6
3	.5	$\tfrac{1}{6}$	.5/6
4	.5	$\tfrac{1}{6}$	.5/6
5	1.5	$\tfrac{1}{6}$	1.5/6
6	2.5	$\tfrac{1}{6}$	2.5/6
		Sum	1.5

**Table 3-2 Calculation of variance for die
random variable**

x	$x - \mu$	$(x - \mu)^2$	$f(x)$	$(x - \mu)^2 f(x)$
1	-2.5	6.25	$\frac{1}{6}$	$6.25/6$
2	-1.5	2.25	$\frac{1}{6}$	$2.25/6$
3	$-.5$	$.25$	$\frac{1}{6}$	$.25/6$
4	$.5$	$.25$	$\frac{1}{6}$	$.25/6$
5	1.5	2.25	$\frac{1}{6}$	$2.25/6$
6	2.5	6.25	$\frac{1}{6}$	$6.25/6$
			Sum	$35\frac{}{12} = 2.917$

properties possessed by the variance, which we will consider next.

The *variance* is defined to be

$$\sigma^2 = E[(x - \mu)^2] \tag{3-3}$$

For continuous distributions the evaluation of (3-3) is a calculus problem which need not concern us. Let us illustrate the calculation for the discrete random variable used in Table 3-1. The results are summarized in Table 3-2. The square root of the variance σ is called the *standard deviation*. For the die random variable $\sigma^2 = 2.917, \sigma = 1.708$. Both σ^2 and σ are measures of variability in the sense that the more the random variable is dispersed about the mean, the larger they become. It is generally true that σ is larger than the mean deviation.

In the kind of problems mentioned at the beginning of the section, the population variance σ^2 is usually not available. Consequently, an estimate must be used in its place. If $x_1, \ldots, x_n$ is a random sample from a population, then

$$s^2 = \frac{(x_1 - \bar{x})^2 + \cdots + (x_n - \bar{x})^2}{n - 1} = \frac{\sum_{i=1}^{n} (x_i - \bar{x})^2}{n - 1} \tag{3-4}$$

is called the *sample variance* and s is called the *sample standard deviation*. As we shall demonstrate in Sec. 3-6, the sample variance is an unbiased estimate of the population variance σ^2.

EXAMPLE 3-1

Suppose that 10 throws of die yield 6, 4, 4, 5, 2, 5, 3, 4, 6, 1. Compute the sample mean, sample variance, and sample standard deviation.

Solution

$$\bar{x} = \frac{6 + 4 + 4 + 5 + 2 + 5 + 3 + 4 + 6 + 1}{10} = 4$$

$$s^2 = [(6 - 4)^2 + (4 - 4)^2 + (4 - 4)^2 + (5 - 4)^2 + (2 - 4)^2$$
$$+ (5 - 4)^2 + (3 - 4)^2 + (4 - 4)^2 + (6 - 4)^2 + (1 - 4)^2]/9$$
$$= (4 + 0 + 0 + 1 + 4 + 1 + 1 + 0 + 4 + 9)/9 = 24/9 = 2.67$$

$$s = \sqrt{2.67} = 1.63$$

Formula (3-4) is not well adapted for use with the hand calculator. It worked out nicely in Example 3-1 because each difference $x_i - \bar{x}$ was an integer. To obtain the computational formula, expand each square in the numerator of s^2. This gives

$$s^2 = \frac{x_1^2 - 2\bar{x}x_1 + \bar{x}^2 + \cdots + x_n^2 - 2\bar{x}x_n + \bar{x}^2}{n - 1}$$

$$= \frac{x_1^2 + \cdots + x_n^2 - 2\bar{x}x_1 - \cdots - 2\bar{x}x_n + \bar{x}^2 + \cdots + \bar{x}^2}{n - 1}$$

$$= \frac{\sum_{i=1}^{n} x_i^2 - 2\bar{x}(x_1 + \cdots + x_n) + n\bar{x}^2}{n - 1}$$

$$= \frac{\sum_{i=1}^{n} x_i^2 - 2\bar{x}n\bar{x} + n\bar{x}^2}{n - 1}$$

$$= \frac{\sum_{i=1}^{n} x_i^2 - n\bar{x}^2}{n - 1} \tag{3-5}$$

$$= \frac{\sum_{i=1}^{n} x_i^2 - n\left(\sum_{i=1}^{n} x_i/n\right)^2}{n - 1}$$

$$= \frac{n\sum_{i=1}^{n} x_i^2 - \left(\sum_{i=1}^{n} x_i\right)^2}{n(n - 1)} \tag{3-6}$$

Both (3-5) and (3-6), particularly the latter, are easily evaluated on a hand-operated computing machine.

EXAMPLE 3-2

Use (3-6) to find s^2 for Example 3-1.

Solution

The calculator gives

$$6 + 4 + 4 + 5 + 2 + 5 + 3 + 4 + 6 + 1 = 40$$
$$6^2 + 4^2 + 4^2 + 5^2 + 2^2 + 5^2 + 3^2 + 4^2 + 6^2 + 1^2 = 184$$

Thus

$$s^2 = \frac{10(184) - 40^2}{10(9)} = \frac{1840 - 1600}{90} = 2.67$$

EXERCISES

3-1 The table of random digits yields the following sample: 10, 37, 8, 99, 12, 66, 31, 85, 63, 73. Compute the sample mean, sample variance, and sample standard deviation. Also find the sample median.

3-2 Use Appendix D-2 to draw a random sample of size 20 of one-digit integers. Compute the sample mean, sample variance, and sample standard deviation. Show that $\mu = 4.5$, $\sigma^2 = 8.25$.

3-3 Find the variance and standard deviation for the random variable of Exercise 1-31.

3-4 Find the variance and standard deviation for the random variable of Exercise 1-32.

3-5 Find the variance and standard deviation for the random variable of Exercise 1-36.

3-6 Find the variance and standard deviation for the random variable of Exercise 1-37.

3-7 Suppose that in Exercise 1-37 the exact probabilities are unknown. To estimate the mean and variance for a particular individual, the experiment is repeated 10 times with the following numbers of correct identifications: 2, 0, 0, 0, 2, 1, 1, 0, 1, 0. Assume that no learning takes place, so that sampling is random, and estimate the mean and variance by the sample mean and sample variance.

3-4 THE NORMAL DISTRIBUTION

In Sec. 2-8 we discussed the standard normal random variable Z. By using calculus it is possible to show that the random variable Z has mean $\mu = 0$ and variance $\sigma^2 = \sigma = 1$. Formula (2-17) is a special case of

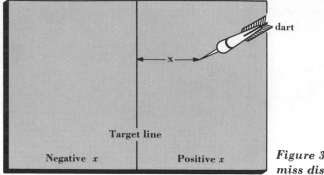

Target line

Negative x Positive x

Figure 3-1   x is the dart miss distance.

$x = 0$

$$f(x;\mu,\sigma^2) = \frac{1}{\sigma\sqrt{2\pi}}\, e^{-(x-\mu)^2/2\sigma^2} \qquad (3\text{-}7)$$

A random variable x with density function (3-7) is said to have a normal distribution with mean μ and variance σ^2. It is often assumed that random variables are normally, or approximately normally, distributed. Experience has shown that (3-7) with $\mu = 0$ is a good model to use to describe the behavior of aiming errors arising when darts are thrown at a vertical line through the origin (see Fig. 3-1). Other more practical examples of random variables that can be adequately characterized by (3-7) include heights of individuals belonging to a certain population, lengths of machined parts turned out on a lathe, yields per acre of a variety of wheat, and IQ's of individuals. In Sec. 3-5 we shall encounter another important use of the normal distribution. As we shall see, some statistics are approximately normally distributed even though they are computed from random samples arising from nonnormal populations.

The graph of the density function (3-7) is shown in Fig. 3-2. It is very similar to the one for standard normal. The curve is symmetric

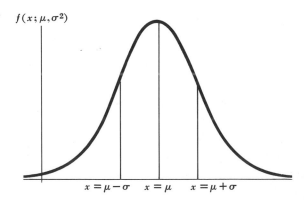

$f(x;\mu,\sigma^2)$

$x = \mu - \sigma$ $x = \mu$ $x = \mu + \sigma$

Figure 3-2   Normal distribution with mean μ, standard deviation σ.

76

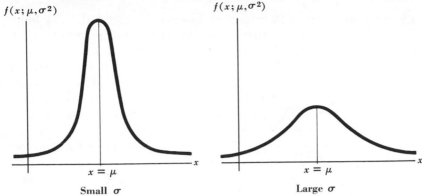

Figure 3-3   Effect of σ on the shape of the normal curve.

about the vertical axis through $x = \mu$.   Practically all of the area is between $\mu - 3\sigma$ and $\mu + 3\sigma$; thus, σ controls the shape of the curve. If σ is small, the curve has most of its area near μ.   The larger σ, the more the area is spread out (see Fig. 3-3).

Fortunately, no new tables are needed to evaluate areas under the curve.   It is known that

$$\Pr(x_1 < x < x_2) = \Pr(Z_1 < Z < Z_2) \tag{3-8}$$

where the Z's are obtained from the x's by the relationship

$$Z = \frac{x - \mu}{\sigma} \tag{3-9}$$

The random variable Z has a standard normal distribution.

EXAMPLE 3-3

Suppose that it is known that IQ's are normally distributed with $\mu = 100$, $\sigma = 10$.   Find the probability that a randomly selected individual has an IQ between 90 and 120.

Solution

Let x be the individual's IQ.   Then

$$\Pr(90 < x < 120) = \Pr\left(\frac{90 - 100}{10} < \frac{x - 100}{10} < \frac{120 - 100}{10}\right)$$
$$= \Pr(-1 < Z < 2)$$
$$= \Pr(Z < 2) - \Pr(Z < -1)$$
$$= .9773 - .1587 \quad \textit{from Appendix D-5}$$
$$= .8186$$

3-8   By using the information of Example 3-3, find the probability that a randomly selected individual has an IQ greater than 115.

◆ 3-9   Suppose a machine turns out bolts whose diameters are normally distributed with mean $\mu = \frac{1}{2}$ inch and standard deviation $\sigma = .01$ inch. What is the probability that a randomly selected bolt has a diameter between .48 and .52 inch? If the bolts are useless when the diameter is less than .47 or greater than .53, what is the probability of turning out a useless bolt?

3-10   Suppose that wheat yields are normally distributed with a mean of $\mu = 35$ bushels per acre and standard deviation $\sigma = 8$ bushels per acre. What is the probability that a randomly selected acre will produce more than 50 bushels?

3-5 SOME CHARACTERISTICS OF THE SAMPLING DISTRIBUTION OF THE SAMPLE MEAN

We have already mentioned that the sample mean is an unbiased estimate of the population mean. To demonstrate this fact by a numerical example, consider again the die random variable whose probability distribution is given in Table 1-1.

If the die is rolled twice, then the sample space (Exercise 1-5) consists of the 36 sample points appearing in Table 3-3, where the first number represents the outcome on the first throw and the second the outcome on the second throw. It is reasonable to assign a weight of $\frac{1}{36}$ to each point in the sample space if the die is true, or unbiased. The number pairs of Table 3-3 represent all possible samples of size 2 that can be obtained from the population of outcomes for the die. Dividing the sum of each pair by 2 yields the 36 sample means of Table 3-4. In other words, these are the 36 possible values of the random variable $\bar{x}$. Since the weight $\frac{1}{36}$ is associated with each

Table 3-3   Enumeration of all possible samples of size 2 obtained from a die

1, 1	2, 1	3, 1	4, 1	5, 1	6, 1
1, 2	2, 2	3, 2	4, 2	5, 2	6, 2
1, 3	2, 3	3, 3	4, 3	5, 3	6, 3
1, 4	2, 4	3, 4	4, 4	5, 4	6, 4
1, 5	2, 5	3, 5	4, 5	5, 5	6, 5
1, 6	2, 6	3, 6	4, 6	5, 6	6, 6

Table 3-4   *Enumeration of sample means for Table 3-3*

1.0	1.5	2.0	2.5	3.0	3.5
1.5	2.0	2.5	3.0	3.5	4.0
2.0	2.5	3.0	3.5	4.0	4.5
2.5	3.0	3.5	4.0	4.5	5.0
3.0	3.5	4.0	4.5	5.0	5.5
3.5	4.0	4.5	5.0	5.5	6.0

sample point of Table 3-3, this weight is associated with each $\bar{x}$ appearing in Table 3-4.   From the latter table we can construct the probability distribution of $\bar{x}$ which is presented in Table 3-5.

The mean of the sampling distribution of $\bar{x}$ computed from Table 3-5 is

$$
\begin{aligned}
\mu_{\bar{x}} = E(\bar{x}) &= 1.0(\tfrac{1}{36}) + 1.5(\tfrac{2}{36}) + 2.0(\tfrac{3}{36}) + 2.5(\tfrac{4}{36}) + 3.0(\tfrac{5}{36}) \\
&\quad + 3.5(\tfrac{6}{36}) + 4.0(\tfrac{5}{36}) + 4.5(\tfrac{4}{36}) + 5.0(\tfrac{3}{36}) \\
&\quad + 5.5(\tfrac{2}{36}) + 6.0(\tfrac{1}{36}) \\
&= \tfrac{126}{36} = 3.5 = \mu_x = E(x)
\end{aligned}
$$

Although we have used a discrete random variable x, the result

$$\mu_{\bar{x}} = \mu_x \tag{3-10}$$

is true whether x is discrete or continuous and holds if the population sampled is finite or infinite, regardless of the sample size.

In Sec. 3-3 we found that $\sigma_x^2 = \tfrac{35}{12}$.   Let us see how this compares to $\sigma_{\bar{x}}^2$, the variance of $\bar{x}$.   By definition of variance we have for Table 3-5

$$
\begin{aligned}
\sigma_{\bar{x}}^2 &= (1.0 - 3.5)^2(\tfrac{1}{36}) + (1.5 - 3.5)^2(\tfrac{2}{36}) + (2.0 - 3.5)^2(\tfrac{3}{36}) \\
&\quad + (2.5 - 3.5)^2(\tfrac{4}{36}) + (3.0 - 3.5)^2(\tfrac{5}{36}) + (3.5 - 3.5)^2(\tfrac{6}{36}) \\
&\quad + (4.0 - 3.5)^2(\tfrac{5}{36}) + (4.5 - 3.5)^2(\tfrac{4}{36}) + (5.0 - 3.5)^2(\tfrac{3}{36}) \\
&\quad + (5.5 - 3.5)^2(\tfrac{2}{36}) + (6.0 - 3.5)^2(\tfrac{1}{36}) \\
&= \frac{35}{24} = \frac{35}{12}\frac{1}{2} = \frac{\sigma_x^2}{2}
\end{aligned}
$$

Table 3-5   *Probability distribution of $\bar{x}$ from Table 3-4*

$\bar{x}$	1.0	1.5	2.0	2.5	3.0	3.5	4.0	4.5	5.0	5.5	6.0
$f(\bar{x})$	$\tfrac{1}{36}$	$\tfrac{2}{36}$	$\tfrac{3}{36}$	$\tfrac{4}{36}$	$\tfrac{5}{36}$	$\tfrac{6}{36}$	$\tfrac{5}{36}$	$\tfrac{4}{36}$	$\tfrac{3}{36}$	$\tfrac{2}{36}$	$\tfrac{1}{36}$

The general result which holds for random samples of size n drawn from an infinite population is

$$\sigma_{\bar{x}}^2 = \frac{\sigma_x^2}{n} \tag{3-11}$$

When drawing a random sample of size n without replacement from a finite population containing N items (so that the probability distribution is uniform with all probabilities equal to $1/N$), (3-11) must be replaced by

$$\sigma_{\bar{x}}^2 = \frac{\sigma^2}{n}\left(\frac{N-n}{N-1}\right) \tag{3-12}$$

Formulas (3-11) and (3-12) are very important when considering estimates of μ based upon $\bar{x}$. A small value of $\sigma_{\bar{x}}^2$ indicates that the sample means tend to be fairly close to μ. Of course, $\sigma_{\bar{x}}^2$ can be made quite small by taking a large sample. In the finite case if $n = N$, then $\sigma_{\bar{x}}^2 = 0$. One of the objectives of statistical analysis is to obtain reasonably accurate results without taking unnecessarily large samples.

Our numerical illustrations have been based upon samples of size 2, primarily to keep calculations simple. Graphically, the probability distributions of x and $\bar{x}$ (given in Tables 1-1 and 3-5) could be pictured as in Figs. 3-4 and 3-5. If we were to repeat the construction of the probability distribution of $\bar{x}$, replacing Table 3-5 and Fig. 3-5 by their counterparts first with $n = 3$ (for which the graph appears in Fig. 3-6), then with $n = 4$, then with $n = 5$, etc., we would find that, as n increases, (1) the number of entries in the probability distribution (and the number of points on the graph) increases each time (by 5), (2) the graph looks more and more like a normal curve, and (3) calculations become increasingly complicated. We might suspect that probabilities for $\bar{x}$ could be based upon a normal approximation if n is not too small. This is indeed the case, a consequence of the

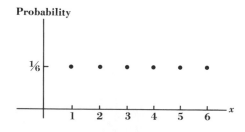

Figure 3-4 Probability distribution for a single die.

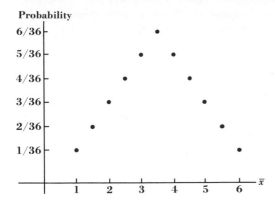

Figure 3-5 *Probability distribution for sample means generated by rolling a die twice.*

central limit theorem, one of the most remarkable theorems in mathematical literature. The theorem is as follows:

Let $x_1, \ldots, x_n$ be a random sample of size n drawn from any population with a mean μ and variance σ^2. Then the distribution of

$$\frac{\bar{x} - \mu}{\sigma/\sqrt{n}} = \frac{\bar{x} - \mu}{\sigma_{\bar{x}}} \tag{3-13}$$

approaches the standard normal as n increases.

The approximation is good even for relatively small n and, of course, improves as n increases. For most practical problems an n of 20 is large enough, and in some cases the approximation is satisfactory with even smaller sample sizes. The theorem implies that the distribution of $\bar{x}$ is approximately normal with mean μ and variance σ^2/n for moderate or large n.

One special case is worth mentioning. If the random sample is drawn from a normal population, no approximation is involved. The

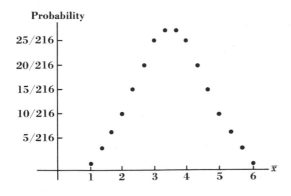

Figure 3-6 *Probability distribution for sample means generated by rolling a die three times.*

81

distribution of $\bar{x}$ is then normally distributed for every n. Thus perhaps we might expect that the more nearly normal the original population, the better the approximation provided by the central limit theorem.

EXAMPLE 3-4

A die is thrown 105 times. Approximate the probability that $\bar{x}$ is between 3 and 4.

Solution

We have already found $\mu_x = \mu_{\bar{x}} = 3.5$ and $\sigma_x^2 = {}^{35}\!/_{12}$. The central limit theorem implies that $\bar{x}$ is approximately normal with mean 3.5 and variance $\sigma_{\bar{x}}^2 = ({}^{35}\!/_{12})({}^1\!/_{105}) = {}^1\!/_{36}$. Thus

$$\Pr(3 < \bar{x} < 4) = \Pr\left(\frac{3 - 3.5}{{}^1\!/_6} < \frac{\bar{x} - 3.5}{{}^1\!/_6} < \frac{4 - 3.5}{{}^1\!/_6}\right)$$
$$\cong \Pr(-3 < Z < 3)$$
$$= \Pr(Z < 3) - \Pr(Z < -3)$$
$$= .998650 - .001350 \qquad \textit{from Appendix D-5}$$
$$= .997300$$

EXAMPLE 3-5

Consider again the population of IQ's described in Example 3-3. If a random sample of 25 individuals is selected, what is the probability that their average IQ is less than 99?

Solution

If it is known that IQ's are normally distributed, then $\bar{x}$ is normally distributed and no approximation is involved. We have $\mu_{\bar{x}} = 100$, $\sigma_{\bar{x}} = 10/\sqrt{25} = 2$. Hence

$$\Pr(\bar{x} < 99) = \Pr\left(\frac{\bar{x} - 100}{2} < \frac{99 - 100}{2}\right)$$
$$= \Pr(Z < -.5)$$
$$= .3085 \qquad \textit{by Appendix D-5}$$

The central limit theorem, as we have stated it, implies that each observation is drawn from the same population. A slightly more general formulation of the theorem is frequently used to argue that random variables arising from frequently encountered sampling situa-

82

tions are normally (or approximately normally) distributed. The more general statement is as follows.

Let $x_1, x_2, \ldots, x_n$ be independently drawn observations from n populations with means $\mu_1, \mu_2, \ldots, \mu_n$ and variances $\sigma_1^2, \sigma_2^2, \ldots, \sigma_n^2$. Let

$$
\begin{aligned}
S &= x_1 + x_2 + \cdots + x_n \\
\mu &= \mu_1 + \mu_2 + \cdots + \mu_n \\
\sigma^2 &= \sigma_1^2 + \sigma_2^2 + \cdots + \sigma_n^2
\end{aligned}
\tag{3-14}
$$

Then S is approximately normally distributed with μ and σ^2 given by (3-14).

It is then contended that some random variables can be considered as being the sum S of certain other random variables and that the more general formulation of the theorem justifies considering S to be approximately normal. For example, the miss distance x of Fig. 3-1 can be regarded as the sum of several random variables which determine x. These might include errors produced by standing a particular way when throwing, releasing the dart from a certain position, the result of last throw, the lighting at the time of the throw, disturbing noises, etc. Similarly, we might argue that a person's IQ is the result of a sum of variables affecting intelligence. These could include health, home background, emotional stability, climate, educational opportunities, etc. Although this type of argument is reasonably sound, again we state that there is no substitute for experience in determining the adequacy of a model.

EXERCISES

3-11 Three slips of paper numbered 1, 2, and 3 are placed in a hat. A slip is drawn and the number is recorded. The slip is then returned to the hat, the numbers are mixed, and a second number is drawn and recorded. Write down the sample space, find the probability distribution of $\bar{x}$, and verify that formulas (3-10) and (3-11) are correct.

3-12 Repeat Exercise 3-11 for the slip not replaced after the first draw. Verify that formulas (3-10) and (3-12) are correct.

3-13 A hybrid seed corn company claims that its product will average 120 bushels of corn to the acre. Twenty-five acres yield an average of 115 bushels per acre. If you are willing to assume that the standard deviation σ is 5 bushels per acre, the same as for other varieties, what is the probability of obtaining a sample average of 115 or less? What conclusion might be drawn?

3-14 Suppose that a random sample of four bolts is selected from those produced by the machine in Exercise 3-9. What is the probability that the average diameter is between .49 and .51?

3-6 SOME CHARACTERISTICS OF THE SAMPLING DISTRIBUTION OF THE SAMPLE VARIANCE

Consider once more the sample space of Table 3-3 resulting from two throws of a die. Let us next compute the sample variance of each of the 36 possible samples. Since $n = 2$, the sample variance is $s^2 = (x_1 - \bar{x})^2 + (x_2 - \bar{x})^2$. Thus we get

$$s^2 = (1 - 1)^2 + (1 - 1)^2 = 0 \qquad \text{for 1, 1}$$
$$s^2 = (1 - 1.5)^2 + (2 - 1.5)^2 = .5 \qquad \text{for 1, 2}$$
$$s^2 = (1 - 2)^2 + (3 - 2)^2 = 2 \qquad \text{for 1, 3}$$

and so on. The 36 sample variances are given in Table 3-6. Again it is reasonable to associate a weight of $\frac{1}{36}$ with each sample point and hence each s^2. From Table 3-6 we obtain the probability distribution of s^2 given in Table 3-7. The average value of s^2 is

$$E(s^2) = 0(\tfrac{6}{36}) + .5(\tfrac{10}{36}) + 2.0(\tfrac{8}{36}) + 4.5(\tfrac{6}{36}) + 8.0(\tfrac{4}{36})$$
$$+ 12.5(\tfrac{2}{36})$$
$$= \tfrac{105}{36} = \tfrac{35}{12} = \sigma^2$$

Although we have used a particular random variable x, which is discrete, the result

$$E(s^2) = \sigma^2 \qquad (3\text{-}15)$$

is true whether x is discrete or continuous and holds if the population sampled is infinite, regardless of the sample size. [In the sampling situation associated with (3-12), $(N - 1)s^2/N$ has average value σ^2.] From Table 3-7 the probability distribution of s could be obtained by replacing s^2 by s. It would be easy to verify that $E(s) \neq \sigma$. If n is fairly large, however, then the average value of s is approximately σ.

Table 3-6   Enumeration of sample variances for Table 3-3

0	.5	2.0	4.5	8.0	12.5
.5	0	.5	2.0	4.5	8.0
2.0	.5	0	.5	2.0	4.5
4.5	2.0	.5	0	.5	2.0
8.0	4.5	2.0	.5	0	.5
12.5	8.0	4.5	2.0	.5	0

Table 3-7   Probability distribution of s^2 from Table 3-6

s^2	0	.5	2.0	4.5	8.0	12.5
$f(s^2)$	$\frac{6}{36}$	$\frac{10}{36}$	$\frac{8}{36}$	$\frac{6}{36}$	$\frac{4}{36}$	$\frac{2}{36}$

EXERCISES

3-15 For the situation described in Exercise 3-11 show that $E(s^2) = \sigma^2$ and $E(s) \neq \sigma$.

3-16 For the situation described in Exercise 3-12 show that $E[(N-1)s^2/N] = \sigma^2$.

3-17 A bowl contains ten slips of paper. The number 1 is written on four slips, 2 on three slips, 3 on two slips, and 4 on one slip. Let x be the number on one slip of paper drawn from the bowl by a blindfolded individual. (a) Find the probability distribution of x, $E(x)$, and σ^2. (b) Suppose the number is recorded, the slip is replaced, and a second number is drawn and recorded. Find the probability distribution of $\bar{x}$ for samples of size 2 drawn in this manner and show that $E(\bar{x}) = E(x)$, $\sigma_{\bar{x}}^2 = \sigma^2/2$. (c) Find the probability distribution of s^2 and show that $E(s^2) = \sigma^2$.

CHAPTER FOUR

Testing Statistical Hypotheses

4-1 INTRODUCTION

A statistical hypothesis is an assumption about the model formula; in other words, it is a statement concerning the distribution of a random variable. Usually in statistical problems a hypothesis specifies one or more parameters associated with the population. As we observed in Sec. 3-1, a hypothesis for the population of potatoes is $p = .90$.

It is sometimes difficult to formulate a hypothesis for a given problem. However, assuming that this step has been accomplished, our next objective is to test the hypothesis. In order to do this, we observe a statistic whose sampling distribution is known if the hypothesis is true. Some values of the statistic may lead us to believe that the hypothesis is unreasonable and should be rejected. Other values

86

may be regarded as support for the hypothesis. However, obtaining a reasonable value of the statistic does not prove the hypothesis is true; it merely fails to contradict it. Thus 22 successes out of 25 trials under the conditions of a binomial may be a reasonable result when $p = .85$ as well as when $p = .90$.

We now turn to some examples of hypothesis testing.

4-2 A DISCRETE EXAMPLE

Let us again return to the potato problem discussed in Example 2-5 and Sec. 3-1. We have already decided that the model formula for the distribution of x, the number of good potatoes in a sample of size n, is $b(x;n,p) = \binom{n}{x} p^x q^{n-x}$. We are undecided about p but wish to investigate the claim that $p = .90$. Thus $p = .90$ is the hypothesis. The other parameter n has yet to be chosen. Suppose we decide to look at a random sample of $n = 25$ and base our decision about p on x. Now if the hypothesis is true, the model formula is completely determined, being $b(x;25,.90) = \binom{25}{x} (.90)^x (.10)^{25-x}$.

The next issue to be decided is the selection of the values of x which cast doubt upon the hypothesis. Hardly anyone would believe that $p = .90$ if 0, 1, or 2 good potatoes are in the sample. Not many people would be willing to believe the hypothesis if $x = 10$. Nearly everyone would feel that $p = .90$ is not unreasonable if $x = 23$. We must make a statistical judgment as to what we are going to regard as unreasonable results. To be specific, suppose that we decide that we will reject $p = .90$ if x takes on a value of 19 or less. In other words our test is: Reject $p = .90$ if $x \leq 19$. Let us examine some of the consequences of our test rule.

First, if $p = .90$

$$
\begin{aligned}
\Pr(x \leq 19) &= \sum_{x=0}^{19} \binom{25}{x} (.90)^x (.10)^{25-x} \\
&= \sum_{x=6}^{25} \binom{25}{x} (.10)^x (.90)^{25-x} \\
&= 1 - \sum_{x=0}^{5} \binom{25}{x} (.10)^x (.90)^{25-x} \\
&= 1 - .96660 \quad \textit{from Appendix D-1} \\
&= .03340
\end{aligned}
$$

Thus, the probability of rejecting the hypothesis when it is true is .03340. In other words, 3 out of every 100 samples would lead us to an incorrect decision. A hypothesis would be rejected when it is true. This kind of mistake is known as a *Type I error*. The probability of committing a Type I error is called the *level of significance* and is denoted by α. Here $\alpha = .03340$. The set of outcomes for the experiment which lead to rejection of the hypothesis ($x = 0,1,2, \ldots ,19$) is called the *critical region*.

Next suppose that the true value of p is .80, not .90. Then

$$
\begin{aligned}
\Pr(x \leqq 19) &= \sum_{x=0}^{19} \binom{25}{x} (.80)^x (.20)^{25-x} \\
&= 1 - \sum_{x=0}^{5} \binom{25}{x} (.20)^x (.80)^{25-x} \\
&= 1 - .61669 \\
&= .38331
\end{aligned}
$$

Of course, since the hypothesis is now false, we would like to reject with a very high probability. We would much prefer to have $\Pr(x \leq 19)$ near 1 instead of equal to .38331. The probability that we accept the hypothesis $p = .90$ using the test rule is .61669. By accepting a false hypothesis, we commit another kind of mistake called a *Type II error*. The probability of making a Type II error is designated by β (here $\beta = .61669$ if $p = .80$).

The various possibilities regarding the hypothesis are summarized in Table 4-1.

If the hypothesis $p = .90$ is rejected by obtaining an x less than or equal to 19, then we conclude that $p < .90$. The latter conclusion is referred to as the *alternative hypothesis*. We shall designate the hypothesis (sometimes called *null hypothesis*) by H_0 and the alternative hypothesis by H_1. Thus, in our example we choose between $H_0 : p = .90$ and $H_1 : p < .90$, the choice being made on the basis of the size of the binomial random variable x. As we shall see, it is important to formulate the alternative hypothesis at the time the hypothesis is selected and before the statistic used to reach a decision is observed.

Table 4-1 Decision versus hypothesis

	Decision	
	Accept	Reject
Hypothesis true	Correct decision	Type I error
Hypothesis false	Type II error	Correct decision

Another important concept is *power*. The power of the test is defined to be the probability of rejecting the hypothesis. In our example the power is .03340 if $p = .90$ and .38331 if $p = .80$. We can compute $\Pr(x \leq 19)$ for any p given in the binomial table. Appendix D-1 yields

$$
\begin{aligned}
\text{Power} &= B(19;25,.75) = 1 - B(5;25,.25) = 1 - .37828 = .62172 \\
&\qquad\qquad\qquad\qquad\qquad\qquad\qquad\qquad\qquad\qquad \text{if } p = .75 \\
&= B(19;25,.70) = 1 - B(5;25,.30) = 1 - .19349 = .80651 \\
&\qquad\qquad\qquad\qquad\qquad\qquad\qquad\qquad\qquad\qquad \text{if } p = .70 \\
&= B(19;25,.60) = 1 - B(5;25,.40) = 1 - .02936 = .97064 \\
&\qquad\qquad\qquad\qquad\qquad\qquad\qquad\qquad\qquad\qquad \text{if } p = .60 \\
&= B(19;25,.50) = .99796 \text{ if } p = .50
\end{aligned}
$$

Of course, power could be obtained for many more values of p by consulting more extensive tables. Plotting the power points on a graph yields Fig. 4-1. An ideal power curve would be of height 1 for all values of the parameter specified by H_1 and of height 0 for values specified by H_0. That is, if the hypothesis is true, we would always like to accept; and if the hypothesis is false, we would always like to reject. Much of the literature of mathematical statistics is concerned with finding tests for a given H_0 with the largest power when H_1 is true.

In constructing a test for the potato example it appears that we arbitrarily selected the critical region to be $x = 0, 1, 2, \ldots , 19$. Usually the statistician selects α instead and finds the corresponding critical region. Common choices for α are .05 and .01, although consideration of the consequences of a Type I error may lead to some other choice. Suppose we had selected $\alpha = .05$ for the potato problem. The binomial table gives (with $p = .90$) $\Pr(x \leq 19) = .03340$

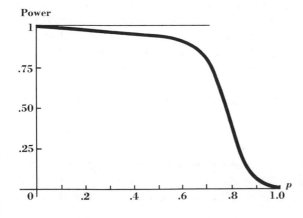

Figure 4-1 Power curve for test of H_0: $p = .90$ against H_1: $p < .90$ with $n = 25$.

and $\Pr(x \leqq 20) = .09799$, showing that this was an impractical choice for α. We either take the critical region $x = 0, 1, 2, \ldots, 19$ with $\alpha = .03340$ or the critical region $x = 0, 1, 2, \ldots, 20$ with $\alpha = .09799$. As we shall see, if the statistic used for the test has a continuous distribution, then an α of .05 or .01 or any other choice can be achieved.

EXERCISES

4-1 Suppose that we had selected as a critical region $x = 0, 1, 2, \ldots, 18$ for the potato example. Verify that α has been reduced to .00948. With the new critical region, what is the power of the test when $p = .80, .75, .70, .60, .50$? Compare with the values obtained when $\alpha = .03340$. What would you say is the effect on β when α is decreased?

4-2 Suppose that we had selected a sample of size $n = 100$ for the potato example. Verify that the critical region $x = 0, 1, 2, \ldots, 84$ has associated with it an $\alpha = .03989$. If $p = .90$ is rejected when $x = 0, 1, 2, \ldots, 84$, find the power of the test when $p = .80, .75, .70, .60, .50$. Compare with the values obtained when $n = 25$. What does increasing n do to the power curve? To the probability of making a Type II error?

4-3 A CONTINUOUS EXAMPLE

Suppose that a smoker is hopelessly enslaved by the cigarette habit. Even though he is aware that he may contract lung cancer, it is impossible for him to quit. Suppose that it has been definitely established by scientists that if cigarettes average 30 milligrams or more of nicotine, lung cancer is certain to develop in the user. The smoker is willing to take his chances if the average μ is less than 30 milligrams. Tests on a random sample of 100 brand A cigarettes yield $\bar{x} = 26$ milligrams of nicotine. If it is known that $\sigma = 8$ milligrams, what decision is he apt to make?

Certainly he will be willing to use brand A if $\bar{x}$ is small enough. Had $\bar{x}$ turned out to be 10, he would have no doubts. An $\bar{x}$ of 31 would not encourage him to use brand A. Somewhere in between lies a borderline or critical value.

One way to proceed would be to compute $\Pr(\bar{x} \leqq 26)$ under the assumption that $\mu = 30$. Then the central limit theorem implies that $\bar{x}$ is approximately normally distributed with mean 30 and standard deviation $8/\sqrt{100} = .8$. Hence

$$
\begin{aligned}
\Pr(\bar{x} \le 26) &= \Pr(\bar{x} < 26) \\
&= \Pr\left(\frac{\bar{x} - 30}{.8} < \frac{26 - 30}{.8}\right) \\
&\cong \Pr(Z < -5) \\
&= \text{practically zero}
\end{aligned}
$$

More extensive tables of the standard normal give a value of about .0000003 for the probability. The two most obvious conclusions are (1) $\mu = 30$ and a miracle has occurred or (2) μ is something less than 30. Certainly (2) is the more reasonable.

Regarding the example as a hypothesis-testing problem, a statistician would probably select for the hypothesis H_0: $\mu = 30$ and for the alternative H_1: $\mu < 30$. If $\bar{x}$ is small enough to reject H_0 with a high degree of confidence, then a reasonable conclusion is that brand A is safe. Suppose the smoker decides before observing $\bar{x}$ that he is willing to take his chances if $\bar{x}$ is some value $\bar{x}_0$ or smaller such that $\Pr(\bar{x} \le \bar{x}_0) = .01$ if the hypothesis is true. Actually, the statistic

$$
Z = \frac{\bar{x} - \mu}{\sigma/\sqrt{n}} = \frac{\bar{x} - 30}{.8}
$$

might as well be used as $\bar{x}$, since the standard normal tables are necessary to evaluate probabilities. Then in terms of Z the smoker will believe that H_0 is true unless the statistic Z is so small that it falls in an interval at the left end of the distribution with which is associated a probability of .01. The last row of Appendix D-6 gives

$$\Pr(Z < -2.326) = .01$$

The critical region for Z is shown in Fig. 4-2. Consequently, the smoker will compute Z and conclude that H_0 is true unless $Z < -2.326$. Since the observed $\bar{x}$ yields a Z of -5, he prefers to believe H_1.

Let us examine the consequences of Type I and Type II errors. If a Type I error is made, the conclusion is that the mean is less than 30 when in reality it is not. Presumably this would be a very serious type of mistake to make, since the smoker would adopt a brand of cigarettes that would endanger his life. Although the probability α was set at .01, this may be way too high when a life hangs in the balance. A figure of .001, or even .0001, would be more appealing. A Type II error is made when the observed $\bar{x}$ leads to a conclusion that $\mu = 30$ when actually $\mu < 30$. Brand A cigarettes would not be used

91

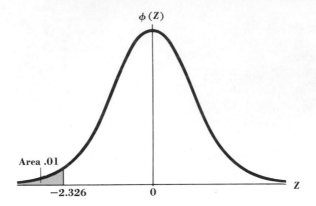

*Figure 4-2   A one-sided critical region and
associated level of significance for testing
H_0: $\mu = 30$ against H_1: $\mu < 30$.*

even though they satisfy the requirement set up by the smoker.   Perhaps the smoker would then test another brand.   At any rate, the
consequences of a Type II error do not seem to be very serious.   Thus,
in this example it is likely that a very small probability α would be
chosen and not much concern be given to β or power.

   When $\alpha = .01$, the test is: Reject if $(\bar{x} - 30)/.8 < -2.326$.   The
power of the test is

$$\text{Pr}\left(\frac{\bar{x} - 30}{.8} < -2.326\right)$$

which takes on different values for different values of μ.   In particular,
we already know that

$$\text{Pr}\left(\frac{\bar{x} - 30}{.8} < -2.326\right) = .01 \qquad \text{if } \mu = 30$$

since $Z = (\bar{x} - 30)/.8$ then has a standard normal distribution.   If
$\mu = 29$, then $(\bar{x} - 29)/.8$ is a random variable with the Z distribution.
Consequently, the variable on the left side of the inequality must be
converted before a probability can be evaluated.   We get

$$\text{Pr}\left(\frac{\bar{x} - 30}{.8} < -2.326\right) = \text{Pr}\left(\frac{\bar{x} - 29}{.8} + \frac{29 - 30}{.8} < -2.326\right)$$
$$\cong \text{Pr}(Z - 1.25 < -2.326)$$
$$= \text{Pr}(Z < -1.076)$$
$$= .141 \qquad \text{from Appendix D-5}$$

92

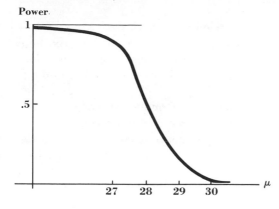

Figure 4-3 Power curve
for test of $H_0: \mu = 30$
against $H_1: \mu < 30$ with
$n = 100$.

Similarly, if $\mu = 28$, the power is

$$\Pr\left(\frac{\bar{x} - 30}{.8} < -2.326\right) = \Pr\left(\frac{\bar{x} - 28}{.8} + \frac{28 - 30}{.8} < -2.326\right)$$
$$\cong \Pr(Z - 2.50 < -2.326)$$
$$= \Pr(Z < .174)$$
$$= .569$$

and if $\mu = 27$, the power is

$$\Pr(Z < 1.424) = .923$$

After obtaining a few more points the power curve of Fig. 4-3 can be drawn. A number of power curves are available for tests based upon continuous random variables. Some of these will be discussed in later chapters.

EXERCISES

◆ 4-3 Suppose that $\alpha = .05$ had been selected in the cigarette problem. Verify that the critical region $(\bar{x} - 30)/.8 < -1.645$ has this α. With this new critical region compute the power when $\mu = 27, 28, 29, 30$ and compare with the values obtained when $\alpha = .01$. What would you say is the effect on β when α is increased?

4-4 Suppose that $n = 25$, not 100, in the cigarette problem. By using the critical region obtained with $\alpha = .01$, compute the power when $\mu = 27, 28, 29, 30$ and compare with the values obtained when $n = 100$. What does decreasing n do to the power curve? To the probability of making a Type II error?

In the potato and cigarette examples only small values of the statistic led to rejection of the hypothesis. The alternative to the hypothesis was one-sided in each case. A number of problems require two-sided alternatives with both large and small values of the statistic leading to rejection. Let us consider an example.

A tomato juice cannery attempts to put 46 ounces in each can. The automatic measuring device puts in x ounces, a random variable which is normally distributed. If the average content is below 46 ounces, the company may get into trouble with the government inspectors. On the other hand, if the average content is above 46 ounces, the company will make less profit. A reasonable hypothesis to test is $H_0: \mu = 46$ regarding either large or small values of $\bar{x}$ as evidence to the contrary. The alternative is $H_1: \mu \neq 46$, the conclusion we reach if H_0 is rejected.

Suppose that it is known that the standard deviation σ is .5 of an ounce. To test the hypothesis, a random sample of size $n = 25$ is to be taken and $\bar{x}$ determined. The plant statistician is satisfied with an α of .05, since this is the figure the government inspector uses. Consequently, since $\sigma_{\bar{x}} = .5/\sqrt{25} = .1$, the statistic $Z = (\bar{x} - 46)/.1$ will be computed and H_0 accepted unless a large or small Z is obtained. A reasonable critical region for Z is pictured in Fig. 4-4. Obviously the probability that Z falls in the critical region if H_0 is true is .05, and both large and small Z are regarded as equally objectionable.

After determining the critical region, the plant statistician takes a random sample of 25 cans and finds $\bar{x} = 46.18$. Since

$$(\bar{x} - 46)/.1 = (46.18 - 46)/.1 = 1.8$$

Figure 4-4   A two-sided critical region and associated level of significance for testing $H_0: \mu = 46$ against $H_1: \mu \neq 46$.

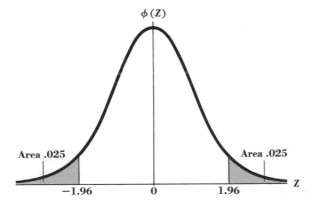

the hypothesis is accepted. In other words, the sample has not produced an $\bar{x}$ that departs from 46 by enough of a margin to cast doubt upon H_0.

Let us suppose that the statistician selected his sample and computed $\bar{x}$ before he decided upon a hypothesis or an alternative. Since $\bar{x}$ is larger than 46, he may be tempted to choose an alternative H_1: $\mu > 46$. Consequently, if he rejects H_0: $\mu = 46$ in favor of the new H_1, he will "prove" that the mean is larger than 46 ounces. Only large $\bar{x}$'s (and hence large Z's) support the new H_1. A reasonable critical region to choose with the new H_1 is pictured in Fig. 4-5 (using the same α). Now the observed Z of 1.8 falls in the critical region and the statistician concludes that the average weight per can is above 46. Thus if an alternative suggested by the data is chosen, an unwarranted conclusion is apt to be drawn. In general, it is not an acceptable procedure to use the data to formulate a hypothesis and then use the same data for the test. Only in comparatively few situations can a hypothesis be chosen after the experiment is conducted.

The power of the two-tailed test is

$$\Pr\left(\frac{\bar{x} - 46}{.1} < -1.96\right) + \Pr\left(\frac{\bar{x} - 46}{.1} > 1.96\right)$$

$$= 1 - \Pr\left(-1.96 < \frac{\bar{x} - 46}{.1} < 1.96\right) \quad (4\text{-}1)$$

This is, of course, equal to .05 if $\mu = 46$, for then $Z = (\bar{x} - 46)/.1$ has a standard normal distribution. If $\mu = 46.1$, then $Z = (\bar{x} - 46.1)/.1$ is standard normal and we must convert to this variable before we can

Figure 4-5 A one-sided critical region and associated level of significance for testing H_0: $\mu = 46$ against H_1: $\mu > 46$.

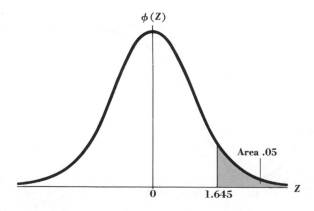

make probability statements. The probability (4-1) can be written

$$1 - \Pr\left(-1.96 < \frac{\bar{x} - 46.1}{.1} + \frac{46.1 - 46}{.1} < 1.96\right)$$
$$= 1 - \Pr(-1.96 < Z + 1 < 1.96)$$
$$= 1 - \Pr(-2.96 < Z < .96)$$
$$= 1 - (.8315 - .0015) = .170$$

If $\mu = 46.2$, the power is

$$1 - \Pr(-1.96 < Z + 2 < 1.96)$$
$$= 1 - \Pr(-3.96 < Z < -.04)$$
$$= 1 - .4840 = .516$$

and if $\mu = 46.3$, the power is

$$1 - \Pr(-1.96 < Z + 3 < 1.96)$$
$$= 1 - \Pr(-4.96 < Z < -1.04)$$
$$= 1 - .1492 = .8508$$

Similarly, using

$\mu = 45.9$ yields   power = .170
$\mu = 45.8$ yields   power = .516
$\mu = 45.7$ yields   power = .8508

Plotting the power curve yields Fig. 4-6. We see that the curve is symmetric about $\mu = 46$.

Figure 4-6   *Power curve for testing H_0: $\mu = 46$ against H_1: $\mu \neq 46$.*

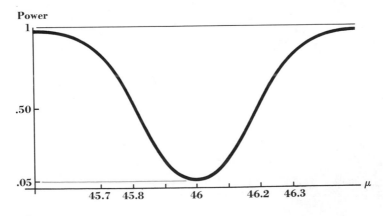

96

EXERCISES

◆ 4-5 Suppose that $\alpha = .10$ in the tomato juice problem. Verify that $(\bar{x} - 46)/.1 < -1.645$ and $(\bar{x} - 46)/.1 > 1.645$ is a critical region with this α. With this new critical region compute the power when $\mu = 45.7, 45.8, 45.9, 46, 46.1, 46.2, 46.3$ and compare with the values obtained when $\alpha = .05$. How does increasing α affect β?

4-6 Suppose that $n = 100$ and not 25 in the tomato juice problem. Using the critical region obtained with $\alpha = .05$, compute the power when $\mu = 45.7, 45.8, 45.9, 46, 46.1, 46.2, 46.3$ and compare with the values obtained when $n = 25$. What does increasing n do to the power curve? To the probability of making a Type II error?

4-5 SOME GENERAL COMMENTS

In the examples considered in this chapter there has been no attempt to justify the choice of either the test statistic or the critical region. It does seem reasonable, however, to use a binomial random variable to test hypotheses concerning the proportion of a population having a certain characteristic. Similarly, it is reasonable to use $\bar{x}$ to test hypotheses concerning μ. The critical region selected in each case was appealing on an intuitive basis. It is conceivable that other tests for these same hypotheses might exist and that some other test with the same significance level α might have a better power curve and hence be preferable. Determining which test is best is a mathematical problem which is beyond the level of our discussion. In the following chapters we shall in general use tests that are chosen on the basis of power, but we shall rely on intuitive justification.

We have already seen that α and β depend upon one another. For a fixed sample size increasing α usually decreases β, and vice versa. In some situations, such as in the smoker problem, a Type I error is much more serious than a Type II error. Consequently, when this happens, a small α should be chosen regardless of the effect on Type II error. In the tomato juice example a Type II error is apt to be more serious. If $H_0: \mu = 46$ is rejected when it should not be, perhaps all that is lost is a little time for checking the weighing device. On the other hand, if H_0 is accepted when it should be rejected, the cannery runs the risk of a large fine or loss of profit. Thus it may be worthwhile to raise α to .10, thereby increasing the power and reducing β for every $\mu \neq 46$. If the time lost in examining the weighing device is costly because of curtailed production, then Type I and Type II may be equally serious and an attempt should be made to keep both α and β small. The exercises of this chapter have demonstrated that β can be decreased for a fixed α if the sample size is increased. This is, of course, consistent with common sense, since one should be able to make better decisions if he possesses more information.

More often than not, α is selected somewhat arbitrarily, with .01 and .05 being the most common choices. Unless the experimenter is willing to increase the sample size, he is stuck with a fixed power curve and a fixed set of β's. The choice of α may be influenced by the reasonableness of the hypothesis being tested. If an experimenter is convinced that male and female high school seniors in the United States have the same average IQ, only a very unusual experimental result will change his mind and he will select a low α. On the other hand, he may believe that high school seniors have a higher average IQ than Bushmen of the same age from the interior of Australia. Consequently, in testing a hypothesis of no difference he will be willing to set α much higher.

In general, power calculations should be performed in the planning stage of the experiment. Usually α should be specified first. Then the sample size required to achieve a certain power at a specified alternative value of the parameter can be computed. We shall see how this is done in the chapters that follow. It would be disappointing to conduct the experiment first and then find that the test was not as powerful as might be desired. A well-planned experiment is much more useful and economical than one in which the experimenter just starts collecting data with no well-defined objectives in mind.

The cigarette example demonstrates one further idea that is fairly important. It is often a good statistical procedure to choose as the hypothesis the conclusion that one hopes to disprove. Thus the alternative states what the experimenter would like to prove. For the nicotine test we selected H_0: $\mu = 30$ against H_1: $\mu < 30$. Since an $\bar{x}$ of 26 or less is almost impossible to obtain if H_0 is true, we have overwhelming confidence in H_1. Suppose we had made the choice H_0: $\mu < 30$ against H_1: $\mu = 30$. Then only large values of $\bar{x}$ would cause us to reject H_0. Very likely an $\bar{x}$ of 30.4 would be regarded as support for H_0 [since $\Pr(\bar{x} > 30.4) = .31$]. Certainly we would be somewhat reluctant to use brand A if the observed $\bar{x}$ were 30.4.

Our original selection of a hypothesis and an alternative placed the burden of proof on the cigarette. This is usually the position we would like to adopt when considering a new and somewhat expensive machine to replace an old one still in good working condition. Unfortunately, some statistical experiments do not permit the manipulation of the hypothesis and the alternative. In others, the desirable choice may be unreasonable on the basis of economic or realistic considerations. In the cigarette problem the possibility exists that no brand will be acceptable unless we modify the statistical procedure. Ruling out all brands may leave the smoker with a choice of either inviting lung cancer or dying of nervous convulsions.

4-6 AN OUTLINE FOR HYPOTHESIS TESTING

When testing a statistical hypothesis, it is good procedure to follow an outline. There are a number of obvious advantages, especially for those not familiar with hypothesis testing. It may even prove worthwhile for an experienced statistician, because others may desire to read and study his results. An outline should include the following steps:

1 State the hypothesis and the alternative hypothesis.
2 Choose α, the level of significance.
3 Select a statistic whose sampling distribution is known if the hypothesis is true and certain other assumptions are satisfied. For the choice of a statistic we must rely on the results obtained by mathematical statisticians. In the following chapters we shall list good tests to use in standard situations, usually those considered best from the standpoint of power. Assumptions under which the sampling distribution is derived should be listed and their reasonableness questioned. We already know the underlying assumptions for some sampling distributions.
4 Find the critical region. The choice may be intuitively obvious. Critical regions will be given for some standard situations.
5 Compute the statistic and show a summary of all calculations.
6 Draw the conclusions. If the statistic falls in the critical region, reject the hypothesis. Otherwise, accept it.

Two further comments concerning the outline should be made. First, if the experimenter desires that the power be a given fraction (such as .90) when a specified alternative is true, this fact should be listed under step 2. Under these circumstances an additional calculation to determine the sample size n will be necessary. This can be accomplished under step 4. That is, step 4 can be changed to read: "Find the sample size n and then determine the critical region." (Of course, two steps can be used if one so desires.)

Although these modifications are worthwhile, in general we shall not include them with the outline, primarily because of the difficulty in selecting a specified alternative value and an accompanying power which are realistic for the particular problem at hand. We shall, however, demonstrate the modifications with the smoker problem.

Second, the sample should be drawn after step 4 is completed. Perhaps it would be preferable to include either as an additional step between 4 and 5 or as part of step 5 the statement: "Draw a random sample of size n." However, we shall not repeat this phrase every time but shall regard the drawing of a random sample at this stage as understood. Now let us illustrate the outline by using the three examples discussed earlier in the chapter.

EXAMPLE 4-1

Write out the outline for the potato problem of Sec. 4-2.

Solution

1 $H_0: p = .90$, $H_1: p < .90$.
2 We arbitrarily select α as large as possible but smaller than .05.
3 The statistic used is x, the number of good potatoes in a sample of size 25. If the hypothesis is true, the sampling distribution of x is binomial with $n = 25$, $p = .90$ provided that:
   (a) Each potato can be classified good or bad.
   (b) The probability of a success is constant from trial to trial.
   (c) Potatoes are independently good or bad.
   (d) The number of trials is fixed.
   We decided that the assumptions are reasonable in Example 2-5.
4 Appendix D-1 yields a critical region of $x = 0, 1, 2, \ldots, 19$ with $\alpha = .03340$.
5 No computation is necessary. The statistic is the observed value of x. Since a specific value was not given, let us assume 20 good potatoes were in the sample.
6 Accept H_0 and conclude $p = .90$, since the statistic does not fall in the critical region. As we have previously observed, it has not been proved that $p = .90$. Rather, if $p = .90$, 20 good potatoes is a reasonable result.

EXAMPLE 4-2

Write out the outline for the cigarette problem of Sec. 4-3.

Solution

1 $H_0: \mu = 30$, $H_1: \mu < 30$.
2 We arbitrarily selected $\alpha = .01$, although we commented that .001 or .0001 might be better.

3 The statistic used is $Z = (\bar{x} - \mu)/\sigma_{\bar{x}} = (\bar{x} - 30)/\sigma_{\bar{x}}$. If the hypothesis is true, the random variable Z has a standard normal distribution provided that:

(a) The sample $x_1, \ldots, x_n$ is drawn randomly.

(b) The population of nicotine contents is normally distributed.

(c) The standard deviation of nicotine contents is 8 milligrams.

We try to collect the sample in a manner which makes (a) reasonable, probably taking one cigarette from a pack and selecting each pack from a different stock. Since $n = 100$, assumption (b) is not necessary. Assumption (c) may not be realistic, but we assume $\sigma = 8$ to simplify the problem (the case of unknown σ will be considered in the next chapter). The random variable Z will be approximately normally distributed regardless of the distribution of the original x's because of the central limit theorem.

4 The critical region is $Z < -2.326$ as pictured in Fig. 4-2.

5 The computations are

$$\sigma_{\bar{x}} = \frac{\sigma}{\sqrt{n}} = \frac{8}{\sqrt{100}} = .8$$

The observed $\bar{x} = 26$. Thus the observed Z is

$$Z = \frac{26 - 30}{.8} = -5$$

6 Since the observed Z falls in the critical region, H_0 is rejected. This means brand A is regarded as safe. Not only is H_0 rejected at the .01 level of significance, it is also rejected at the .0000003 level of significance. When H_0 is rejected, it is generally good procedure to report this additional figure in step 6 if it is available.

Now suppose that the smoker had specified in advance that he wanted the power to be .90 if $\mu = 28$. Then the following changes would be made in the outline:

2 We select $\alpha = .01$ and power $= .90$ if $\mu = 28$.

4 The sample size n is calculated to be 207 (Example 5-3) and the critical region is $Z < -2.326$. (Here the critical region does not depend upon n, but that is usually not the case.)

5 The observed value of Z would be recalculated with the new $\bar{x}$ and $n = 207$.

6 The appropriate conclusion would be drawn.

EXAMPLE 4-3

Write out the outline for the tomato juice problem of Sec. 4-4.

Solution

1    $H_0: \mu = 46$, $H_1: \mu \neq 46$.

2    $\alpha = .05$ is selected primarily because it is the α used by the government inspector.

3   The statistic used is $Z = (\bar{x} - \mu)/\sigma_{\bar{x}} = (\bar{x} - 46)/\sigma_{\bar{x}}$. Again if the hypothesis is true, the sampling distribution of Z is standard normal provided:

    (a) The cans of tomato juice are selected randomly.

    (b) The population of weights is normally distributed. To compute Z, we must also assume (c) σ is known.

In order to make (a) reasonable, one can might be selected off the production line every 2 minutes. It was assumed that (b) is true but, because of the central limit theorem, the assumption is not critical. Although assumption (c) is probably more realistic than in the cigarette problem, it may not be fulfilled. To simplify the problem, we accept $\sigma = .5$ as the truth.

4   The critical region is $Z < -1.96$ and $Z > 1.96$ as pictured in Fig. 4-4.

5   The computations are

$$\sigma_{\bar{x}} = \frac{\sigma}{\sqrt{n}} = \frac{.5}{\sqrt{25}} = .1$$

The observed $\bar{x} = 46.18$. Thus the observed Z is

$$Z = \frac{46.18 - 46}{.1} = 1.8$$

6   The observed value of Z does not fall in the critical region. Consequently, H_0 is accepted and it is concluded that the standard of a 46-ounce average is being met.

EXERCISES

◆ 4-7   Write out the outline for the experiment described in Exercise 4-1. Use the largest α possible less than .01 and assume that the observed x is 16.

4-8   Write out the outline for the experiment described in Exercise 4-5. Use $\alpha = .10$ and use 46.18 for the observed value of $\bar{x}$.

CHAPTER FIVE

Some Statistical Inference for Means and Variances

5-1 INTRODUCTION

We are now in a position to make a systematic study of some of the standard problems of statistical inference. The procedures described in this and the following chapters are based upon sound mathematical principles. In particular, most of the tests have the property that their power curves are in general better than power curves associated with other tests for the same hypothesis. As we have implied previously, mathematical justification is a topic for more advanced courses in statistics. Consequently, our main objectives will be to learn how and when to use these standard techniques.

5-2 TESTING HYPOTHESES CONCERNING A MEAN WHEN σ^2 IS KNOWN

The three most commonly occurring situations for hypotheses and alternatives are used in the examples of the preceding chapter. The cigarette problem of Sec. 4-3 is a special case of testing

$$H_0: \mu = \mu_0 \text{ against } H_1: \mu < \mu_0 \qquad (5\text{-}1)$$

in which $\mu_0 = 30$. Frequently, one may be interested in testing

$$H_0: \mu = \mu_0 \text{ against } H_1: \mu > \mu_0 \qquad (5\text{-}2)$$

This situation was demonstrated in Sec. 4-4 with the tomato juice problem, although it was incorrectly used because the alternative was suggested by data. Finally, the correct analysis at the tomato juice cannery led to testing

$$H_0: \mu = \mu_0 \text{ against } H_1: \mu \neq \mu_0 \qquad (5\text{-}3)$$

with $\mu_0 = 46$. In most of the cases which one is likely to encounter when testing a hypothesis about a single mean, H_0 and H_1 can be expressed in one of the three forms (5-1), (5-2), or (5-3).

When the variance is known, the statistic

$$Z = \frac{\bar{x} - \mu_0}{\sigma/\sqrt{n}} \qquad (5\text{-}4)$$

is used to test hypotheses about the mean. If the population mean is μ_0, then the sampling distribution of Z is standard normal provided the

Figure 5-1 Critical region and associated level of significance for testing $H_0: \mu = \mu_0$ against $H_1: \mu < \mu_0$ with σ^2 known.

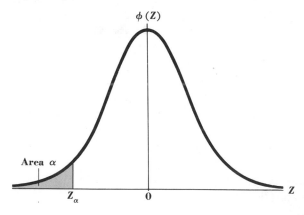

104

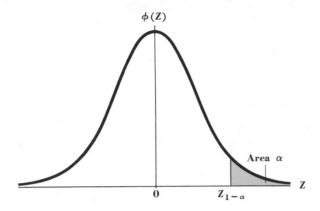

Figure 5-2 Critical region and associated level of significance for testing $H_0: \mu = \mu_0$ against $H_1: \mu > \mu_0$ with σ^2 known.

observations $x_1, \ldots, x_n$ are (a) selected randomly and (b) drawn from a normal population. As we have observed, assumption b is not critical if n is moderately large because of the central limit theorem. In order to compute the statistic in step 5, we must further assume (c) σ is known.

When testing (5-1), only small $\bar{x}$, and hence small Z, support H_1. Consequently, H_0 is rejected if Z is small. If the significance level is α, then the critical region is

$$\frac{\bar{x} - \mu_0}{\sigma/\sqrt{n}} < Z_\alpha \qquad (5\text{-}5)$$

as pictured in Fig. 5-1. This is the same as Fig. 4-2 except that α is specifically .01 in the earlier figure. Similarly, only large $\bar{x}$, and large Z, support the H_1 of (5-2). A test of significance level α is obtained by rejecting H_0 when

$$\frac{\bar{x} - \mu_0}{\sigma/\sqrt{n}} > Z_{1-\alpha} \qquad (5\text{-}6)$$

The critical region is shown in Fig. 5-2. Figure 4-5 conveys the same information except that it shows the specific region for $\alpha = .05$.

When testing (5-3), both large and small values of $\bar{x}$ (and hence Z) provide support for H_1. Thus it is reasonable to expect that both large and small values of Z comprise the critical region. For a test with significance level α, the hypothesis H_0 is rejected if

$$\frac{\bar{x} - \mu_0}{\sigma/\sqrt{n}} < Z_{\alpha/2} \qquad \text{or} \qquad \frac{\bar{x} - \mu_0}{\sigma/\sqrt{n}} > Z_{1-\alpha/2} \qquad (5\text{-}7)$$

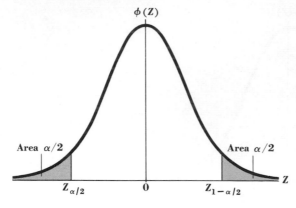

Area $\alpha/2$

Area $\alpha/2$

$\phi(Z)$

$Z_{\alpha/2}$ 0 $Z_{1-\alpha/2}$ Z

Figure 5-3   Critical region and associated level of significance for testing H_0: $\mu = \mu_0$ against H_1: $\mu \neq \mu_0$ with σ^2 known.

The critical region, pictured in Fig. 5-3, is a generalization of the one shown in Fig. 4-4, where $\alpha = .05$. Owing to the symmetry of the curve, $Z_{\alpha/2} = -Z_{1-\alpha/2}$.

EXAMPLE 5-1

A large corporation uses thousands of light bulbs every year. The brand that has been used in the past has an average life of 1,000 hours with a standard deviation of 100 hours. A new brand is offered to the corporation at a price far lower than the one they are paying for the old brand. It is decided that they will switch to the new brand unless the new brand is proved to have a smaller average life at the $\alpha = .05$ level of significance. Consequently, a sample of 100 new-brand bulbs is tested, yielding an average life of 985 hours. Assuming that the standard deviation for the new brand is the same as the old, what conclusion should be drawn?

Solution

We shall follow the outline proposed in Sec. 4-6.

1 For the population of new bulbs we test H_0: $\mu = 1,000$ against H_1: $\mu < 1,000$. If H_0 is rejected, we conclude that the new-brand average is lower than the old-brand average.

2 $\alpha = .05$ has already been specified.

3 The statistic to use is $Z = (\bar{x} - \mu_0)/\sigma_{\bar{x}} = (\bar{x} - 1,000)/\sigma_{\bar{x}}$. If the mean is 1,000, then Z has a standard normal distribution provided:

(a) The sample of light bulbs tested was selected randomly.

(b) The population of light bulb lives is normally distributed.

With $n = 100$, assumption (b) is unnecessary. In order to compute the statistic, we must assume:

(c) σ is known to be 100.

106

4 The critical region is $(\bar{x} - 1{,}000)/\sigma_{\bar{x}} < -1.645$ (Fig. 5-1 applies with $\alpha = .05$).

5 Computations: We are given $\sigma = 100$, so that

$$\sigma_{\bar{x}} = \frac{100}{\sqrt{100}} = 10$$

The observed $\bar{x}$ is 985. Thus

$$\frac{\bar{x} - 1{,}000}{\sigma_{\bar{x}}} = \frac{985 - 1{,}000}{10} = -1.5$$

6 Since the statistic does not lie in the critical region, the hypothesis that the new brand average is 1,000 is not rejected. The corporation will switch to the new brand. (The problem has been over-simplified somewhat to provide a simple illustration. The assumption about the variance may be unrealistic. Other considerations such as cost per hour or side benefits from extra good service may alter the decision.)

Perhaps it would make more sense to test H_0: $\mu \geq 1{,}000$ against H_1: $\mu < 1{,}000$ in Example 5-1. Thus we would be choosing between (1) the average life of the new brand is as high or higher than that of the old and (2) the average life of the new brand is lower than that of the old. The test statistic, the critical regions, and the outline (except for H_0) remain unchanged. However, some further comment concerning step 2 is necessary. Allowing the parameter μ to be one of a whole range of values produces a new complication in computing Type I error. The hypothesis is true when $\mu = 1{,}001$ as well as when $\mu = 1{,}000$. The probability of rejecting the hypothesis for a chosen critical region will change depending upon which value of $\mu \geq 1{,}000$ one selects. We have already observed in the preceding chapter that the power is different for different values of μ. The critical region of step 4 yields a power of .05 if $\mu = 1{,}000$ and a power of less than .05 if $\mu > 1{,}000$ (see Fig. 5-4). Consequently, as we have defined the term, "Type I error" is somewhat ambiguous. If we are going to permit μ to assume more than one value under H_0, the Type I error should be regarded as the maximum value of the power when H_0 is true.

Thus instead of using (5-1) or (5-2) we might prefer to test

$$H_0: \mu \geq \mu_0 \text{ against } H_1: \mu < \mu_0 \tag{5-8}$$

in the first case and

$$H_0: \mu \leq \mu_0 \text{ against } H_1: \mu > \mu_0 \tag{5-9}$$

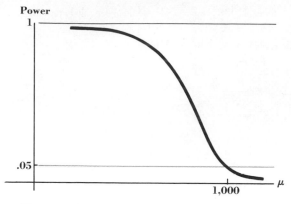

Figure 5-4 Power curve arising from critical region of Example 5-1.

in the second.   No change in procedure is required.   The test statistic, the critical region, and the outline (except for H_0) remain unchanged. That is, (5-1) and (5-8) are handled in exactly the same way, and so are (5-2) and (5-9).   The only difference occurs in the new interpretation of α, which is now regarded as the largest power under H_0.   This largest value is the predetermined α and is achieved when $\mu = \mu_0$.

EXERCISES

Use the recommended outline.

◆ 5-1   A company that sells frozen shrimp prints "Contents 12 Ounces" on the package.   A sample of 25 packages yields an average of 11.83 ounces.   Suppose it is known from past experience that the population of package weights has a standard deviation of .5 ounce.   Using $\alpha = .05$, what conclusion would be drawn concerning the standard which the company is trying to achieve?

5-2   A manufacturer of flashlight batteries claims that the average life of his product will exceed 30 hours.   A company is willing to buy a very large shipment of batteries if the claim is true.   A random sample of 36 batteries is tested, and it is found that the sample mean is 40 hours.   If the population of batteries has a standard deviation of 5 hours, is it likely that the batteries will be purchased?

◆ 5-3   Incoming freshmen are given entrance examinations in a number of fields including English.   Over a period of years it has been found that the average score in the English examination is 67 and that the standard deviation of the scores is 7.5.   An English I

108

instructor looks up the scores for his class of 25 and finds that their average is 70. Assuming the standard deviation of 7.5 can be used, can the instructor claim that the average has increased?

5-4 A fisherman decides that he needs a line that will test more than 10 pounds if he is to catch the size fish he desires. He tests 16 pieces of brand F line and finds a sample mean of 10.4. If it is known that $\sigma = .5$ pound, what can he conclude about brand F?

5-3 POWER CALCULATIONS

The calculation of power for the tests of the preceding section is fairly simple and has already been demonstrated in Chap. 4. Appendix D-10 contains graphs from which power can be read. The curve $f = \infty$ applies to the tests based upon the Z random variable of Sec. 5-2. The other curves are for the t test, which will be discussed in Sec. 5-5. The graphs are specifically designed to give power for one-sided tests, but they can be used for two-sided tests with practically no error if $\delta \geqq 1$ and with a maximum error of $\alpha/2$ if $\delta < 1$. The quantity $\delta = |\mu - \mu_0| \sqrt{n}/\sigma$, where μ must be in the range designated under H_1. The given values of $\alpha = .005, .01, .025, .05$ apply to one-sided tests. For two-sided tests double the α given above the graphs. Hence, power can be read for two-sided tests with $\alpha = .01, .02, .05, .10$.

EXAMPLE 5-2

In discussing the smoker problem in Sec. 4-3 we found, using $\alpha = .01$,

Power = .141 $\mu = 29$
Power = .569 $\mu = 28$
Power = .923 $\mu = 27$

Verify these figures with the proper graph of Appendix D-10.

Solution

If $\mu = 29$ $\delta = |29 - 30| \sqrt{100}/8 = 1.25$
If $\mu = 28$ $\delta = |28 - 30| \sqrt{100}/8 = 2.50$
If $\mu = 27$ $\delta = |27 - 30| \sqrt{100}/8 = 3.75$

Turning to the graph labeled $\alpha = .01$, we see that the vertical line through $\delta = 1.25$ crosses the curve $f = \infty$ opposite power = .14. Similarly, $\delta = 2.50, 3.75$ yield power = .57, .92.

EXAMPLE 5-3 ═══════════════════════════════

A power of .57 was obtained in Example 5-2 when $\mu = 28$. How large would n have to be (instead of 100) to increase the power to .90?

Solution

Using the graph labeled $\alpha = .01$, we see that $\delta = 3.6$ makes the power .90. Hence we need to solve $|28 - 30| \sqrt{n}/8 = 3.6$ for n. This gives $\sqrt{n} = 14.4$, $n = (14.4)^2 = 207.36$. Since n must be an integer, we could use $n = 207$. An n of 208 would make the power slightly over .90.

EXAMPLE 5-4 ═══════════════════════════════

In Sec. 4-4 for the tomato juice example we found, by using $\alpha = .05$,

Power = .170 $\mu = 46.1, 45.9$
Power = .516 $\mu = 46.2, 45.8$
Power = .851 $\mu = 46.3, 45.7$

Verify these figures with the proper graph of Appendix D-10.

Solution

For $\mu = 46.1$ $\delta = |46.1 - 46| \sqrt{25}/.5 = 1$
For $\mu = 46.2$ $\delta = |46.2 - 46| \sqrt{25}/.5 = 2$
For $\mu = 46.3$ $\delta = |46.2 - 46| \sqrt{25}/.5 = 3$

Since the test was two-sided, we look under the graph labeled $\alpha = .025$, which gives us power for a two-sided test with $\alpha = .05$. With no difficulty we read power of .17, .52, .85, respectively, from the $f = \infty$ curve. Since 45.9, 45.8, 45.7 reproduce the same δ's, the same power values are obtained.

EXAMPLE 5-5 ═══════════════════════════════

A power of .516 or .52 (rounded to two decimal places) was obtained in Example 5-4 when $\mu = 46.2$. How large would n have to be to raise this to .98?

Solution

Using the graph labeled $\alpha = .025$ shows that $\delta = 4$ makes the power = .98. Hence $|46.2 - 46| \sqrt{n}/.5 = 4$, $\sqrt{n} = 10$, $n = 100$.

EXERCISES

◆ 5-5   In Exercise 5-1 find the power if $\mu = 11.8$. The company might want to be fairly certain that a change in standard will be detected if the mean weight has shifted by .2 ounce. Suppose that a power of .99 is required when $\mu = 11.8$. How large a sample size is needed?

5-6   In Exercise 5-2 find the power if $\mu = 32$. How large should n be to raise this to .90? Use $\alpha = .01$.

◆ 5-7   In Exercise 5-4 suppose that on the average the line actually tests out at 10.4 pounds. With an $\alpha = .01$ what is the probability of rejecting H_0?

5-4   CONFIDENCE INTERVALS

In most of the examples considered thus far, the problem under consideration has specified a value for the parameter. We have then proceeded to test a hypothesis concerning the specified value. If the problem does not imply a parameter value about which hypotheses can be formulated, perhaps an interval estimate will provide useful information. Even if a hypothesis is tested, an interval estimate may prove very useful if the hypothesis is rejected.

Suppose that the sample of light bulbs in Example 5-1 has yielded a mean of 950 hours. The hypothesis that $\mu = 1,000$ would then be rejected. Of course, our best guess as to the average life is the point estimate 950 hours. Since estimates may vary considerably from sample to sample, we would probably find it more satisfying to know that we are fairly confident that the unknown average μ is somewhere between 931.4 and 969.6. Let us see how the interval and the degree of confidence are obtained.

Regardless of the value of the true mean μ, the random variable $Z = (\bar{x} - \mu)/\sigma_{\bar{x}}$ still has a standard normal distribution if n is moderately large or if the original population is normal. Consequently

$$\Pr\left(-1.96 < \frac{\bar{x} - \mu}{\sigma_{\bar{x}}} < 1.96\right) = .95 \qquad (5\text{-}10)$$

or more generally

$$\Pr\left(-Z_{1-\alpha/2} < \frac{\bar{x} - \mu}{\sigma_{\bar{x}}} < Z_{1-\alpha/2}\right) = 1 - \alpha \qquad (5\text{-}11)$$

Consider the two inequalities in (5-10). One is $-1.96 < (\bar{x} - \mu)/\sigma_{\bar{x}}$. Since inequalities, like equations, can be multiplied by a positive number, we can write $-1.96\sigma_{\bar{x}} < \bar{x} - \mu$. The same number can be added to or subtracted from each side of an equality without changing the sense of the inequality. Hence $-1.96\sigma_{\bar{x}} < \bar{x} - \mu$ and $-1.96\sigma_{\bar{x}} - \bar{x} < -\mu$ are equivalent. Finally, if both sides of an inequality are multiplied by a negative number, the sense is reversed. Thus if $-1.96\sigma_{\bar{x}} - \bar{x} < -\mu$, then $1.96\sigma_{\bar{x}} + \bar{x} > \mu$ or $\mu < \bar{x} + 1.96\sigma_{\bar{x}}$. These rules for manipulation of inequalities can be quickly recalled by numerical illustrations. For example, the inequality $2 < 4$ remains true in sense if both sides are divided by 2, becoming $1 < 2$. However, if both sides are divided by -2, it becomes $-1 > -2$, with the sense reversed. The second inequality $(\bar{x} - \mu)/\sigma_{\bar{x}} < 1.96$ can be rewritten $\bar{x} - 1.96\sigma_{\bar{x}} < \mu$. Thus

$$-1.96 < \frac{\bar{x} - \mu}{\sigma_{\bar{x}}} < 1.96 \qquad \text{and} \qquad \bar{x} - 1.96\sigma_{\bar{x}} < \mu < \bar{x} + 1.96\sigma_{\bar{x}}$$

are equivalent inequalities. That is, if the former is true, then so is the latter, and vice versa. Thus (5-10) and (5-11) could be rewritten as

$$\Pr\left(\bar{x} - 1.96\,\frac{\sigma}{\sqrt{n}} < \mu < \bar{x} + 1.96\,\frac{\sigma}{\sqrt{n}}\right) = .95 \qquad (5\text{-}12)$$

and

$$\Pr\left(\bar{x} - Z_{1-\alpha/2}\,\frac{\sigma}{\sqrt{n}} < \mu < \bar{x} + Z_{1-\alpha/2}\,\frac{\sigma}{\sqrt{n}}\right) = 1 - \alpha \qquad (5\text{-}13)$$

In the light bulb example, $\sigma = 100$, $\sqrt{n} = 10$, $\bar{x} = 950$, and (5-12) becomes

$$\Pr(950 - 19.6 < \mu < 950 + 19.6) = .95$$

or

$$\Pr(931.4 < \mu < 969.6) = .95 \qquad (5\text{-}14)$$

The interval 931.4 to 969.6 is called a confidence interval for μ with coefficient .95.

Care must be exercised in the interpretation of (5-14) [or more generally, (5-13)]. It would appear that the statement implies that the probability is .95 that μ is between 931.4 and 969.6. A little thought reveals that this interpretation is incorrect. The parameter μ has a definite constant value even though it is unknown. Consequently, the number μ either is in the interval 931.4 to 969.6 or is not, and the probability that μ is in the interval is either 0 or 1. Thus (5-14) is a nonsensical statement if interpreted directly as a probability statement. The interval, not μ, is the random variable. If thousands of such intervals were calculated in the same way, each based upon a different random sample, then in the long run about 95 out of every 100 intervals would include or capture μ. The procedure is somewhat analogous to throwing intervals at a point target in such a way that 95 per cent of the time the interval will cover the point.

Since the same statistic Z is used to obtain a confidence interval for μ and to test hypotheses about μ, we might expect that the interval and one of the tests are equivalent. Using $\alpha = .05$, it is easy to verify that an $\bar{x}$ of 950 leads to rejection of $H_0 \colon \mu = 1,000$ when tested against $H_1 \colon \mu \neq 1,000$ (since $Z = -5$) with the light-bulb example. We have observed that the interval computed from this $\bar{x}$, using the same α, does not contain 1,000. On the other hand, an $\bar{x}$ of 985 leads to acceptance of H_0 at the .05 level. The interval computed from this second $\bar{x}$ with $\alpha = .05$ is $(985 - 19.6,\ 985 + 19.6)$ or $(965.4, 1004.6)$, which does cover 1,000. The conclusion to be drawn is that the test of $H_0 \colon \mu = \mu_0$ against $H_1 \colon \mu \neq \mu_0$ accepts or rejects H_0 if, and only if, the interval

$$\left(\bar{x} - Z_{1-\alpha/2} \frac{\sigma}{\sqrt{n}},\ \bar{x} + Z_{1-\alpha/2} \frac{\sigma}{\sqrt{n}} \right)$$

covers μ_0 when the same α is used. Thus we could compute the interval, rather than the Z statistic, to test H_0 if we so desired.

The length of the interval given by (5-13) is

$$\bar{x} + Z_{1-\alpha/2} \frac{\sigma}{\sqrt{n}} - \left(\bar{x} - Z_{1-\alpha/2} \frac{\sigma}{\sqrt{n}} \right) = 2Z_{1-\alpha/2} \frac{\sigma}{\sqrt{n}} \qquad (5\text{-}15)$$

We note two rather obvious facts. First, the larger $Z_{1-\alpha/2}$, the larger the confidence interval. The higher the probability we associate with the interval, the larger it becomes for a fixed n. This is only common sense, since the larger the interval becomes, the more confident we can be that it contains μ. However, it is not as useful to know that μ is between 0 and 5,000 as it is to know that μ is between 940 and 960. Second, the length can be decreased by increasing n. In fact, for a given α, it can be made into any specified length L. To find the required n, we need to solve

$$2Z_{1-\alpha/2} \frac{\sigma}{\sqrt{n}} = L$$

for n, which gives

$$n = \left(\frac{2\sigma Z_{1-\alpha/2}}{L} \right)^2 \qquad (5\text{-}16)$$

Of course, we would probably use the nearest integer for n.

The confidence interval given by (5-13) has some desirable mathematical features. First, it is the shortest possible interval that can be obtained for μ with σ known and α and n fixed. It is easy to verify that longer intervals can be obtained by starting with nonsymmetric intervals in (5-10) and (5-11). Second, the probability that the interval covers wrong values of μ is smaller than for any other interval which can be obtained for fixed α and n.

EXAMPLE 5-6

Compute a confidence interval with coefficient .99 for the average nicotine content of brand A cigarettes. Use the information given in Sec. 4-3.

Solution

We have $\bar{x} = 26$, $\sigma = 8$, $n = 100$. With $1 - \alpha = .99$, $\alpha = .01$, $\alpha/2 = .005$, and $Z_{1-\alpha/2} = Z_{.995} = 2.576$. Thus the interval is $26 - 2.576(8/\sqrt{100})$ to $26 + 2.576(8/\sqrt{100})$, which reduces to 23.94 to 28.06.

EXAMPLE 5-7

In Example 5-6 how large would n have to be to decrease the interval to 2 milligrams?

Solution

Use (5-16) with $L = 2$, $\sigma = 8$, $Z_{1-\alpha/2} = Z_{.995} = 2.576$. Thus

$$n = \left[\frac{2(8)(2.576)}{2} \right]^2 = 424.8$$

Hence a sample size of 425 is required.

One-sided confidence intervals can be obtained by starting with a one-sided region in (5-10) and (5-11). Thus

$$\Pr\left(\frac{\bar{x} - \mu}{\sigma_{\bar{x}}} < 1.645 \right) = .95$$

can be converted to

$$\Pr\left(\bar{x} - 1.645 \, \frac{\sigma}{\sqrt{n}} < \mu \right) = .95$$

However, we shall not pursue this topic.

114

5-8   Use the information in Exercise 5-1 to find a confidence interval with confidence coefficient .95 for the average weight of a package of shrimp.   Does the interval include 12?   What is the relationship of the interval to the hypothesis-testing problem of Exercise 5-1?   How large would n have to be to reduce the length of the interval to .1 ounce?

♦ 5-9   Use the information given in Exercise 5-3 to find a confidence interval with confidence coefficient .99 for the average score of the population of students attracted by the instructor.   Does the interval include 67?   What can be said about the corresponding hypothesis-testing problem?   How many students would be required to reduce the length of the interval to 2 units?

5-5 INFERENCES ABOUT A MEAN WHEN σ^2 IS UNKNOWN

More often than not the variance is unknown in real-life problems. When σ^2 is not known, the Z statistic given by (5-4) can no longer be used to test hypotheses and obtain confidence intervals.   It seems reasonable to develop procedures in which s^2 is used for σ^2.   Instead of the statistic Z, we shall now use

$$t_{n-1} = \frac{\bar{x} - \mu_0}{s/\sqrt{n}} \tag{5-17}$$

to draw inferences about the mean.   If the mean of the population is μ_0, then the sampling distribution of t_{n-1} is a t distribution provided the observations $x_1, \ldots, x_n$ are (a) selected randomly and (b) drawn from a normal population.

Except that t_{n-1} is used instead of Z, the testing procedures for (5-1), (5-2), (5-3), (5-8), and (5-9) are the same as given in Sec. 5-2. Of course, the critical regions are obtained from Appendix D-6, which is entered with degrees of freedom equal to one less than the sample size. The hypotheses of (5-1) and (5-8) lead to a left-hand critical region as before, with H_0 being rejected if

$$\frac{\bar{x} - \mu_0}{s/\sqrt{n}} < t_{n-1;\alpha} \tag{5-18}$$

Similarly, the H_0's of (5-2) and (5-9) are rejected if $\bar{x}$ and t_{n-1} are too large, giving a critical region

$$\frac{\bar{x} - \mu_0}{s/\sqrt{n}} > t_{n-1;\,1-\alpha} \tag{5-19}$$

Finally, for the situation of (5-3), H_0 is rejected if

$$\frac{\bar{x} - \mu_0}{s/\sqrt{n}} < t_{n-1;\alpha/2} \qquad \text{or} \qquad \frac{x - \mu_0}{s/\sqrt{n}} > t_{n-1;\,1-\alpha/2} \qquad (5\text{-}20)$$

EXAMPLE 5-8

Suppose that in Example 5-1 the sample had contained 25 bulbs, yielding $\bar{x} = 985$, $s = 90.2$. Use the same α as before and rewrite the outline.

Solution

1 Same as in Example 5-1
2 Same as in Example 5-1
3 The statistic we use is

$$t_{n-1} = \frac{\bar{x} - 1{,}000}{s/\sqrt{n}}$$

If the mean is 1,000, then t_{n-1} has a t distribution provided:
(a) The sample of light bulbs tested was randomly selected.
(b) The population of light bulb lives is normally distributed.
4 The critical region is

$$\frac{\bar{x} - 1{,}000}{s/\sqrt{n}} < -1.711 = t_{24;.05}$$

5 Computations:
We are given $\bar{x} = 985$, $s = 90.2$, $n = 25$. Thus

$$\frac{\bar{x} - 1{,}000}{s/\sqrt{n}} = \frac{985 - 1{,}000}{90.2/5} = -.83$$

6 Again, H_0: $\mu = 1{,}000$ is not rejected.

Assumption b of Example 5-8, concerning normality, is not too critical if the sample size is moderately large. That is, probabilities computed by using the t distribution will still be approximately correct if the population is not normal. Mild departures from normality do not seriously affect the tests even for small n.

For tests based upon the Z statistic we have computed power by using the standard normal table. However, the t table is of no use in power calculations for t tests, and special tables or graphs are needed. We shall use the charts of Appendix D-10. As we have seen in Sec. 5-3, one of the entries in the table is $\delta = |\mu - \mu_0| \sqrt{n}/\sigma$, which depends upon the unknown quantity σ. One way out of this difficulty is to choose $|\mu - \mu_0|$ as a multiple of σ. Thus if $|\mu - \mu_0| = a\sigma$, $\delta = a\sqrt{n}$. A second way to avoid σ requires that a two-stage sample be taken. The latter procedure will be discussed in the next section. Except that we need to find the curve with the appropriate degrees of freedom, all other comments relative to the use of the charts given at the beginning of Sec. 5-3 still apply.

EXAMPLE 5-9

Find the power of the test used in Example 5-8 if the true mean μ is one-half a standard deviation below the hypothesized value $\mu_0 = 1,000$.

Solution

We are given that $\mu = 1,000 - \sigma/2$, $n = 25$. Hence $|\mu - \mu_0| = \sigma/2$ and

$$\delta = \frac{(\sigma/2)\sqrt{25}}{\sigma} = 2.5$$

The degrees of freedom are $n - 1 = f = 24$. Since the test is one-sided with significance level .05, turn to the graph of Appendix D-10 labeled $\alpha = .05$. The vertical line through $\delta = 2.5$ crosses the curve for $f = 24$ opposite .80. Hence the required power is .80.

EXAMPLE 5-10

In Example 5-9 how large does n have to be to raise the power to .99 if $\mu = 1,000 - \sigma/2$?

Solution

Now

$$\delta = \frac{(\sigma/2)\sqrt{n}}{\sigma} = \frac{\sqrt{n}}{2}$$

The page of Appendix D-10 used in Example 5-9 reveals that for a power of .99 we need $\delta = 3.97$ (approximately) when $f = \infty$. Hence, if we solve $\sqrt{n}/2 = 3.97$, we shall have an approximate solution. This gives $\sqrt{n} = 7.94$, $n = 63.04$. We would probably take a sample of size 63. Since $n = 63$ means $f = 62$ and we have used $f = \infty$ to get δ, the power will be slightly less than .99. There are graphs from which n can be read directly for this type of problem (see [2],† pages 37 to 40) provided n does not exceed 100. These graphs give $n = 65$ as the solution to our problem. Thus the approximate method leads to a very small relative error, and the error gets smaller as f increases.

---

† Numbers in brackets are those of references listed at the end of the chapter.

EXAMPLE 5-11

Rework Example 5-9 for $n = 16$.

Solution

Now

$$\delta = \frac{(\sigma/2)\sqrt{16}}{\sigma} = 2 \quad \text{and} \quad f = n - 1 = 15$$

Curves are included for $f = 12$ and $f = 24$, but not for $f = 15$. The graph yields

Power $= .60$ if $f = 12$
Power $= .63$ if $f = 24$

Interpolating, the power is approximately .61 when $\delta = 2$, $f = 15$. The curves on the charts are so close together that it is almost impossible to make a reading error that is apt to be of practical significance no matter how badly one interpolates.

To obtain a confidence interval for μ with coefficient $1 - \alpha$, we start with

$$\Pr\left(-t_{n-1;\,1-\alpha/2} < \frac{\bar{x} - \mu}{s/\sqrt{n}} < t_{n-1;\,1-\alpha/2}\right) = 1 - \alpha \tag{5-21}$$

Except that t_{n-1} has replaced Z and s has replaced σ, (5-21) is the same as (5-11). The inequality manipulation previously outlined converts (5-21) to

$$\Pr\left(\bar{x} - t_{n-1;\,1-\alpha/2}\frac{s}{\sqrt{n}} < \mu < \bar{x} + t_{n-1;\,1-\alpha/2}\frac{s}{\sqrt{n}}\right) = 1 - \alpha \tag{5-22}$$

which can be written down by looking at (5-13) and making the necessary replacements. Hence the desired confidence interval is

$$\left(\bar{x} - t_{n-1;\,1-\alpha/2}\frac{s}{\sqrt{n}}, \; \bar{x} + t_{n-1;\,1-\alpha/2}\frac{s}{\sqrt{n}}\right) \tag{5-23}$$

The probability statement (5-22) has to be interpreted in the same way as (5-13). As with the Z statistic, the interval (5-23) covers a value μ_0 if, and only if, the test accepts $H_0: \mu = \mu_0$ against $H_1: \mu \neq \mu_0$ when the same n and α are used. Thus we could compute the interval, rather than the t statistic, to test H_0 if we so desired.

EXAMPLE 5-12

Find a confidence interval with coefficient .95 for the mean for the light bulb data of Example 5-8.

Solution

We had $\bar{x} = 985$, $s = 90.2$, $n = 25$. Since $\alpha = .05$, $\alpha/2 = .025$, we need $t_{24;.975}$. Appendix D-6 yields $t_{24;.975} = 2.064$. Thus the required interval is

$$\left(985 - 2.064\,\frac{90.2}{\sqrt{25}},\ 985 + 2.064\,\frac{90.2}{\sqrt{25}}\right)$$

which reduces to (947.8, 1022.2).

The length of the confidence interval (5-23) is

$$2t_{n-1;\,1-\alpha/2}\,\frac{s}{\sqrt{n}} \tag{5-24}$$

Unlike (5-15), this is a random variable. The average value of (5-24) is less than the average value of lengths of other intervals which can be constructed for μ. As with σ known, the probability that the interval covers wrong values of μ is smaller than for any other interval which can be obtained for fixed α and n. When σ is known, the length of the interval as given by (5-15) is known as soon as α and n are determined. The best we can do with (5-24) is to make probability statements concerning the length. Suppose we want to know

$$\Pr\left(2t_{n-1;\,1-\alpha/2}\,\frac{s}{\sqrt{n}} < L\right) \tag{5-25}$$

where we shall specify L. The probability (5-25) and

$$\Pr\left(\frac{s^2}{\sigma^2} < \frac{nL^2}{4\sigma^2 t_{n-1;\,1-\alpha/2}^2}\right) \tag{5-26}$$

are equivalent, as can be verified by easy algebraic manipulations. If the observations $x_1, \ldots, x_n$ are (a) randomly selected and (b) drawn from a normal population, then the sampling distribution of s^2/σ^2 is chi-square divided by degrees of freedom. Since σ^2 is unknown, we must choose L as a multiple of σ to enable us to evaluate (5-26).

EXAMPLE 5-13

In example 5-12 we found a confidence interval with $\alpha = .05$ and a sample of size 25. Find the probability that a random sample of size 25 drawn from a normal distribution produces an interval (with coefficient .95) (a) shorter than σ and (b) shorter than $.8\sigma$.

Solution

We have $n = 25$, degrees of freedom $= 24$, $t_{24;.975} = 2.064$, $L = \sigma$. Hence

$$\frac{nL^2}{4\sigma^2 t_{n-1;1-\alpha/2}^2} = \frac{25\sigma^2}{4\sigma^2(2.064)^2} = 1.47$$

and we seek

$$\Pr\left(\frac{s^2}{\sigma^2} < 1.47\right)$$

Turning to Appendix D-8 with degrees of freedom (d.f.) $= 24$ we find

$$\Pr\left(\frac{s^2}{\sigma^2} < 1.38\right) = .90$$

$$\Pr\left(\frac{s^2}{\sigma^2} < 1.52\right) = .95$$

Thus $\Pr\left(\dfrac{s^2}{\sigma^2} < 1.47\right) = .93$, approximately. If $L = .8\sigma$, $L^2 = .64\sigma^2$, then we need

$$\Pr\left(\frac{s^2}{\sigma^2} < .64(1.47)\right) = \Pr\left(\frac{s^2}{\sigma^2} < .94\right)$$

The table gives

$$\Pr\left(\frac{s^2}{\sigma^2} < .902\right) = .40 \qquad \Pr\left(\frac{s^2}{\sigma^2} < .972\right) = .50$$

Hence

$$\Pr\left(\frac{s^2}{\sigma^2} < .94\right) = .45, \text{ approximately}$$

Appendix D-8 can be used in conjunction with Appendix D-6 to find the n required to make (5-25) and (5-26) equal to any desired probability level for a given α and a given L (as a multiple of σ). A trial-and-error method would have to be used, however. That is, different values of n would be tried until (5-26) yielded approximately the desired probability level. Appendix D-11 contains graphs from which n can be read for $\alpha = .05, .10$, and probability levels .30, .50, .70, .90, .99. The sample size is plotted against L (in σ units).

EXAMPLE 5-14

Use Appendix D-11 to find the n required if it is desired to obtain a confidence interval for μ with coefficient .95 such that the probability will be .90 that the interval will be shorter than $.5\sigma$.

120

Solution

Turn to the graph headed by $\alpha = .05$, confidence coefficient .95. The vertical line above $L = .5\sigma$ crosses the curve labeled Pr $= .90$ opposite $n = 77$, approximately. Thus the probability is .90 that a random sample of size 77 drawn from a normal distribution will produce a confidence interval with coefficient .95 that is shorter than $.5\sigma$.

Observe that the graphs of Appendix D-11 can also be used to obtain an approximate answer for a problem like Example 5-13. That is, with a given n we can approximate the probability that a random sample from a normal distribution produces a confidence interval (with given coefficient) for the mean shorter than L. For example, with the information given in Example 5-13 ($\alpha = .05$, $L = \sigma$, $n = 25$), we see that the horizontal line through $n = 25$ and the vertical line through $L = 1$ cross between the curves labeled Pr $= .90$ and Pr $= .99$. Crude interpolation yields a probability of .92 or .93, agreeing with the result previously obtained in Example 5-13.

It has been pointed out previously that the t random variable of (5-17) has a sampling distribution that is approximately a t distribution if the population is not normal and samples are of moderate size. Consequently, nonnormality does not seriously affect probability statements, tests, and confidence intervals based upon (5-17). However, the variable s^2/σ^2 may have a sampling distribution quite unlike chi-square divided by degrees of freedom if the population is not normal. As a result, probabilities based on (5-26) may be seriously inaccurate if the normality condition is not satisfied.

EXERCISES

◆ 5-10 Suppose that the frozen shrimp company of Exercise 5-1 obtains $\bar{x} = 12.24$ ounces and $s = .60$ ounce from a random sample of size 25. If $\alpha = .05$, what conclusion can be drawn with regard to the standard of 12 ounces that the company is trying to achieve? Follow the recommended outline for hypothesis testing and assume σ is unknown.

◆ 5-11 Find the power of the test in Exercise 5-10 if the true mean μ differs from the hypothesized value by one-half of a standard deviation. Approximately how large would n have to be to raise this to .99?

◆ 5-12 In Exercise 5-10 find a confidence interval for μ with coefficient .95. How does the interval relate to the test of Exercise 5-10?

◆ 5-13 In Exercise 5-12 a confidence interval was found using a coefficient of .95 and a sample of size 25. Find the probability that a random sample of size 25 drawn from a normal distribution produces an interval (with coefficient .95) shorter than $.75\sigma$. How large would n have to be to raise this probability to .99?

5-14 A famous bridge player has found that his average score for a session of tournament play is 60.0 per cent when he uses standard bidding methods. When he uses a new system for 16 sessions, his average is 62.1 with a standard deviation of 3.0 per cent. Unless the player is convinced at the .01 level of significance that the new system produces a higher average, he will discontinue using it. Assuming his scores are normally distributed, what decision should he make? Follow the recommended outline.

5-15 Find the power of the test in Exercise 5-14 if the true mean using the new system is actually one-half of a standard deviation above 60.0. Approximately how large would n have to be to raise this to .90?

5-16 For the data of Exercise 5-14 find a confidence interval for the μ of the new system with a coefficient of .90.

5-17 In Exercise 5-16 a confidence interval was requested using a coefficient of .90 and a sample of size 16. Find the probability that a random sample of size 16 drawn from a normal population produces an interval (with coefficient .90) shorter than σ. Shorter than $.5\sigma$. How large would n have to be to raise the probability to .90 for $.5\sigma$?

◆ 5-18 A standard variety of wheat yields, on the average, 30 bushels per acre in a certain region. A new imported variety is planted on nine randomly selected acre plots. The average yield from the new variety is 33.4 bushels. If the sample standard deviation is 5.1 bushels, what conclusion can be drawn by using $\alpha = .05$? Follow the standard outline for hypothesis testing.

5-19 For the new variety of Exercise 5-18 find a confidence interval with coefficient .95 for the mean yield.

5-6 INFERENCES ABOUT A MEAN WITH A TWO-STAGE PROCEDURE

In Sec. 5-5 we found that both power calculations and the probability statement (5-26) concerning the length of a confidence interval depend upon the unknown quantity σ. The obstacle is overcome by choosing $|\mu - \mu_0|$ and L as multiples of σ. A two-stage procedure due to Stein [4] yields (1) t tests for the mean with power independent of σ and (2) confidence intervals of fixed length, guaranteed with a prechosen probability independent of σ. The two-stage sampling scheme consists of the following steps:

1 Specify a preliminary sample size, say, n_0.
2 Compute a value of k determined by the conditions of the problem.
3 Observe a random sample of size n_0.
4 Compute

$$s^2 = \frac{\displaystyle\sum_{i=1}^{n_0} (x_i - \bar{x})^2}{n_0 - 1}$$

for the preliminary sample.
5 If $ks^2 \leq n_0$, take no more observations and the total sample size is $n = n_0$. If $ks^2 > n_0$, continue sampling until the total sample size n just exceeds ks^2.

The statistic used to test hypotheses about the mean is

$$t_{n_0-1} = \frac{\bar{x} - \mu_0}{s/\sqrt{n}} \tag{5-27}$$

where s is computed from the n_0 observations and $\bar{x}$ is computed from all n observations. The sampling distribution of (5-27) is a t distribution with $n_0 - 1$ degrees of freedom provided (a) the sample is selected randomly and (b) the population is normal. The critical regions are determined exactly as before. That is, when testing (5-1) or (5-8), small values of t support H_1 and lead to rejection. When testing (5-2) or (5-9), reject H_0 for large values. Finally, for (5-3), H_0 is rejected for both large and small values.

We still have to find k, which in turn determines n. Let us consider one-sided tests first. Suppose that we would like to have a power of p if the true mean is μ and not μ_0. Then

$$k = \left(\frac{t_{n_0-1; 1-\alpha} + t_{n_0-1; p}}{\mu - \mu_0} \right)^2 \tag{5-28}$$

Of course, μ must be one of the values specified by H_1. Using the k of (5-28) guarantees that the power will be at least p if the mean is actually μ. For two-sided tests replace α by $\alpha/2$ in (5-28). A power of p is achieved for most realistic situations. (If α is large and p is small, the power could be a little less than p, the maximum possible difference being $\alpha/2$.)

EXAMPLE 5-15

For the tomato juice problem of Sec. 4-4 we tested H_0: $\mu = 46$ against H_1: $\mu \neq 46$ with $\alpha = .05$. Suppose that σ is unknown and we desire that the power $= .99$ if the mean is really 45.5 or 46.5 so that $|\mu - \mu_0| = .5$. Find k if a preliminary sample of size 10 is to be used. If the preliminary sample yields $s = .61$, how large should n be? Suppose that $\bar{x}$ based on all n observations turns out to be 46.18. What conclusion is reached?

Solution

Since the test for H_0 is two-sided, we replace α by $\alpha/2$ in (5-28). Thus $\alpha/2 = .025$, $1 - \alpha/2 = .975$, $p = .99$, $n_0 = 10$, $t_{9;.975} = 2.262$, $t_{9;.99} = 2.821$, $|\mu - \mu_0| = .50$. Thus

$$k = \left(\frac{2.262 + 2.821}{.50}\right)^2 = \left(\frac{5.083}{.5}\right)^2 = (10.166)^2 = 103.35$$

and $n \geqq (103.35)(.61)^2 = 38.46$, so that the necessary total sample size is 39. Hence, 29 more observations are needed. The statistic takes on the value

$$t_9 = \frac{46.18 - 46}{.61/\sqrt{39}} = 1.84$$

Since the critical region is $t_9 > 2.262$ and $t_9 < -2.262$, H_0 is accepted.

Next suppose that we want a confidence interval of length L such that the probability is at least $1 - \alpha$ that the interval covers μ. If the two-stage procedure is used with

$$k = \left(\frac{2t_{n_0-1;\,1-\alpha/2}}{L}\right)^2 \tag{5-29}$$

then the interval $(\bar{x} - L/2,\ \bar{x} + L/2)$ is a confidence interval for μ with coefficient at least $1 - \alpha$.

EXAMPLE 5-16

Use the information from the preliminary sample in Example 5-15 to compute k and then the n necessary to ensure that a confidence interval of length .5 ounce is an interval for μ with coefficient at least .95.

Solution

We have $\alpha = .05$, $1 - \alpha/2 = .975$, $t_{9;.975} = 2.262$, $s = .61$, $L = .5$. Thus

$$k = \left[\frac{2(2.262)}{.5}\right]^2 = 9.048^2 = 81.87$$

and $n \geq 81.87(.61^2) = 30.46$. Hence a total of 31 observations, or 21 more, are required. If $\bar{x}$ based upon the 31 observations is 46.18, then $(46.18 - .25, \ 46.18 + .25)$ or $(45.93,46.43)$ is a confidence interval for μ with coefficient at least .95.

EXERCISES

◆ 5-20　In the light bulb problem discussed in Example 5-1 we tested H_0: $\mu = 1,000$ against H_1: $\mu < 1,000$ with $\alpha = .05$. Now assume that σ is unknown and suppose that we desire to have a power of .90 if $\mu = 975$. Find k if a preliminary sample of size 20 is to be used. If the preliminary sample yields $s = 90.2$, how large should n be? Suppose that $\bar{x}$ based upon all n observations turns out to be 970. What conclusion is reached? Follow the standard six-step outline.

◆ 5-21　Use the information from the preliminary sample in Exercise 5-20 to compute k and the n necessary to ensure that a confidence interval for μ of length 50 hours has a confidence coefficient of at least .95. Exhibit the interval if $\bar{x}$ based upon all n observations is 985.

5-22　Consider again the frozen shrimp problem discussed in Exercises 5-1 and 5-10 and assume σ is unknown. Suppose that we would like to have the power = .95 if the mean is actually 11.75 or 12.25 so that $|\mu - \mu_0| = .25$. Use $\alpha = .05$ to find k if a preliminary sample of size 25 is used. If the preliminary sample yields $s = .60$, how large should n be? Suppose that $\bar{x}$ based upon all n observations turns out to be 12.24. What conclusion is reached? Follow the six-step outline.

5-23　Use the information from the preliminary sample in Exercise 5-22 to compute k and the n necessary to ensure that a confidence interval for μ of length .25 ounce has a confidence coefficient of at least .95. Exhibit the interval if $\bar{x}$ based upon all n observations is 12.24 ounces.

5-7　INFERENCES ABOUT A VARIANCE

In Sec. 3-3 we mentioned some situations in which variability is of interest and pointed out that, because of nice mathematical properties, variance (or standard deviation) is usually used to measure this characteristic. The hypothesis-testing problems which occur most frequently when studying variability give rise to hypotheses and alternatives similar to those encountered with the mean.

Suppose that we have been using a standard machine to make bolts and have established that the variance of diameters produced by the machine is σ_0^2 (to be specific, we could take $\sigma_0^2 = .00042$). A salesman is trying to sell us a new machine which he claims produces bolts with smaller variability of diameters, say, σ^2. If we decide to buy the new machine only if its variance is smaller, we will test

$$H_0: \sigma^2 = \sigma_0^2 \text{ against } H_1: \sigma^2 < \sigma_0^2 \qquad (5\text{-}30)$$

with $\sigma_0^2 = .00042$ and replace our present equipment if we conclude H_1 is true. If the new machine is capable of producing many more parts than the old, we may decide to switch unless the variance associated with the new machine is larger than that associated with the old. Under the latter circumstances we would test

$$H_0: \sigma^2 = \sigma_0^2 \text{ against } H_1: \sigma^2 > \sigma_0^2 \qquad (5\text{-}31)$$

and replace the present machine unless we conclude H_1 is true.

Some problems lead to two-sided alternatives. For example, suppose that it is known that a standard method for the teaching of reading produces a variance σ_0^2 in reading rates. A new method is tried, and it is desired to know whether the new method has the same variance as the old. In this instance it would be appropriate to test

$$H_0: \sigma^2 = \sigma_0^2 \text{ against } H_1: \sigma^2 \neq \sigma_0^2 \qquad (5\text{-}32)$$

In some problems we may prefer to replace (5-30) by

$$H_0: \sigma^2 \geqq \sigma_0^2 \text{ against } H_1: \sigma^2 < \sigma_0^2 \qquad (5\text{-}33)$$

or (5-31) by

$$H_0: \sigma^2 \leqq \sigma_0^2 \text{ against } H_1: \sigma^2 > \sigma_0^2 \qquad (5\text{-}34)$$

In so doing we run into the same difficulty concerning Type I error as with (5-8) and (5-9). Again α has to be regarded as the largest power under H_0.

The statistic

$$\chi_{n-1}^2 = \frac{(n-1)s^2}{\sigma_0^2} \qquad (5\text{-}35)$$

is used to test hypotheses about the variance. If the variance of the population is σ_0^2, then the sampling distribution of χ_{n-1}^2 is a chi-square distribution with $n - 1$ degrees of freedom provided the observations $x_1, \ldots, x_n$ are (a) selected randomly and (b) drawn from a normal population. The effect of nonnormality is much more serious for tests of hypotheses for the variance than for the mean. Instead of (5-35) we can use s^2/σ_0^2, whose sampling distribution is chi-square divided by degrees of freedom.

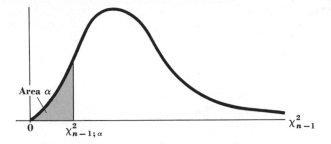

Figure 5-5 Critical region and associated level of significance for testing $H_0: \sigma^2 = \sigma_0^2$ against $H_1: \sigma^2 < \sigma_0^2$.

When testing (5-30), only small values of s^2, and hence small χ_{n-1}^2, support H_1. If the significance level is α, then the critical region is

$$\frac{(n-1)s^2}{\sigma_0^2} < \chi_{n-1;\alpha}^2 \tag{5-36}$$

as pictured in Fig. 5-5. Similarly, only large s^2 and large χ_{n-1}^2 support the H_1 of (5-31). A test of significance level α is obtained by rejecting H_0 when

$$\frac{(n-1)s^2}{\sigma_0^2} > \chi_{n-1;1-\alpha}^2 \tag{5-37}$$

The critical region is shown in Fig. 5-6. Finally, when testing (5-32), both large and small values of s^2, and hence χ_{n-1}^2, provide support for

Figure 5-6 Critical region and associated level of significance for testing $H_0: \sigma^2 = \sigma_0^2$ against $H_1: \sigma^2 > \sigma_0^2$.

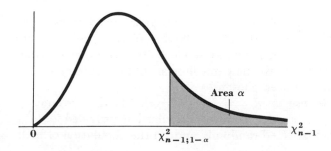

127

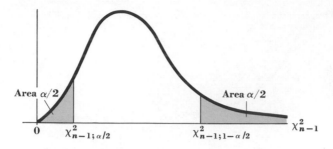

Figure 5-7   Critical region and associated
level of significance for testing $H_0: \sigma^2 = \sigma_0^2$ against
$H_1: \sigma^2 \neq \sigma_0^2$.

H_1.   The hypothesis is rejected if

$$\frac{(n-1)s^2}{\sigma_0^2} < \chi_{n-1;\alpha/2}^2 \qquad \text{or} \qquad \frac{(n-1)s^2}{\sigma_0^2} > \chi_{n-1;1-\alpha/2}^2 \qquad (5\text{-}38)$$

The critical region is pictured in Fig. 5-7.   In the two-sided case, a slightly better critical region (from a theoretical point of view) can be found by using special tables (see [3] and [5]).   However, even for relatively small n, the latter region differs very little from the one shown in Fig. 5-7.

EXAMPLE 5-17 ━━

A standard machine produces ½-inch bolts with a variance of .00042 for diameters.   A random sample of 25 bolts produced by a new machine yields a sample variance of .00028.   We are willing to buy the new machine if we can "prove" (using $\alpha = .05$) that it produces ½-inch bolts with smaller variance.   On the basis of the sample, what decision should be made?

Solution

We shall follow the six-step outline.

1   For the population of bolts from the new machine we test $H_0: \sigma^2 = .00042$ against $H_1: \sigma^2 < .00042$.   If H_0 is rejected, we conclude that the new machine produces bolts with lower variance for diameters and that the new machine should be purchased.
2 $\alpha = .05$ has already been chosen.
3   The statistic to use is $\chi_{n-1}^2 = (n-1)s^2/\sigma_0^2$.   If the variance is .00042, then χ_{n-1}^2 has a chi-square distribution provided (*a*) the sample of bolts is selected randomly and (*b*) the population of bolts

128

produced by the new machine has diameters which are normally distributed. Experience has shown that the normality assumption is reasonable for this type of measurement.

4   The critical region is $\chi^2_{24} < 13.85$ (or $\chi^2_{24}/24 < .577$). Figure 5-5 applies with $\alpha = .05$, $n = 25$.
5   Computations: The observed value of χ^2_{24} is $24(.00028)/.00042 = 16$. (The observed value of χ^2_{24} is $.00028/.00042 = .667$.)
6   H_0 is accepted and the old machine is retained.

EXAMPLE 5-18

A standard method of teaching statistics produces final-examination scores with a standard deviation of 10. A new method involving the use of a new textbook is tried on a class of 81 students. The final-examination scores have a standard deviation of 12. Does this result indicate that the standard deviation with the new method is not 10?

Solution

We shall follow the six-step outline.

1   For the population of scores obtained by the new method we test $H_0: \sigma^2 = 100$ against $H_1: \sigma^2 \neq 100$.
2   Select $\alpha = .05$, an arbitrary choice.
3   The statistic to use is $\chi^2_{n-1} = (n-1)s^2/\sigma_0^2$ (or chi-square divided by degrees of freedom). The necessary assumptions are (a) the sample of students producing the scores is randomly selected and (b) the population of scores is normally distributed. The normality assumption is fairly reasonable for this type of score.
4   The critical region is $\chi^2_{80} < 57.15$, $\chi^2_{80} > 106.6$ (or $\chi^2_{80}/80 < .714$, $\chi^2_{80}/80 > 1.33$). Figure 5-7 applies with $\alpha = .05$, $n = 81$.
5   Computations: The observed value of χ^2_{80} is $80(144)/100 = 115.2$. (The observed value of $\chi^2_{80}/80 = 144/100 = 1.44$.)
6   Reject H_0. We would probably conclude that the new method produces scores which are more variable than the old method produces.

Approximate values for the power of the tests discussed in this section are easily obtained from the table of chi-square divided by degrees of freedom. Suppose that for the hypothesis tested in Example 5-17 we would like to know the power if $\sigma^2 = .00028$. The power is

$$\Pr\left(\frac{s^2}{\sigma_0^2} < .577\right) = \Pr\left(\frac{s^2}{\sigma^2} < .577 \frac{\sigma_0^2}{\sigma^2}\right)$$

which is, of course, equal to .05 if $\sigma^2 = \sigma_0^2$. If, however, the variance is actually σ^2, and not σ_0^2, then s^2/σ^2 has a chi-square divided by degrees of freedom distribution and we can evaluate

$$\Pr\left(\frac{s^2}{\sigma^2} < .577 \frac{.00042}{.00028}\right) = \Pr\left(\frac{s^2}{\sigma^2} < .866\right)$$

from Appendix D-8. The table gives

$$\Pr\left(\frac{s^2}{\sigma^2} < .831\right) = .30 \qquad \Pr\left(\frac{s^2}{\sigma^2} < .902\right) = .40$$

Hence the power is approximately .35 when $\sigma^2 = .00028$.

An easier way to obtain the power is to use the graphs of Appendix D-12. The first set of three give power for testing $H_0: \sigma^2 = \sigma_0^2$ against $H_1: \sigma^2 < \sigma_0^2$ with $\alpha = .01, .025, .05$. The second set of three are for testing $H_0: \sigma^2 = \sigma_0^2$ against $H_1: \sigma^2 > \sigma_0^2$ with the same α's. All six graphs can be used to approximate the power of the test of $H_0: \sigma^2 = \sigma_0^2$ against $H_1: \sigma^2 \neq \sigma^2$ with maximum error $\alpha/2$ (which occurs when H_0 is true) and negligible error if power is larger than .30. When using the graphs with a two-tailed test, use the ones with one-half the significance level of the test. Thus they apply to two-tailed tests with $\alpha = .02$, .05, .10. In order to find power, enter the horizontal scale with $R = \sigma/\sigma_0$, follow this line up to the curve with the appropriate degrees of freedom, and read off power on the vertical scale. Thus, for the situation of Example 5-17, we have, if $\sigma^2 = .00028$, $R^2 = .00028/.00042 = \frac{2}{3}$, $R = .816$. Since the degrees of freedom $= 24$, we interpolate between the curves $\nu = 20$ and $\nu = 30$ and read a power of .35.

EXAMPLE 5-19

If a sample size of 101 is used in Example 5-17, what is the power when $\sigma^2 = .00028$?

Solution

If $n = 101$, the critical value of chi-square divided by degrees of freedom is $\chi^2_{100;.05}/100 = .779$ and the power is

$$\Pr\left(\frac{s^2}{\sigma_0^2} < .779\right) = \Pr\left(\frac{s^2}{\sigma^2} < .779\frac{\sigma_0^2}{\sigma^2}\right)$$

$$= \Pr\left(\frac{s^2}{\sigma^2} < .779\frac{.00042}{.00028}\right)$$

$$= \Pr\left(\frac{s^2}{\sigma^2} < 1.169\right)$$

For 100 degrees of freedom the table gives

$$\Pr\left(\frac{s^2}{\sigma^2} < 1.12\right) = .80 \qquad \Pr\left(\frac{s^2}{\sigma^2} < 1.18\right) = .90$$

130

Hence the power is approximately .88 (or slightly under .90) when $\sigma^2 = .00028$. From the lower-tail graphs in Appendix D-12 with $\alpha = .05$ and $\nu = 100$, we read power $= .88$ above $R = .816$.

EXAMPLE 5-20

In Example 5-19 how large would n have to be to raise the power to .95 when $\sigma^2 = .00028$?

Solution

One way to approximate n is by trial and error. Since $n = 101$ gives a power of .88, a larger sample is needed. Try $n = 121$, which gives a critical value of .798 for s^2/σ_0^2. The power is

$$\Pr\left(\frac{s^2}{\sigma^2} < \frac{.798(3)}{2}\right) = \Pr\left(\frac{s^2}{\sigma^2} < 1.20\right) \cong .93$$

With $n = 141$, the critical value is .812 and the power is

$$\Pr\left(\frac{s^2}{\sigma^2} < \frac{.812(3)}{2}\right) = \Pr\left(\frac{s^2}{\sigma^2} < 1.22\right) \cong .96$$

Thus the n required is roughly two-thirds of the way between 121 and 141, or approximately 134. In a real-life problem any n close to 134 (say 130 to 140) would be satisfactory. The graphs of Appendix D-12 can also be used for this type of problem. Entering above $R = .816$, a power of .95 is obtained between $\nu = 100$ and $\nu = 150$. Interpolation yields ν equal to approximately 139.

EXAMPLE 5-21

Find the approximate power of the test in Example 5-18 if $\sigma = 11$.

Solution

The power is

$$\Pr\left(\frac{s^2}{\sigma_0^2} < .714\right) + \Pr\left(\frac{s^2}{\sigma_0^2} > 1.33\right)$$

$$= \Pr\left(\frac{s^2}{\sigma^2} < .714\,\frac{\sigma_0^2}{\sigma^2}\right) + \Pr\left(\frac{s^2}{\sigma^2} > 1.33\,\frac{\sigma_0^2}{\sigma^2}\right)$$

$$= \Pr\left(\frac{s^2}{\sigma^2} < \frac{.714(100)}{121}\right) + \Pr\left(\frac{s^2}{\sigma^2} > \frac{1.33(100)}{121}\right)$$

$$= \Pr\left(\frac{s^2}{\sigma^2} < .59\right) + \Pr\left(\frac{s^2}{\sigma^2} > 1.10\right)$$

$$\cong .001 + (1 - .74) = .26$$

Using the graph of Appendix D-12 for upper-tail tests headed by $\alpha = .025$ requires some interpolation. We enter the horizontal scale with $R = \sigma/\sigma_0 = {}^{11}\!/_{10} = 1.1$. For $\nu = 75$, the power is about .22; for $\nu = 100$, about .30. Hence, our estimate of the power from the graphs is about .24. Since the curves rise almost vertically in this region, it is difficult to read the graph accurately.

To obtain a confidence interval for σ^2 and σ with coefficient $1 - \alpha$, we start with

$$\Pr\left(\chi^2_{n-1;\alpha/2} < \frac{(n-1)s^2}{\sigma^2} < \chi^2_{n-1;1-\alpha/2}\right) = 1 - \alpha \tag{5-39}$$

Easy manipulation of inequalities yields

$$\Pr\left(\frac{(n-1)s^2}{\chi^2_{n-1;1-\alpha/2}} < \sigma^2 < \frac{(n-1)s^2}{\chi^2_{n-1;\alpha/2}}\right) = 1 - \alpha \tag{5-40}$$

Taking square roots in (5-40) yields the equivalent statement

$$\Pr\left(\sqrt{\frac{(n-1)s^2}{\chi^2_{n-1;1-\alpha/2}}} < \sigma < \sqrt{\frac{(n-1)s^2}{\chi^2_{n-1;\alpha/2}}}\right) = 1 - \alpha \tag{5-41}$$

The probability statements (5-40) and (5-41) have to be interpreted in the usual way for confidence intervals. The interval

$$\left(\sqrt{\frac{(n-1)s^2}{\chi^2_{n-1;1-\alpha/2}}}, \sqrt{\frac{(n-1)s^2}{\chi^2_{n-1;\alpha/2}}}\right) \tag{5-42}$$

covers a value σ_0 if, and only if, the test accepts $H_0: \sigma^2 = \sigma_0^2$ against $H_1: \sigma^2 \neq \sigma_0^2$ with the same α. Thus again we could compute the interval, rather than the χ^2_{n-1} statistic, to test H_0.

EXAMPLE 5-22

Find a confidence interval with coefficient .95 for the σ^2 and σ of Example 5-18.

Solution

We have $s = 12$, $n = 81$, $\alpha = .05$, $\alpha/2 = .025$. Appendix D-7 yields $\chi^2_{80;.025} = 57.15$, $\chi^2_{80;.975} = 106.6$. Thus the confidence interval for σ^2 is

$$\left(\frac{80(144)}{106.6}, \frac{80(144)}{57.15}\right)$$

which reduces to (108.1, 201.6). Taking square roots yields $(\sqrt{108.1}, \sqrt{201.6})$ or (10.4, 14.2) as a confidence interval for σ with coefficient .95.

132

The length of the confidence interval (5-42) is

$$I = \sqrt{\frac{(n-1)s^2}{\chi^2_{n-1;\alpha/2}}} - \sqrt{\frac{(n-1)s^2}{\chi^2_{n-1;1-\alpha/2}}} \qquad (5\text{-}43)$$

Suppose we want to know

$$\Pr(I < L) \qquad (5\text{-}44)$$

where L is a specified length for the confidence interval. The probability (5-44) is equivalent to

$$\Pr\left[\frac{s^2}{\sigma^2} < \frac{L^2/\sigma^2}{\left(\sqrt{\dfrac{n-1}{\chi^2_{n-1;\alpha/2}}} - \sqrt{\dfrac{n-1}{\chi^2_{n-1;1-\alpha/2}}}\right)^2}\right] \qquad (5\text{-}45)$$

which can be evaluated from Appendix D-8 if L is chosen as a multiple of σ.

EXAMPLE 5-23

Find the probability that a random sample of size 81 drawn from a normal population produces a confidence interval for σ with coefficient .95 which is shorter than $.35\sigma$.

Solution

We have $n = 81$, $\chi^2_{80;.025}/80 = .714$, $\chi^2_{80;.975}/80 = 1.33$, $L = .35\sigma$. Hence we seek

$$\Pr\left[\frac{s^2}{\sigma^2} < \frac{(.35)^2}{\left(\sqrt{\dfrac{1}{.714}} - \sqrt{\dfrac{1}{1.33}}\right)^2}\right] = \Pr\left(\frac{s^2}{\sigma^2} < 1.23\right)$$

Entering Appendix D-8 with 80 degrees of freedom reveals that the probability is between .90 and .95. Interpolation yields about .92.

Appendix D-8 can be used to find the n required to make (5-44) and (5-45) equal to any desired probability level for a given α and a given L (as a multiple of σ). A trial-and-error method must be used, however. Different values of n are tried until (5-45) yields approximately the desired probability level. Appendix D-13 contains graphs from which n can be read for $\alpha = .05, .10$ and probability levels .30, .50, .70, .90, .99.

EXAMPLE 5-24

Use Appendix D-13 to find the n required if it is desired to obtain a confidence interval for σ with coefficient .90 such that the probability will be .99 that the interval will be less than $.5\sigma$.

Solution

Turn to the graph in Appendix D-13 headed by $\alpha = .10$, confidence coefficient .90. The vertical line above $L = .5\sigma$ crosses the graph labeled Pr $= .99$ opposite $n = 39$. Thus the probability is .99 that a random sample of size 39 drawn from a normal population will produce a confidence interval with coefficient .90 that is shorter than $.5\sigma$.

Observe that the graphs of Appendix D-13 can also be used to obtain an approximate answer for a problem like Example 5-23. That is, with a given n we can approximate the probability that a random sample from a normal distribution produces a confidence interval (with given coefficient) for the standard deviation shorter than L. For example, with the information given in Example 5-23 ($\alpha = .05$, $n = 81$, $L = .35\sigma$), we see that a horizontal line drawn through $n = 81$ crosses a vertical line drawn through $L = .35$ between the curves labeled Pr $= .90$ and Pr $= .99$. Crude interpolation yields a probability slightly over .90, agreeing with the .92 obtained in Example 5-23.

Some other tables which can be used to determine sample size associated with short confidence intervals for the standard deviation are discussed in Sec. 3-3 of [2].

EXERCISES

◆ 5-24 Assume that the frozen shrimp company of Exercise 5-1 does not know the standard deviation of package weights. Suppose that the company desires to maintain a standard deviation of ½ ounce or less. A random sample of 25 packages yields a sample standard deviation of .60 ounce. Assuming that package weights are normally distributed, should we conclude that the desired standard deviation is not being maintained? Use $\alpha = .05$ and follow the six-step outline.

◆ 5-25 Find the power of the test used in Exercise 5-24 if the actual value of σ is .60. If $\sigma = .75$.

◆ 5-26 Approximately how large does n have to be in Exercise 5-24 if a power of .95 is desired when $\sigma = .75$?

◆ 5-27 Find a confidence interval for σ in Exercise 5-24 with coefficient .95.

134

5-28 Find the probability that a random sample of size 25 drawn from a normal population produces a confidence interval for σ with coefficient .95 which is shorter than $.7\sigma$. How large would n have to be to raise the probability to .90?

5-29 Grade-point averages for students at a certain university have had a standard deviation of .5 units over a number of years. A random sample of 20 grade-point averages is selected from last semester's reports from the College of Education and yields a sample standard deviation of .35. Does this indicate that last semester's College of Education grades have a different standard deviation? Follow the six-step outline. Find the approximate power of the test if $\sigma = .40$.

5-30 Exercise 5-14 deals with a famous bridge player and a new system. Suppose that a player with somewhat less talent finds that he averages about 52.0 per cent whether he uses the old or new bidding system. He would like to use the new system, even though it entails more memory work, if he can "prove" that it yields scores with a larger standard deviation, since that would increase his chances of occasionally obtaining a really high score and thus winning. Using the old system, his standard deviation is 5.0 per cent. Using the new system for 10 sessions, his standard deviation is 8.0 per cent. If $\alpha = .01$, should he adopt the new system? Follow the six-step outline.

5-31 In Exercise 5-30 find the probability of adopting the new system if the actual value of σ is 7.0 per cent. If $n = 36$ (not 10), what is the probability of adopting the new system if $\sigma = 7.0$?

5-32 Find a confidence interval for σ in Exercise 5-30 with coefficient .90.

5-8 INFERENCES ABOUT TWO VARIANCES

In the preceding section we encountered some problems in which we tested hypotheses about the variance of a random variable associated with a new process or procedure. In both Examples 5-17 and 5-18 the σ_0^2 used in step 1 was the variance, assumed to be known, arising from a standard process. Situations in which an experimenter may want to test hypotheses about two variances, neither of which is known, frequently arise. Instead of having a standard and a new machine, as in Example 5-17, we may be choosing between two new machines on the basis of variance. Instead of the situation encountered in Example 5-18, two new statistics textbooks may be under consideration with both variances unknown. The frozen shrimp company may have two methods of packaging which yield an average content of 12 ounces and wish to choose one on the basis of variability.

Suppose that two machines both produce $\frac{1}{2}$-inch bolts. Machine 1 is somewhat more expensive than machine 2. We would like to buy machine 2 unless we can prove that machine 1 makes bolts with lower variance of diameters. Let σ_1^2 and σ_2^2 be the unknown variances associated with machines 1 and 2, respectively. Then we would test

$$H_0: \sigma_1^2 = \sigma_2^2 \text{ against } H_1: \sigma_1^2 < \sigma_2^2 \tag{5-46}$$

and buy the cheaper machine if H_0 is accepted. If the two machines are about the same price and machine 1 turns out more parts than machine 2, we may decide to buy machine 1 unless the variance associated with machine 1 can be proved to be larger than the variance for machine 2. Under the latter circumstances we would test

$$H_0: \sigma_1^2 = \sigma_2^2 \text{ against } H_1: \sigma_1^2 > \sigma_2^2 \tag{5-47}$$

and buy machine 1 unless H_0 is rejected. Note that the alternative of (5-47) can be written $H_1: \sigma_2^2 < \sigma_1^2$. If we interchange the names of the machines, calling the one that turns out more parts machine 2, then (5-46) and (5-47) are exactly the same and need not be considered separate cases. We can always use (5-46) and associate the smaller variance under H_1 with the subscript 1.

Some problems lead to two-sided alternatives. A test for equality of two means, to be encountered later in the chapter, depends upon the assumption that two unknown variances are equal. The assumption may be tested by comparing

$$H_0: \sigma_1^2 = \sigma_2^2 \text{ against } H_1: \sigma_1^2 \neq \sigma_2^2 \tag{5-48}$$

In some problems we may prefer to replace (5-46) by

$$H_0: \sigma_1^2 \geqq \sigma_2^2 \text{ against } H_1: \sigma_1^2 < \sigma_2^2 \tag{5-49}$$

or (5-47) by

$$H_0: \sigma_1^2 \leqq \sigma_2^2 \text{ against } H_1: \sigma_1^2 > \sigma_2^2 \tag{5-50}$$

Again, α must be regarded as the largest value of the power under H_0.

Let $x_{11}, x_{21}, \ldots, x_{n_1 1}$ and $x_{12}, x_{22}, \ldots, x_{n_2 2}$ denote samples from populations having variances σ_1^2 and σ_2^2, respectively. The sample variances are

$$s_1^2 = \frac{\sum_{i=1}^{n_1} (x_{i1} - \bar{x}_1)^2}{n_1 - 1} \quad \text{and} \quad s_2^2 = \frac{\sum_{i=1}^{n_2} (x_{i2} - \bar{x}_2)^2}{n_2 - 1} \tag{5-51}$$

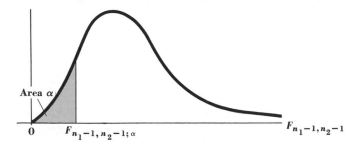

Figure 5-8   Critical region and associated level of significance for testing $H_0: \sigma_1^2 = \sigma_2^2$ against $H_1: \sigma_1^2 < \sigma_2^2$.

where $\bar{x}_1$ and $\bar{x}_2$ are the sample means.   Then

$$F_{n_1-1, n_2-1} = \frac{s_1^2/\sigma_1^2}{s_2^2/\sigma_2^2} = \frac{s_1^2}{s_2^2}\left(\frac{\sigma_2^2}{\sigma_1^2}\right) = \frac{s_1^2}{s_2^2}\left(\frac{1}{R_0^2}\right) \tag{5-52}$$

is used to test hypotheses about the ratio of variances.   Although other ratios could be used in tests, the H_0's of (5-46), (5-47), and (5-48) specify the ratio as 1.   Consequently, in these situations (5-52) reduces to

$$F_{n_1-1, n_2-1} = \frac{s_1^2}{s_2^2} \tag{5-53}$$

If $\sigma_1^2 = \sigma_2^2$, then the sampling distribution of s_1^2/s_2^2 is the F distribution with $n_1 - 1$ and $n_2 - 1$ degrees of freedom provided (*a*) both samples are selected randomly and (*b*) both populations are normal.   Again nonnormality may produce serious error in probability statements.

When testing (5-46) or (5-49), H_1 is supported only if s_1^2 is small by comparison to s_2^2.   Consequently, H_0 is rejected if F_{n_1-1, n_2-1} is small.

Figure 5-9   Critical region and associated level of significance for testing $H_0: \sigma_1^2 = \sigma_2^2$ against $H_1: \sigma_1^2 > \sigma_2^2$.

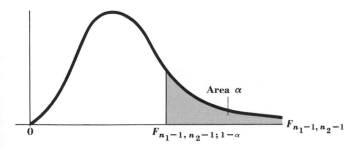

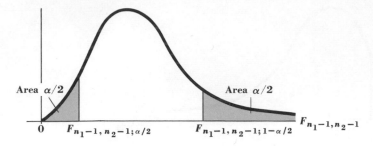

*Figure 5-10   Critical region and associated level of signifi-
cance for testing $H_0: \sigma_1^2 = \sigma_2^2$ against $H_1: \sigma_1^2 \neq \sigma_2^2$.*

If the significance level is α, then the critical region is

$$\frac{s_1^2}{s_2^2} < F_{n_1-1,n_2-1;\alpha} \qquad (5\text{-}54)$$

as shown in Fig. 5-8.   Similarly, when testing (5-47) or (5-50), only
large values of s_1^2 (when compared to s_2^2) support H_1 and a test of significance level α is obtained by rejecting H_0 when

$$\frac{s_1^2}{s_2^2} > F_{n_1-1,n_2-1;1-\alpha} \qquad (5\text{-}55)$$

The latter critical region is shown in Fig. 5-9.   Finally, when testing
(5-48), H_0 is rejected when s_1^2/s_2^2 is either too large or too small.   The
critical region which is usually used is pictured in Fig. 5-10.   Thus we
reject when

$$\frac{s_1^2}{s_2^2} < F_{n_1-1,n_2-1;\alpha/2}, \quad \frac{s_1^2}{s_2^2} > F_{n_1-1,n_2-1;1-\alpha/2} \qquad (5\text{-}56)$$

From a theoretical point of view a region slightly better than (5-56)
exists.   However, there is very little difference between the two even
for small n_1 and n_2.

EXAMPLE 5-25

Consider again the two machines used to illustrate (5-46).   Suppose
that a random sample of 25 bolts is taken from each machine and the
sample variances for diameters are $s_1^2 = .00028$ and $s_2^2 = .00045$ from
machines 1 and 2, respectively.   What decision should be made if
$\alpha = .05$?

138

Solution

We shall follow the six-step outline:

1   We test $H_0: \sigma_1^2 = \sigma_2^2$ against $H_1: \sigma_1^2 < \sigma_2^2$ and buy machine 2 unless H_0 is rejected.

2   $\alpha = .05$ is given.

3   The statistic to use is $F_{n_1-1,n_2-1} = s_1^2/s_2^2$. If $\sigma_1^2 = \sigma_2^2$, then F_{n_1-1,n_2-1} has an F distribution provided (a) both samples are selected randomly and (b) both populations are normal.

4   The critical region is $F_{24,24} < .504$. Figure 5-8 applies with $\alpha = .05$.

5   Computations: Since the sample variances are given, we need only compute $F_{24,24} = .00028/.00045 = .62$.

6   H_0 is accepted and machine 2 is purchased.

EXAMPLE 5-26

A standard and a new method of teaching statistics are being compared. It is desired to know whether or not there is a difference in variability, as measured by variance, of final-examination scores produced by the two methods. One class is taught by each method, and both classes take the same final examination. The sample variances are $s_1^2 = 100$ and $s_2^2 = 144$, where the subscript 1 is used for the standard method and 2 is used for the new. If the classes contain $n_1 = 101$ and $n_2 = 61$ students, what conclusion would be drawn with $\alpha = .05$?

Solution

We shall follow the six-step outline.

1   We test $H_0: \sigma_1^2 = \sigma_2^2$ against $H_1: \sigma_1^2 \neq \sigma_2^2$, since the problem does not suggest a particular one-sided alternative.

2   $\alpha = .05$ is given.

3   Same as in Example 5-25.

4   The critical region is $F_{100,60} < .641$, $F_{100,60} > 1.60$. Figure 5-10 applies with $\alpha = .05$.

5   Computations:

$$F_{100,60} = \frac{s_1^2}{s_2^2} = \frac{100}{144} = .694$$

6   H_0 is accepted. The sample variances are such that it is reasonable that populations with equal variances could have produced them.

Approximate values for the power of the test discussed in this section can be obtained from Appendix D-9. Suppose that for the hypothesis tested in Example 5-25 we would like to know the power if $\sigma_1^2/\sigma_2^2 = .5$. The power is

$$\Pr\left(\frac{s_1^2}{s_2^2} < .504\right) \tag{5-57}$$

According to (5-52), if $R_0^2 = \sigma_1^2/\sigma_2^2 = .5$, then $2s_1^2/s_2^2$ has an F distribution. Consequently, to evaluate (5-57), each side of the inequality has to be multiplied by 2. We get

$$\text{Power} = \Pr\left[2\frac{s_1^2}{s_2^2} < 2(.504)\right]$$
$$= \Pr(F_{24,24} < 1.008)$$

The table gives

$$\Pr(F_{24,24} < 1.00) = .50 \qquad \Pr(F_{24,24} < 1.32) = .75$$

Hence the power is just slightly larger than .50, or about .51, when $\sigma_1^2/\sigma_2^2 = .5$. In general, the power of the test for (5-46) and (5-49) is

$$\Pr\left(F_{n_1-1,n_2-1} < \frac{F_{n_1-1,n_2-1;\alpha}}{R_0^2}\right) \tag{5-58}$$

Of course, if $R_0^2 = 1$, (5-58) reduces to α. Similarly, the power of test for (5-48) is

$$\Pr\left(F_{n_1-1,n_2-1} < \frac{F_{n_1-1,n_2-1;\alpha/2}}{R_0^2}\right) + \Pr\left(F_{n_1-1,n_2-1} > \frac{F_{n_1-1,\,n_2-1;\,1-\alpha/2}}{R_0^2}\right) \tag{5-59}$$

If both sample sizes are the same, power can be obtained from the graphs of Appendix D-14. These give power for testing $H_0: \sigma_1^2 = \sigma_2^2$ against $H_1: \sigma_1^2 < \sigma_2^2$ with $\alpha = .01, .025, .05$. The graphs can be used for (5-47) by interchanging the roles of the 1 and 2 subscripts. They also yield approximate power of the test for $H_0: \sigma_1^2 = \sigma_2^2$ against $H_1: \sigma_1^2 \neq \sigma_2^2$ with maximum error $\alpha/2$ (which occurs when H_0 is true) and negligible error if power is larger than .30. Before entering the graphs with a two-tailed test, divide the significance level of the test by 2. In order to find power, enter the horizontal scale with $R_0 = \sigma_1/\sigma_2$, follow this line up to the curve with the appropriate degrees of freedom, and read off power on the vertical scale. Hence if $R_0^2 = .5$, $R_0 = .707$, $\nu_1 = \nu_2 = \nu = 24$, $\alpha = .05$, we read a power of about .52 by interpolating between $\nu = 20$ and $\nu = 30$, which agrees with the value calculated above. When using the graphs with two-tailed tests and $R_0 > 1$, enter the horizontal scale at $1/R_0$.

EXAMPLE 5-27

If samples of size 61 are used for the problem of Example 5-25, what is the power if $R_0^2 = \sigma_1^2/\sigma_2^2 = .5$? What is the answer if the sample sizes are 121?

Solution

Equation (5-58) becomes

$$\Pr\left(F_{60,60} < \frac{.652}{R_0^2}\right)$$

If $R_0^2 = .5$, then the power is $\Pr(F_{60,60} < 1.304)$. Appendix D-9 yields

$$\Pr(F_{60,60} < 1.19) = .75 \qquad \Pr(F_{60,60} < 1.40) = .90$$

Thus the power is between .75 and .90. Interpolation yields about .83. Entering the page of Appendix D-14 headed by $\alpha = .05$, we read a power of about .84 for $\nu = 60$, $R_0 = .707$.

When the sample sizes are 121, then the power is

$$\Pr\left(F_{120,120} < \frac{.740}{R_0^2}\right) = \Pr(F_{120,120} < 1.48)$$

According to the F table, the latter probability is about .98. The graphs of Appendix D-14 give a power of .983.

EXAMPLE 5-28

Find the approximate power of the test used in Example 5-26 if $R_0^2 = \sigma_1^2/\sigma_2^2 = .5$.

Solution

Equation (5-59) becomes

$$\Pr\left(F_{100,60} < \frac{.641}{.5}\right) + \Pr\left(F_{100,60} > \frac{1.60}{.5}\right)$$
$$= \Pr(F_{100,60} < 1.28) + \Pr(F_{100,60} > 3.20)$$

The second probability is practically zero. To evaluate the first one, we see that

$$\Pr(F_{100,60} < 1.17) = .75 \qquad \Pr(F_{100,60} < 1.36) = .90$$

Interpolation gives about .84 for $\Pr(F_{100,60} < 1.28)$.

To obtain a confidence interval for σ_1^2/σ_2^2 (or σ_1/σ_2) with coefficient $1 - \alpha$, we start with

$$\Pr\left(F_{n_1-1,n_2-1;\alpha/2} < \frac{s_1^2}{s_2^2}\left(\frac{\sigma_2^2}{\sigma_1^2}\right) < F_{n_1-1,n_2-1;1-\alpha/2}\right) = 1 - \alpha \qquad (5\text{-}60)$$

After manipulating the inequalities in (5-60), we get

$$\Pr\left(\frac{s_1^2}{s_2^2}\frac{1}{F_{n_1-1,n_2-1;1-\alpha/2}} < \frac{\sigma_1^2}{\sigma_2^2} < \frac{s_1^2}{s_2^2}\frac{1}{F_{n_1-1,n_2-1;\alpha/2}}\right) = 1 - \alpha \qquad (5\text{-}61)$$

Taking the square roots in (5-61) yields

$$\Pr\left(\frac{s_1}{s_2}\frac{1}{\sqrt{F_{n_1-1,n_2-1;1-\alpha/2}}} < \frac{\sigma_1}{\sigma_2} < \frac{s_1}{s_2}\frac{1}{\sqrt{F_{n_1-1,n_2-1;\alpha/2}}}\right) = 1 - \alpha \qquad (5\text{-}62)$$

As in previous cases, the probability statements (5-61) and (5-62) have to be interpreted in the usual way for confidence intervals. The interval

$$\left(\frac{s_1}{s_2}\frac{1}{\sqrt{F_{n_1-1,n_2-1;1-\alpha/2}}}, \frac{s_1}{s_2}\frac{1}{\sqrt{F_{n_1-1,n_2-1;\alpha/2}}}\right) \qquad (5\text{-}63)$$

covers a 1 if, and only if, the test of (5-48) accepts H_0 using the same α.

EXAMPLE 5-29

Find a confidence interval with coefficient .95 for σ_1^2/σ_2^2 and σ_1/σ_2 in Example 5-25.

Solution

We have $s_1^2 = .00028$, $s_2^2 = .00045$, $n_1 = n_2 = 25$. Also, $\alpha = .05$, $F_{24,24;.025} = .441$, $F_{24,24;.975} = 2.27$. Thus the interval given by (5-61) is

$$\left(\frac{28}{45}\frac{1}{2.27}, \frac{28}{45}\frac{1}{.441}\right)$$

which reduces to (.274,1.41). Taking square roots yields ($\sqrt{.274}$, $\sqrt{1.41}$) or (.52,1.19) as a confidence interval for σ_1/σ_2 with coefficient .95.

EXERCISES

◆ 5-33 Two methods of packaging frozen shrimp yield about the same average value. However, method 2 is somewhat faster and the company would like to use it unless the variance can be shown to be larger than the variance for method 1 at the .05 level of significance. A sample of 41 packages from those produced by each method is examined. The sample standard deviations are $s_1 = .50$ ounce for method 1 and $s_2 = .62$ ounce for method 2. What decision should be made? Follow the six-step outline.

◆ 5-34   Find the power of the test used in Exercise 5-33 if $\sigma_1/\sigma_2 = .7$. If $\sigma_1/\sigma_2 = .5$.

◆ 5-35   Suppose that two samples of size 61 had been used in Exercise 5-33. What is the power if $\sigma_1/\sigma_2 = .7$? What is the power when $\sigma_1/\sigma_2 = .7$ if two samples of size 121 are used?

◆ 5-36   Find a confidence interval for σ_1/σ_2 in Exercise 5-33 with coefficient .95.

5-37   It is known that two brands of tires have an average life of 25,000 miles. However, there may be some difference in the variability of mileage attained from the two brands. An experiment in which 16 tires from each brand are used is conducted. The tires are run under similar conditions until they wear out. It is found that the two sample standard deviations are $s_1 = 4,200$ miles, $s_2 = 2,800$ miles. If $\alpha = .05$, what are your conclusions? Follow the six-step outline.

5-38   Find the power of test used in Exercise 5-37 if $\sigma_1/\sigma_2 = 2$. If $\sigma_1/\sigma_2 = \frac{1}{2}$.

5-39   Suppose that 41 of each kind of tires had been used in Exercise 5-37. Now what is the power if $\sigma_1/\sigma_2 = 2$? If $\sigma_1/\sigma_2 = \frac{1}{2}$?

5-40   Find a confidence interval for σ_1/σ_2 in Exercise 5-37 with coefficient .95.

◆ 5-41   Two classes are taught statistics, each with a different text. Both classes take the same final examination. The class sizes are $n_1 = 61$, $n_2 = 121$. If the sample standard deviations for the final examination grades are $s_1 = 10$, $s_2 = 15$, what conclusion can be drawn concerning the variability of final-examination scores associated with the two textbooks? Follow the six-step outline.

5-42   Find a confidence interval for σ_1/σ_2 in Exercise 5-41 with coefficient .90.

5-9   INFERENCES ABOUT TWO MEANS WITH TWO RANDOM SAMPLES

In Secs. 5-2 and 5-5 we considered a number of hypothesis-testing problems concerning one mean. In situations that will sometimes be encountered an investigator will want to test hypotheses concerning two means. The large corporation of Example 5-1 may be choosing between two brands of light bulbs and not know either average life. The smoker discussed in Sec. 4-3 may be interested in comparing the average nicotine content of two brands of cigarettes. A wheat grower may want to compare two varieties of wheat for average yield. A teacher may be interested in comparing average results achieved by two teaching methods.

Suppose that two brands of light bulbs are being considered by a large corporation. Brand 1 is slightly less expensive than brand 2. The company would like to buy brand 1 unless there is good evidence that the average life of brand 1 is less than the average life of brand 2. If we let μ_1 and μ_2 be the average length of life for brands 1 and 2, respectively, then we will be interested in testing

$$H_0: \mu_1 = \mu_2 \text{ against } H_1: \mu_1 < \mu_2. \tag{5-64}$$

If H_0 is accepted, the cheaper brand will be purchased. If the two brands sell for about the same price and brand 2 is more attractive than brand 1, we may want to buy brand 2 unless brand 1 has a longer average life. Under the latter circumstances we will test

$$H_0: \mu_1 = \mu_2 \text{ against } H_1: \mu_1 > \mu_2 \tag{5-65}$$

and buy brand 2 unless H_0 is rejected. Actually, (5-64) and (5-65) need not be considered separate cases, because they can be reduced to the same problem merely by interchanging the roles of the subscripts.

Some problems lead to two-sided alternatives. In comparing two varieties of wheat for average yield, it is likely that there would be no other reason to prefer one variety over the other. In such a situation it would be logical to test

$$H_0: \mu_1 = \mu_2 \text{ against } H_1: \mu_1 \neq \mu_2 \tag{5-66}$$

In some problems we may prefer to replace (5-64) by

$$H_0: \mu_1 \geqq \mu_2 \text{ against } H_1: \mu_1 < \mu_2 \tag{5-67}$$

or (5-65) by

$$H_0: \mu_1 \leqq \mu_2 \text{ against } H_1: \mu_1 > \mu_2 \tag{5-68}$$

As before, α must be regarded as the largest power when H_0 is true.

Let $x_{11}, x_{21}, \ldots, x_{n_1 1}$ and $x_{12}, x_{22}, \ldots, x_{n_2 2}$ denote samples from populations having means μ_1 and μ_2 and variances σ_1^2 and σ_2^2, respectively. If the variances are known, then the statistic

$$Z = \frac{\bar{x}_1 - \bar{x}_2 - (\mu_1 - \mu_2)}{\sqrt{\sigma_1^2/n_1 + \sigma_2^2/n_2}} \tag{5-69}$$

where $\bar{x}_1$ and $\bar{x}_2$ are the sample means, is used for testing (5-64) to (5-68). In each case $\mu_1 - \mu_2$ is replaced by 0 when computing the statistic which is to be compared to the critical value. Thus (5-69) reduces to

$$Z = \frac{\bar{x}_1 - \bar{x}_2}{\sqrt{\sigma_1^2/n_1 + \sigma_2^2/n_2}} \tag{5-70}$$

If (a) both samples are drawn randomly and (b) both populations are normal, then the statistic (5-70) has a standard normal distribution when $\mu_1 = \mu_2$. Assumption (b) is not critical if the n's are moderately large because of the central limit theorem. Since the variances are usually unknown, the usage of (5-69) is somewhat limited. If we are willing to assume (a) and (b) and if (c) both populations have the same variance, then

$$t_{n_1+n_2-2} = \frac{\bar{x}_1 - \bar{x}_2 - (\mu_1 - \mu_2)}{s_p \sqrt{1/n_1 + 1/n_2}} \tag{5-71}$$

is used to test hypotheses (5-64) to (5-68). As with (5-69), $\mu_1 - \mu_2$ is replaced by 0 when computing the statistic which is to be compared to the critical value. Here

$$s_p^2 = \frac{(n_1 - 1)s_1^2 + (n_2 - 1)s_2^2}{n_1 + n_2 - 2}$$

and s_1^2 and s_2^2 are the sample variances given by (5-51).

When testing (5-64), or (5-67), only small values of $\bar{x}_1 - \bar{x}_2$, and hence small values of $t_{n_1+n_2-2}$ (assuming variances are unknown) support H_1 and lead to rejection of H_0. If the significance level is α, then the critical region is

$$\frac{\bar{x}_1 - \bar{x}_2}{s_p \sqrt{1/n_1 + 1/n_2}} < t_{n_1+n_2-2;\alpha} \tag{5-72}$$

as pictured in Fig. 5-11. Similarly, when testing (5-65) or (5-68),

Figure 5-11   Critical region and associated level of significance for testing $H_0: \mu_1 = \mu_2$ against $H_1: \mu_1 < \mu_2$.

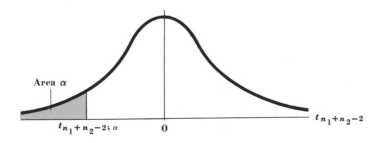

145

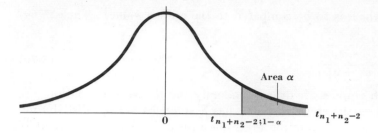

Figure 5-12   Critical region and associated level of significance for testing $H_0\colon \mu_1 = \mu_2$ against $H_1\colon \mu_1 > \mu_2$.

only large values of $\bar{x}_1 - \bar{x}_2$ support H_1 and a test of significance level α is obtained by rejecting H_0 when

$$\frac{\bar{x}_1 - \bar{x}_2}{s_p \sqrt{1/n_1 + 1/n_2}} > t_{n_1+n_2-2;\,1-\alpha} \tag{5-73}$$

The latter critical region is shown in Fig. 5-12.   Finally, when testing (5-66), H_0 is rejected when the statistic is too large or too small.   The critical region is

$$\frac{\bar{x}_1 - \bar{x}_2}{s_p \sqrt{1/n_1 + 1/n_2}} < t_{n_1+n_2-2;\,\alpha/2}, \quad \frac{\bar{x}_1 - \bar{x}_2}{s_p \sqrt{1/n_1 + 1/n_2}} > t_{n_1+n_2-2;\,1-\alpha/2} \tag{5-74}$$

and is shown in Fig. 5-13.

If the variances are unknown and not equal, only approximate solutions are available for testing the hypotheses that we have discussed for two means.   A statistic that can be used in this case is

$$t'_\nu = \frac{\bar{x}_1 - \bar{x}_2 - (\mu_1 - \mu_2)}{\sqrt{s_1^2/n_1 + s_2^2/n_2}} \tag{5-75}$$

Figure 5-13   Critical region and associated level of significance for testing $H_0\colon \mu_1 = \mu_2$ against $H_1\colon \mu_1 \neq \mu_2$.

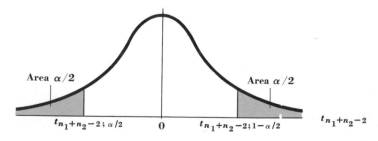

which is approximately distributed as t_ν with degrees of freedom

$$\nu = \frac{(s_1^2/n_1 + s_2^2/n_2)^2}{\dfrac{(s_1^2/n_1)^2}{n_1 - 1} + \dfrac{(s_2^2/n_2)^2}{n_2 - 1}} - 2$$

if the two populations are normal. Since ν will usually not be an integer, round it off to the nearest whole number. If $n_1 = n_2$, (5-71) and (5-75) reduce to the same number. However, the degrees of freedom associated with the two quantities are different.

Experimental evidence seems to indicate that mild departures from the assumptions of normality and equal variances do not seriously influence conclusions drawn from (5-71) provided the sample sizes are equal or nearly so. Consequently, it is likely that we would prefer to use (5-75) only if the sample sizes differ greatly and we are quite sure the variances are unequal.

EXAMPLE 5-30

The large corporation of Example 5-1 wants to choose between two brands of light bulbs on the basis of average life. Brand 1 is slightly less expensive than brand 2. The company would like to buy brand 1 unless the average life for brand 2 is shown to be significantly greater at the .05 level of significance. A sample of 100 bulbs from each brand is tested and it is found that $\bar{x}_1 = 985$ hours, $\bar{x}_2 = 1,003$ hours, $s_1 = 80$ hours, $s_2 = 60$ hours. What conclusion should be drawn?

Solution

We shall follow the six-step outline.

1   We shall test H_0: $\mu_1 = \mu_2$ against H_1: $\mu_1 < \mu_2$.
2   $\alpha = .05$ is given.
3   The statistic to use is (5-71) with $\mu_1 - \mu_2 = 0$. If $\mu_1 - \mu_2 = 0$, then $t_{n_1+n_2-2}$ has a t distribution with $100 + 100 - 2 = 198$ degrees of freedom provided (*a*) the samples are randomly chosen, (*b*) the two populations of lengths of light bulb lives are normally distributed, and (*c*) both populations have the same variance. With equal n's this large, (*b*) and (*c*) are not crucial.
4   The critical region is $t_{198} < -1.653$.
5   Computations:

$$s_p^2 = \frac{99(80)^2 + 99(60)^2}{198} = \frac{6,400 + 3,600}{2} = \frac{10,000}{2}$$

The denominator of (5-71) is

$$s_p \sqrt{\frac{1}{n_1} + \frac{1}{n_2}} = \frac{100}{\sqrt{2}} \sqrt{\frac{1}{100} + \frac{1}{100}} = \frac{100}{\sqrt{2}} \sqrt{\frac{2}{100}} = 10$$

Thus

$$t_{198} = \frac{985 - 1003}{10} = -1.8$$

6 Reject H_0 in favor of H_1. Consequently, brand 2 should be purchased.

EXAMPLE 5-31

In Example 5-30 suppose that both brands sell for the same price and that the company has no reason to prefer one over the other. In comparing the two brands for average length of life, how should Example 5-30 be changed?

Solution

1 Now we test H_0: $\mu_1 = \mu_2$ against H_1: $\mu_1 \neq \mu_2$.
4 The critical region is $t_{198} < -1.972$, $t_{198} > 1.972$.
6 H_0 is now accepted. The difference in sample means is not sufficient to demonstrate that brand 2 is superior. Lacking any other information or considerations, we would no doubt still choose brand 2.

Power calculations are similar to those for Examples 5-9 to 5-11. Again we can use the graphs of Appendix D-10 with

$$\delta = \frac{|\mu_1 - \mu_2|}{\sigma \sqrt{1/n_1 + 1/n_2}},$$

where $\mu_1 - \mu_2$ must be in the range designated by H_1.

EXAMPLE 5-32

Find the power of the test used in Example 5-30 if $\mu_2 = \mu_1 + .5\sigma$; that is, the average life for brand 2 is .5 of a standard deviation longer than for brand 1.

148

Solution

We are given $n_1 = n_2 = 100$, $|\mu_1 - \mu_2| = .5\sigma$. Thus

$$\delta = \frac{.5\sigma}{\sigma \sqrt{1/100 + 1/100}} = .5 \sqrt{50} = 3.54$$

The degrees of freedom are $f = 198$. Turning to the graphs of Appendix D-10 labeled $\alpha = .05$, we find that the vertical line through $\delta = 3.54$ crosses the curves for both $f = 24$ and $f = \infty$ at about .97, which is the required power.

EXAMPLE 5-33

Find the power of the test used in Example 5-31 if $|\mu_1 - \mu_2| = .5\sigma$.

Solution

Again $\delta = 3.54$, $f = 198$. Since the test is two-sided, we look under the graph labeled $\alpha = .025$. With $f = 24$ the power is .925, and with $f = \infty$ the power is .945. Thus for $f = 198$ the power is approximately .94.

To obtain a confidence interval for $\mu_1 - \mu_2$, we start with

$$\Pr\left(-t_{n_1+n_2-2;\, 1-\alpha/2} < \frac{\bar{x}_1 - \bar{x}_2 - (\mu_1 - \mu_2)}{s_p \sqrt{1/n_1 + 1/n_2}} < t_{n_1+n_2-2;\, 1-\alpha/2} \right) = 1 - \alpha \tag{5-76}$$

Except for minor differences in symbols, (5-76) and (5-21) are the same. The usual manipulation with inequalities converts (5-76) to

$$\Pr\left(\bar{x}_1 - \bar{x}_2 - t_{n_1+n_2-2;\, 1-\alpha/2}\, s_p \sqrt{\frac{1}{n_1} + \frac{1}{n_2}} < \mu_1 - \mu_2 \right.$$
$$\left. < \bar{x}_1 - \bar{x}_2 + t_{n_1+n_2-2;\, 1-\alpha/2}\, s_p \sqrt{\frac{1}{n_1} + \frac{1}{n_2}} \right) = 1 - \alpha \tag{5-77}$$

which can be written down by looking at (5-13) and making the necessary replacements. The interval given (5-77) covers 0 if, and only if, the test accepts H_0: $\mu_1 = \mu_2$ against H_1: $\mu_1 \neq \mu_2$.

EXAMPLE 5-34

Find a confidence interval with coefficient .95 for $\mu_1 - \mu_2$ by using the data of Example 5-30.

Solution

We had $\bar{x}_1 - \bar{x}_2 = 985 - 1{,}003 = -18$ hours and $s_p \sqrt{\dfrac{1}{n_1} + \dfrac{1}{n_2}} = 10$.
Also $t_{198;.975} = 1.972$. Thus the required interval is $[-18 - (1.972)10, -18 + (1.972)10]$ which reduces to $(-37.7, 1.7)$.

The two-sample procedure discussed in Sec. 5-6 has been adapted to problems involving two means by Chapman [1]. However, we shall not discuss the topic here.

EXERCISES

◆ 5-43 Two types of wheat are being compared for yield. Thirty-two acres of each kind are planted and are exposed to fairly uniform growing conditions. The results are: variety A, average yield 33 bushels per acre, sample variance 5.9; variety B, average yield 35.7 bushels per acre, sample variance 12.1. Analyze the result by following the six-step outline and using $\alpha = .01$.

◆ 5-44 Find the power of the test used in Exercise 5-43 if the average yield for variety B is σ bushels per acre more than for variety A.

◆ 5-45 In Exercise 5-43 find a confidence interval for $\mu_1 - \mu_2$ with coefficient .99. How does the interval relate to the test of Exercise 5-43?

5-46 A company is trying to decide which of two types of tires to buy for their trucks. They would like to adopt brand G unless there is some evidence that brand F is better. An experiment in which 16 tires from each brand are used is conducted. The tires are run under similar conditions until they wear out. The results are

Brand F: $\bar{x}_1 = 26{,}000$ miles, $s_1 = 4{,}200$ miles
Brand G: $\bar{x}_2 = 25{,}000$ miles, $s_2 = 2{,}800$ miles

What conclusions can be drawn? Follow the six-step outline and use $\alpha = .05$.

5-47 Find the power of the test used in Exercise 5-46 if brand F has an average life that is $\sigma/2$ miles greater than that for brand G. If the average life for brand F is σ miles greater.

5-48 In Exercise 5-46 find a confidence interval for $\mu_1 - \mu_2$ with coefficient .90.

◆ 5-49 Two methods of teaching statistics are being tried by a professor. A class of 64 students is taught by method 1 and a class of 36 by method 2. The two classes are given the same final examina-

tion.   These scores yield $\bar{x}_1 = 67$, $\bar{x}_2 = 63$, $s_1 = 10$, $s_2 = 8$.
Using $\alpha = .05$, can we conclude that the average final-examina-
tion scores produced by the two methods are different?   Follow
the six-step outline.

5-10 INFERENCES ABOUT TWO MEANS
WITH PAIRED OBSERVATIONS

There are many situations in which we may wish to compare two
population means yet find that observations occur in pairs.   Thus,
instead of having two random samples we have one random sample of
pairs.   The two observations of a pair are related to each other.
When this happens, the procedures of Sec. 5-9 no longer apply.   A
typical problem of this type is one that involves before-and-after data.
For example, suppose 20 adults are given a strenuous physical-training
program.   Their weights are recorded before they begin and after
they complete the course.   We desire to know if the program produces
a change in the average weight of individuals.   Obviously, the measurements are related.   That is, if an individual weighs 200 pounds
before beginning, he will probably weigh about 200 pounds at the end.
Similarly, a person who begins at 100 pounds will not differ too greatly
from that weight after completing the course.   The final weight
depends to a large extent upon the initial weight.   Our testing procedure must be changed to meet this situation.

Another important reason for pairing observations is to eliminate
effects in which there is no interest.   Suppose that two teaching
methods are to be compared by using 50 students divided into two
equal classes.   One way to conduct the experiment is to assign randomly 25 students to each class and then compare average scores when
the experiment is concluded.   If one group happens to get better
students, the results may not give a fair comparison of the two methods.
A better procedure is to pair the students according to ability (as
measured by some test or IQ) and assign at random one of each pair to
each class.   Any conclusions reached are then based upon differences
of paired scores, which we hope measure the effects due to different
teaching methods.

When extraneous effects are eliminated, the scores upon which the
test is based are less variable.   If the scores derived from the teaching
experiment measure both ability and difference in methods, the variance will be larger than if the scores reflect only difference in methods,
since each score has two sources of variation instead of one.   Decreas-

ing the variability of the observations increases the accuracy of the conclusions by reducing the probability of a Type II error.

In the teaching-methods example, there is an advantage in having available pairs of different ability. The conclusions are then applicable to a larger class of individuals than would be the case if pairs of about the same ability had been used for the experiment. In general, it is advantageous to choose pairs so that units within a pair are similar and there are wide differences from pair to pair.

Suppose that the experiment yields n pairs of measurements (x_{11}, x_{12}), (x_{21}, x_{22}), . . . , (x_{n1}, x_{n2}). From each pair a difference can be computed. Denote these by $d_1, d_2, \ldots, d_n$, where $d_i = x_{i1} - x_{i2}$, $i = 1$, $2, \ldots, n$. Let

$$\bar{d} = \frac{\sum\limits_{i=1}^{n} d_i}{n} \qquad s_d^2 = \frac{\sum\limits_{i=1}^{n} (d_i - d)^2}{n-1}$$

If it is assumed that (a) $d_1, d_2, \ldots, d_n$ is a random sample of differences and (b) the differences are normally distributed, then

$$t_{n-1} = \frac{\bar{d} - \mu_d}{s_d/\sqrt{n}} \tag{5-78}$$

where $\mu_d = \mu_1 - \mu_2$, is the best statistic to use to test (5-64) to (5-68). Except for the fact that differences, rather than individual x's, form the random variable that is sampled, (5-78) and (5-17) are exactly the same. Consequently, all the remarks made in Secs. 5-5 and 5-6 still apply.

To test (5-64) to (5-68), the statistic (5-78) is computed with $\mu_d = 0$. Critical regions are determined as in preceding sections. When testing (5-64) or (5-67), only small values of $\bar{d}$, and hence t_{n-1}, support H_1 and lead to rejection of H_0. If the significance level is α, then the critical region is

$$\frac{\bar{d}}{s_d/\sqrt{n}} < t_{n-1;\alpha} \tag{5-79}$$

Similarly, when testing (5-65) or (5-68), only large values of $\bar{d}$ support H_1 and a test of significance level α is obtained by rejecting when

$$\frac{\bar{d}}{s_d/\sqrt{n}} > t_{n-1;1-\alpha} \tag{5-80}$$

Finally, when testing (5-66), H_0 is rejected when the statistic is too large or too small and the critical region is

$$\frac{\bar{d}}{s_d/\sqrt{n}} < t_{n-1;\alpha/2} \qquad \frac{\bar{d}}{s_d/\sqrt{n}} > t_{n-1;1-\alpha/2} \tag{5-81}$$

We note that the paired-observations test has only $n - 1$ degrees of freedom for $2n$ observations. If the data are not paired, then the degrees of freedom for the t test are $2(n - 1)$, twice the previous number. This can be a big loss if pairing is not necessary. However, if the paired units are quite similar or highly related, the smaller variance more than compensates for the loss of degrees of freedom.

EXAMPLE 5-35

Ten young men were put through a strenuous physical program by the Army. Their weights were recorded before and after with the following results:

Man	1	2	3	4	5	6	7	8	9	10
Weight before	127	195	162	170	143	205	168	175	197	136
Weight after	135	200	160	182	147	200	172	186	194	141
Difference	-8	-5	2	-12	-4	5	-4	-11	3	-5

Does the program affect the average weight of young men?

Solution

1 Test H_0: $\mu_d = 0$ against H_1: $\mu_d \neq 0$.
2 Choose $\alpha = .05$, an arbitrary choice.
3 The statistic to use is (5-78) with $\mu_d = 0$. If $\mu_d = 0$, then $t_{n-1} = t_9$ has a t distribution provided (a) the young men constitute a random sample from the population of young men about whom we wish to state a conclusion and (b) the distribution of the differences is normal. The sample should be chosen in some manner to make (a) seem realistic. Experience indicates that (b) is a reasonable assumption.
4 The critical region is $t_9 < -2.262$, $t_9 > 2.262$.
5 Computations:

$$\bar{d} = \frac{-8 - 5 + 2 - 12 - 4 + 5 - 4 - 11 + 3 - 5}{10} = \frac{-39}{10}$$
$$= -3.9$$

$$\sum_{i=1}^{10} d_i^2 = (-8)^2 + (-5)^2 + 2^2 + \cdots + (-5)^2 = 449$$

153

$$s_d^2 = \frac{n \sum\limits_{i=1}^{n} d_i^2 - \left(\sum\limits_{i=1}^{n} d_i \right)^2}{n(n-1)} = \frac{10(449) - (-39)^2}{10(9)} = \frac{4,490 - 1,521}{90}$$
$$= 32.99$$

$$s_d = 5.74$$

$$t_9 = \frac{-3.9}{5.74/\sqrt{10}} = \frac{-3.9(3.16)}{5.74} = -2.13$$

6   Accept H_0. The experiment does not provide sufficient evidence to conclude that the program affects average weights.

EXAMPLE 5-36

Suppose that two teaching methods are being compared by using 50 students divided into two equal classes. The students are paired on the basis of IQ, and one of each pair is assigned at random to each group. At the end of the course an examination is given and differences in paired scores are computed by subtracting the scores produced by method 2 from those produced by method 1. The results are $\bar{d} = 5.6$, $s_d = 9.6$. Method 2 requires less work and is preferred unless it can be demonstrated that method 1 is superior. What decision should be made?

Solution

1   We test H_0: $\mu_d = 0$ against H_1: $\mu_d > 0$. If H_0 is rejected, we conclude method 1 produces the superior results.
2   Select $\alpha = .01$, an arbitrary choice.
3   Same as in Example 5-35.
4   The critical region is $t_{24} > 2.492$.
5   Computations:

$$t_{24} = \frac{5.6}{9.6/\sqrt{25}} = \frac{(5.6)5}{9.6} = \frac{28.0}{9.6} = 2.92$$

6   Reject H_0. Use method 1, which on the average produces superior results.

EXAMPLE 5-37

Find the power of the test used in Example 5-36 if $\mu_1 - \mu_2 = \mu_d = \sigma_d/2$.

Solution

$$\delta = \frac{|\mu_d| \sqrt{n}}{\sigma_d} = \frac{\frac{\sigma_d}{2} \sqrt{25}}{\sigma_d} = 2.5 \qquad \text{and} \qquad f = 25 - 1 = 24$$

Turning to the graph of Appendix D-10 labeled $\alpha = .01$, we find that the vertical line through $\delta = 2.5$ crosses the curve for $f = 24$ at .51, the required power.

Except for changes in notation, a confidence interval for μ_d with coefficient $1 - \alpha$ is obtained from (5-23). It is

$$\left(\bar{d} - t_{n-1;\, 1-\alpha/2} \frac{s_d}{\sqrt{n}}, \; \bar{d} + t_{n-1;\, 1-\alpha/2} \frac{s_d}{\sqrt{n}} \right) \qquad (5\text{-}82)$$

EXAMPLE 5-38

Find a confidence interval with coefficient .95 for μ_d in Example 5-35.

Solution

We had $\bar{d} = -3.9$, $s_d = 5.74$, $n = 10$, $t_{9;.975} = 2.262$. Thus the required interval is

$$\left(-3.9 - 2.262 \frac{5.74}{\sqrt{10}}, \; -3.9 + 2.262 \frac{5.74}{\sqrt{10}} \right)$$

which reduces to $(-8.0, .2)$.

EXERCISES

◆ 5-50 Each of two hybrid seed corn companies claims that its product is superior to the other's. Three scientists are hired to settle the dispute. They plant one acre of each kind in eight different localities where soil and climate conditions vary. When the corn is harvested, they record the tabulated yields, in bushels.

			Yield from locality					
Variety	1	2	3	4	5	6	7	8
Long Ear	114	86	93	75	102	89	64	95
Fat Kernel	107	94	86	70	90	82	73	81

What should the scientists say in their report? Test the appropriate hypothesis following the six-step outline and use $\alpha = .05$.

♦ **5-51** Find the power of the test used in Exercise 5-50 if the average yield for Long Ear is σ_d bushels per acre more than for Fat Kernel. What would the power be under these circumstances if 25 acres (instead of 8) had been planted with each brand?

♦ **5-52** In Exercise 5-50 find a confidence interval for μ_d with coefficient .95. How is the interval related to the test?

5-53 Consider once more the bridge player of Exercise 5-14. Suppose that he wishes to compare two bidding systems, say, method 1 and method 2. He prefers method 1 because it is simpler, but he will use method 2 if he can prove at the .01 level of significance that it produces a higher average. In order to reach a decision, he plays two sessions, one using each method, with seven of his favorite partners. The results in percentages are as tabulated. Which method should he use? Follow the six-step outline.

| | **Results with partner** | | | | | |
Method 1	**2**	**3**	**4**	**5**	**6**	**7**
1 59	61	58	59	64	60	61
2 63	67	55	65	67	58	68

5-54 Find the power of the test used in Exercise 5-53 if $\mu_2 = \mu_1 + \sigma_d$. If $\mu_2 = \mu_1 + 2\sigma_d$. To what is the power increased when $\mu_2 = \mu_1 + \sigma_d$ if 25 partners (instead of 7) are used?

5-55 In Exercise 5-53 find a confidence interval for μ_d with coefficient .99.

REFERENCES

1 CHAPMAN, D. G.: Some Two Sample Tests, *Annals of Mathematical Statistics*, vol. 21, pp. 601–606, 1950.

2 OWEN, D. B.: "Handbook of Statistical Tables," Addison-Wesley Publishing Company, Inc., Reading, Mass., 1962.

3 PACHARES, JAMES: Tables for Unbiased Tests of the Variance of a Normal Population, *Annals of Mathematical Statistics*, vol. 32, pp. 84–87, 1961.

4 STEIN, C. M.: A Two Sample Test for a Linear Hypothesis Whose Power Is Independent of the Variance, *Annals of Mathematical Statistics*, vol. 16, pp. 243–258, 1945.

5 TATE, R. F., and G. W. KLETT: Optimal Confidence Intervals for the Variance of a Normal Distribution, *Journal of the American Statistical Association*, vol. 54, pp. 674–682, 1959.

I. Inferences concerning one mean, variance σ^2 known

  A. Standard hypotheses, alternatives, statistics, and critical regions (Sec. 5-2) (significance level α)

Hypothesis	Alternative	Statistic†	Critical region
$H_0: \mu = \mu_0$	$H_1: \mu < \mu_0$	$Z = \dfrac{\bar{x} - \mu_0}{\sigma/\sqrt{n}}$	$Z < Z_\alpha$
$H_0: \mu \geqq \mu_0$	$H_1: \mu < \mu_0$		$Z < Z_\alpha$
$H_0: \mu = \mu_0$	$H_1: \mu > \mu_0$		$Z > Z_{1-\alpha}$
$H_0: \mu \leqq \mu_0$	$H_1: \mu > \mu_0$		$Z > Z_{1-\alpha}$
$H_0: \mu = \mu_0$	$H_1: \mu \neq \mu_0$		$Z < Z_{\alpha/2} = -Z_{1-\alpha/2}, Z > Z_{1-\alpha/2}$

† Note that whenever a statistic is given in this summary, certain assumptions are made. These assumptions, giving the statistic the required distribution, may be found in the text material.

  B. Power calculations (Sec. 5-3)

    1. Use Appendix D-10 with entries α ($\alpha/2$ with two-sided alternatives)

$$\delta = \frac{|\mu - \mu_0|}{\sigma/\sqrt{n}} \qquad f = \infty$$

    2. μ must be in the range specified by the alternative.

    3. Given $|\mu - \mu_0|/\sigma$, α, and power, the n required to yield the specified power is given by $n = [\delta/(|\mu - \mu_0|/\sigma)]^2$.

  C. Two-sided confidence interval with coefficient α (Sec. 5-4)

    1. The interval:

$$\left(\bar{x} - Z_{1-\alpha/2}\,\frac{\sigma}{\sqrt{n}},\ \bar{x} + Z_{1-\alpha/2}\,\frac{\sigma}{\sqrt{n}} \right)$$

    2. Given length in σ units, L/σ, and α, the n required to achieve this length (or shorter) is given by $n \geqq (2\sigma Z_{1-\alpha/2}/L)^2$.

II. Inferences concerning one mean, variance σ^2 unknown (single sample) (Sec. 5-5)

  A. Standard hypotheses, alternatives, statistics, and critical regions (significance level α)

Hypothesis	Alternative	Statistic	Critical region
$H_0: \mu = \mu_0$	$H_1: \mu < \mu_0$	$t_{n-1} = \dfrac{\bar{x} - \mu_0}{s/\sqrt{n}}$	$t_{n-1} < t_{n-1;\,\alpha}$
$H_0: \mu \geqq \mu_0$	$H_1: \mu < \mu_0$		$t_{n-1} < t_{n-1;\,\alpha}$
$H_0: \mu = \mu_0$	$H_1: \mu > \mu_0$		$t_{n-1} > t_{n-1;\,1-\alpha}$
$H_0: \mu \leqq \mu_0$	$H_1: \mu > \mu_0$		$t_{n-1} > t_{n-1;\,1-\alpha}$
$H_0: \mu = \mu_0$	$H_1: \mu \neq \mu_0$		$t_{n-1} < t_{n-1;\,\alpha/2}$
			$= -t_{n-1;\,1-\alpha/2}, t_{n-1} > t_{n-1;\,1-\alpha/2}$

B. Power calculations
  1. Use Appendix D-10 with entries α ($\alpha/2$ with two-sided alternatives), $\delta = |\mu - \mu_0|/(\sigma/\sqrt{n})$, $f = n - 1$.
  2. μ must be in the range specified by the alternative.
  3. Given $|\mu - \mu_0|/\sigma$, α, and power, the n required to yield the specified power can be approximated (by using interpolation) from Appendix D-10.
C. Two-sided confidence interval with coefficient α
  1. The interval:

$$\left(\bar{x} - t_{n-1;\,1-\alpha/2}\, \frac{s}{\sqrt{n}},\; \bar{x} + t_{n-1;\,1-\alpha/2}\, \frac{s}{\sqrt{n}} \right)$$

  2. If α is given, then the relationship between n and the probability that the length of the interval is less than L/σ can be obtained from Appendix D-11.
III. Inferences concerning one mean, variance σ^2 unknown (two-stage sample) (Sec. 5-6)
  A. Standard hypotheses, alternatives, statistics, and critical regions (significance level α)

Hypothesis	Alternative	Statistic	Critical region
$H_0\!: \mu = \mu_0$	$H_1\!: \mu < \mu_0$	$t_{n_0-1} = \dfrac{\bar{x} - \mu_0}{s/\sqrt{n}}$	$t_{n_0-1} < t_{n_0-1;\,\alpha}$
$H_0\!: \mu \geqq \mu_0$	$H_1\!: \mu < \mu_0$		$t_{n_0-1} < t_{n_0-1;\,\alpha}$
$H_0\!: \mu = \mu_0$	$H_1\!: \mu > \mu_0$	where n_0 = preliminary sample size	$t_{n_0-1} > t_{n_0-1;\,1-\alpha}$
$H_0\!: \mu \leqq \mu_0$	$H_1\!: \mu > \mu_0$	n = total sample size	$t_{n_0-1} > t_{n_0-1;\,1-\alpha}$
$H_0\!: \mu = \mu_0$	$H_1\!: \mu \neq \mu_0$	$\bar{x}$ = sample mean of all observations s = sample standard deviation of preliminary sample	$t_{n_0-1} < t_{n_0-1;\,\alpha/2}$, $t_{n_0-1} > t_{n_0-1;\,1-\alpha/2}$

B. Calculation of n required to give a specified power independent of σ
  1. With given α, μ, μ_0, n_0, and power p calculate k as given by (5-28).
  2. Compute ks^2. If $ks^2 \leqq n_0$, no more observations are necessary. If $ks^2 > n_0$, continue sampling until the total sample size just exceeds ks^2.
  3. For two-sided tests replace α by $\alpha/2$ in (5-28).

C. Two-sided confidence interval of specified length L with coefficient α
  1. The interval: $(\bar{x} - L/2,\ \bar{x} + L/2)$.
  2. With given α, n_0, and L, calculate k from (5-29). Then compute ks^2 and determine n as in III-B-2.

IV. Inferences concerning one variance (Sec. 5-7)
  A. Standard hypotheses, alternatives, statistics, and critical regions (significance level α)

Hypothesis	Alternative	Statistic	Critical region
$H_0: \sigma^2 = \sigma_0^2$	$H_1: \sigma^2 < \sigma_0^2$	$\chi_{n-1}^2 = \dfrac{(n-1)s^2}{\sigma_0^2}$ $\left(\text{or } \dfrac{\chi_{n-1}^2}{n-1} = \dfrac{s^2}{\sigma_0^2}\right)$	$\chi_{n-1}^2 < \chi_{n-1;\alpha}^2$
$H_0: \sigma^2 \geqq \sigma_0^2$	$H_1: \sigma^2 < \sigma_0^2$		$\chi_{n-1}^2 < \chi_{n-1;\alpha}^2$
$H_0: \sigma^2 = \sigma_0^2$	$H_1: \sigma^2 > \sigma_0^2$		$\chi_{n-1}^2 > \chi_{n-1;1-\alpha}^2$
$H_0: \sigma^2 \leqq \sigma_0^2$	$H_1: \sigma^2 > \sigma_0^2$		$\chi_{n-1}^2 > \chi_{n-1;1-\alpha}^2$
$H_0: \sigma^2 = \sigma_0^2$	$H_1: \sigma^2 \neq \sigma_0^2$		$\chi_{n-1}^2 < \chi_{n-1;\alpha/2}^2,$ $\chi_{n-1}^2 > \chi_{n-1;1-\alpha/2}^2$

  B. Power calculations
    1. Use Appendix D-12 with entries α ($\alpha/2$ with two-sided alternatives), $R = \sigma/\sigma_0$, and $\nu = n - 1$.
    2. σ must be in the range specified by the alternative.
    3. Given α, R, and power, the n required to yield the specified power can be approximated from Appendix D-12.
  C. Two-sided confidence interval with coefficient α
    1. The interval:

$$\left[\frac{(n-1)s^2}{\chi_{n-1;1-\alpha/2}^2},\ \frac{(n-1)s^2}{\chi_{n-1;\alpha/2}^2}\right]$$

    2. If α is given, then the relationship between n and the probability that the length of the interval is less than L/σ can be obtained from Appendix D-13.

V. Inferences concerning two variances (Sec. 5-8)
  A. Standard hypotheses, alternatives, statistics, and critical regions (significance level α)

Hypothesis	Alternative	Statistic	Critical region
$H_0: \sigma_1^2 = \sigma_2^2$	$H_1: \sigma_1^2 < \sigma_2^2$	F_{n_1-1,n_2-1} $= \dfrac{s_1^2}{s_2^2}$ where s_1^2, s_2^2 are the sample variances	$F_{n_1-1,n_2-1} < F_{n_1-1,n_2-1;\alpha}$
$H_0: \sigma_1^2 \geqq \sigma_2^2$	$H_1: \sigma_1^2 < \sigma_2^2$		$F_{n_1-1,n_2-1} < F_{n_1-1,n_2-1;\alpha}$
$H_0: \sigma_1^2 = \sigma_2^2$	$H_1: \sigma_1^2 > \sigma_2^2$		$F_{n_1-1,n_2-1} > F_{n_1-1,n_2-1;1-\alpha}$
$H_0: \sigma_1^2 \leqq \sigma_2^2$	$H_1: \sigma_1^2 > \sigma_2^2$		$F_{n_1-1,n_2-1} > F_{n_1-1,n_2-1;1-\alpha}$
$H_0: \sigma_1^2 = \sigma_2^2$	$H_1: \sigma_1^2 \neq \sigma_2^2$		$F_{n_1-1,n_2-1} < F_{n_1-1,n_2-1;\alpha/2},$ $F_{n_1-1,n_2-1} > F_{n_1-1,n_2-1;1-\alpha/2}$

B. Power calculations
  1. Use Appendix D-14 with entries α ($\alpha/2$ with two-sided alternatives), $R_0 = \sigma_1/\sigma_2$, and $\nu = n - 1$ if $n_1 = n_2 = n$. If the sample sizes are not equal, use (5-58) or (5-59).
  2. σ_1/σ_2 must be in the range specified by the alternative.
  3. If the sample sizes are equal and if α, R_0, and the power are given, then the n required to yield the specified power can be approximated from Appendix D-14.
C. Two-sided confidence interval with coefficient α for σ_1^2/σ_2^2
  1. The interval:

$$\left(\frac{s_1^2}{s_2^2} \frac{1}{F_{n_1-1,n_2-1;\,1-\alpha/2}}, \; \frac{s_1^2}{s_2^2} \frac{1}{F_{n_1-1,n_2-1;\,\alpha/2}} \right)$$

  2. The interval for σ_1/σ_2 is obtained by taking the square roots of the numbers forming the interval in V-C-1.
VI. Inferences concerning two means (with two random samples) (Sec. 5-9)
  A. Standard hypotheses, alternatives, statistics, and critical regions (significance level α)

Hypothesis	Alternative	Statistic	Critical region
$H_0: \mu_1 = \mu_2$	$H_1: \mu_1 < \mu_2$	$t_{n_1+n_2-2}$	$t_{n_1+n_2-2} < t_{n_1+n_2-2;\,\alpha}$
$H_0: \mu_1 \geqq \mu_2$	$H_1: \mu_1 < \mu_2$	$= \dfrac{\bar{x}_1 - \bar{x}_2}{s_p \sqrt{\dfrac{1}{n_1} + \dfrac{1}{n_2}}}$	$t_{n_1+n_2-2} < t_{n_1+n_2-2;\,\alpha}$
$H_0: \mu_1 = \mu_2$	$H_1: \mu_1 > \mu_2$		$t_{n_1+n_2-2} > t_{n_1+n_2-2;\,1-\alpha}$
$H_0: \mu_1 \leqq \mu_2$	$H_1: \mu_1 > \mu_2$	where s_p^2	$t_{n_1+n_2-2} > t_{n_1+n_2-2;\,1-\alpha}$
$H_0: \mu_1 = \mu_2$	$H_1: \mu_1 \neq \mu_2$	$= \dfrac{(n_1 - 1)s_1^2 + (n_2 - 1)s_2^2}{n_1 + n_2 - 2}$	$t_{n_1+n_2-2} < t_{n_1+n_2-2;\,\alpha/2}$, $\quad t_{n_1+n_2-2} > t_{n_1+n_2-2;\,1-\alpha/2}$

B. Power calculations
  1. Use Appendix D-10 with entries α ($\alpha/2$ with two-sided alternatives)

$$\delta = \frac{|\mu_1 - \mu_2|}{\sigma \sqrt{1/n_1 + 1/n_2}} \qquad f = n_1 + n_2 - 2$$

  2. $\mu_1 - \mu_2$ must be in the range specified by the alternative.
  3. If the sample sizes are equal and if α, $|\mu_1 - \mu_2|/\sigma$, and the power are given, then the n required to yield the specified power can be approximated from Appendix D-10.

C. Two-sided confidence interval with coefficient α for $\mu_1 - \mu_2$
   1. The interval:

$$(\bar{x}_1 - \bar{x}_2 - t_{n_1+n_2-2;\,1-\alpha/2} s_p \sqrt{1/n_1 + 1/n_2},\ \bar{x}_1 - \bar{x}_2$$
$$+ t_{n_1+n_2-2;\,1-\alpha/2} s_p \sqrt{1/n_1 + 1/n_2})$$

VII. Inferences concerning two means (paired observations) (Sec. 5-10)
   A. Standard hypotheses, alternatives, statistics, and critical regions (significance level α)

Hypothesis	Alternative	Statistic	Critical region
$H_0: \mu_1 = \mu_2$	$H_1: \mu_1 < \mu_2$	$t_{n-1} = \dfrac{\bar{d}}{s_d/\sqrt{n}}$	$t_{n-1} < t_{n-1;\,\alpha}$
$H_0: \mu_1 \geqq \mu_2$	$H_1: \mu_1 < \mu_2$		$t_{n-1} < t_{n-1;\,\alpha}$
$H_0: \mu_1 = \mu_2$	$H_1: \mu_1 > \mu_2$	where $\bar{d}$ = sample mean of differences s_d^2 = sample variance of differences	$t_{n-1} > t_{n-1;\,1-\alpha}$
$H_0: \mu_1 \leqq \mu_2$	$H_1: \mu_1 > \mu_2$		$t_{n-1} > t_{n-1;\,1-\alpha}$
$H_0: \mu_1 = \mu_2$	$H_1: \mu_1 \neq \mu_2$		$t_{n-1} < t_{n-1;\,\alpha/2},$ $t_{n-1} > t_{n-1;\,1-\alpha/2}$

   B. Power calculations
   1. Use Appendix D-10 with entries α ($\alpha/2$ with two-sided alternatives), $\delta = |\mu_1 - \mu_2|/(\sigma_d/\sqrt{n})$ $f = n - 1$.
   2. $\mu_1 - \mu_2$ must be in the range specified by the alternative.
   3. If α, $|\mu_1 - \mu_2|/\sigma_d$, and the power are given, then the n required to yield the specified power can be approximated from Appendix D-10.
   C. Two-sided confidence interval with coefficient α for $\mu_1 - \mu_2$
   1. The interval:

$$\left(\bar{d} - t_{n-1;\,1-\alpha/2} \frac{s_d}{\sqrt{n}},\ \bar{d} + t_{n-1;\,1-\alpha/2} \frac{s_d}{\sqrt{n}} \right)$$

   2. If α is given, then the relationship between n and the probability that the length of the interval is less than L/σ can be obtained from Appendix D-11.

CHAPTER SIX

Some Statistical Inference for Parameters of Discrete Random Variables; Approximate Chi-square Tests

6-1 INTRODUCTION

In Chap. 5 most of the inferences that were drawn were based upon techniques derived by using the assumption that the observations come from a normal population. We did observe, however, that the normality assumption is not too crucial for drawing inferences about the mean if the sample size is moderately large. Primarily we were concerned with continuous random variables.

In this chapter our main interest is parameters which arise in discrete probability models. In Example 2-5, if the percentage of good potatoes is unknown, we may wish to test the hypothesis that $p = .90$ or obtain a confidence interval for p. For the situation of Exercise 2-9 we may want to prove that the new cure for tuberculosis is more successful than the old. In Example 2-14 we might wish to test the hypothesis that the secretary's claim of averaging one error per page is correct. Perhaps we would like to have a confidence interval for the average number of calls coming into a telephone switchboard.

As in Chap. 5 our main objectives will be to learn how and when to use some standard techniques.

6-2 INFERENCES ABOUT THE BINOMIAL PARAMETER p

The hypothesis-testing problems which are most frequently encountered when one is concerned with the binomial p are very similar to those we have discussed for means and variances. In Secs. 4-2 and 4-6 we illustrated testing

$$H_0: p = p_0 \text{ against } H_1: p < p_0 \tag{6-1}$$

with the potato problem. If we are considering purchasing a new machine to make bolts, we might decide not to buy if the proportion of bolts requiring rework is too high. In order to reach a decision we could test

$$H_0: p = p_0 \text{ against } H_1: p > p_0 \tag{6-2}$$

and buy the machine if H_0 is accepted. If we are interested in determining whether a coin is unbiased or not, then we will want to test

$$H_0: p = p_0 \text{ against } H_1: p \neq p_0 \tag{6-3}$$

with $p_0 = \frac{1}{2}$.

In some problems we may prefer to replace (6-1) by

$$H_0: p \geqq p_0 \text{ against } H_1: p < p_0 \tag{6-4}$$

and (6-2) by

$$H_0: p \leqq p_0 \text{ against } H_1: p > p_0 \tag{6-5}$$

Again α has to be interpreted as the largest power under H_0.

The statistic used to test hypotheses about p is x, the number of successes in n trials. If the conditions (2-1) are satisfied, then x has a binomial distribution. Further, if the H_0 of (6-1), (6-2), or (6-3) is true, then x is binomial with parameters n and p_0. Of course, n has to be chosen either arbitrarily or to meet some power requirement.

When (6-1) or (6-4) is tested, small values of x support H_1 and lead to rejection of H_0. As we observed near the end of Sec. 4-2, a specified α, say, α_0, for the level of significance is unlikely to be achieved owing to the discreteness of x. Consequently, the critical region usually chosen for (6-1) is $x \leq x_0$, where x_0 is the largest x such that $\Pr(x \leq x_0) \leq \alpha_0$. When we attempted to achieve $\alpha_0 = .05$ with $n = 25$, the critical region for testing

H_0: $p = .90$ against H_1: $p < .90$

turned out to be $x \leq 19$ with an $\alpha = .03340$ instead of .05. Similarly, when we test (6-2) or (6-5), only large x support H_1. Consequently, H_0 is rejected when $x \geq x_0$, where $\Pr(x \geq x_0)$ is the significance level. Again, if we have a predetermined α_0 in mind, x_0 should be the smallest x such that $\Pr(x \geq x_0) \leq \alpha_0$. For the two-sided situation of (6-3) both large and small x contradict H_0 and lead to rejection. If it is desired to have a significance level α_0, the critical region usually selected is $x \leq x_1$, $x \geq x_2$, where x_1 is the largest value of x such that $\Pr(x \leq x_1) \leq \alpha_0/2$ and x_2 is the smallest x such that $\Pr(x \geq x_2) \leq \alpha_0/2$. The true significance level is $\alpha = \Pr(x \leq x_1) + \Pr(x \geq x_2)$. All calculations mentioned above are performed with $p = p_0$.

EXAMPLE 6-1

A coin is tossed 100 times and 43 heads are recorded. Does this result indicate the coin is biased? Use $\alpha_0 = .05$.

Solution

We shall follow the six-step outline.

1 We test H_0: $p = \frac{1}{2}$ against H_1: $p \neq \frac{1}{2}$.
2 The significance level we hope to achieve is $\alpha_0 = .05$. However, the critical region to be selected in step 4 will yield $\alpha < .05$.
3 The statistic we use is x, the number of heads. It is reasonable to use the binomial model for computing probabilities associated with x since (*a*) each toss is a head or a tail, (*b*) the probability of a head remains constant for each throw ($\frac{1}{2}$ if H_0 is true) if the coin is thrown exactly the same way each time, (*c*) tosses are independent, and (*d*) the coin is tossed $n = 100$ times, a fixed number.
4 The critical region is $x \leq x_1 = 39$, $x \geq x_2 = 61$. The true significance level is .

$$\alpha = \Pr(x \leq 39) + \Pr(x \geq 61) = .01760 + .01760 = .0352$$

We observe

$$\Pr(x \leq 40) = .02844 > .025$$
$$\Pr(x \geq 60) = .02844 > .025$$

5 No computations are necessary.
6 Since $x = 43$ does not fall in the critical region, we do not reject H_0.

EXAMPLE 6-2

Suppose we are considering for purchase a new machine which makes bolts. We will buy the machine if the fraction of bolts requiring rework is .10 or less. A sample of 25 bolts produced by the machine is examined, and 4 require rework. With $\alpha_0 = .05$ can we conclude that our requirement is not being met?

Solution

We shall follow the six-step outline.

1 We test $H_0: p \leq .10$ against $H_1: p > .10$.

2 We aim at a significance level of $\alpha_0 = .05$. However, the true significance level will be less than .05.

3 The statistic we use is x, the number of bolts requiring rework. We check the conditions required for the use of the binomial model: (*a*) A bolt requires rework or it does not. (*b*) Unless the machine shows some sign of wear or a setting changes, it is not unreasonable to assume that p remains constant. (*c*) It is reasonable to assume that the classification of one bolt is independent of the classification of other bolts unless something goes wrong with the machine. If the machine is inclined to produce several poor bolts in a row, then the independence condition is more realistic if every fifth (or perhaps every tenth) bolt is taken for the sample. (*d*) The number of trials is fixed at $n = 25$. Thus the binomial seems like a reasonable model to use.

4 The critical region is $x \geq 6$. We see that

$$\alpha = \Pr(x \geq 6) = \sum_{x=6}^{25} \binom{25}{x} (.10)^x (.90)^{25-x} = .03340$$

$$\Pr(x \geq 5) = .09799$$

5 No computations are necessary.

6 Since the sample contained only four bolts requiring rework, H_0 is accepted. The machine will be purchased.

Power calculations are fairly routine, especially when extensive tables of the binomial are used.

EXAMPLE 6-3

Find the power of the test used in Example 6-2 if $p = .20$. If $p = .30$.

Solution

We need $\Pr(x \geqq 6)$ if $p = .20$.

$$\Pr(x \geqq 6) = \sum_{x=6}^{25} \binom{25}{x} (.20)^x (.80)^{25-x}$$
$$= 1 - B(5;25,.20)$$
$$= 1 - .61669 = .38331$$

Similarly, if $p = .30$,

$$\Pr(x \geqq 6) = 1 - B(5;25,.30)$$
$$= 1 - .19349 = .80651$$

EXAMPLE 6-4

Suppose that $n = 100$ bolts is used in Example 6-2. Find the power when $p = .20$. When $p = .30$.

Solution

If $p = .10$, $\Pr(x \geqq 16) = .03989$, $\Pr(x \geqq 15) = .07257$. Hence the critical region is $x \geqq 16$ with $\alpha = .03989$. If $p = .20$,

$$\Pr(x \geqq 16) = \sum_{x=16}^{100} \binom{100}{x} (.20)^x (.80)^{100-x}$$
$$= 1 - B(15;100,.20)$$
$$= 1 - .12851 = .87149$$

If $p = .30$,

$$\Pr(x \geqq 16) = 1 - B(15;100,.30)$$
$$= 1 - .00040 = .99960$$

EXAMPLE 6-5

How large does n have to be in Example 6-2 to raise the power to .95 or greater if $p = .20$?

Solution

Since $n = 100$ does not achieve the desired power, our tables are inadequate. Even with more extensive tables some trial and error is involved. The Harvard University table [2] gives for $n = 130$, $p = .10$, $\Pr(x \geqq 19) = .05957$, $\Pr(x \geqq 20) = .03443$. Hence the critical region is $x \geqq 20$. If $n = 130$, $p = .20$, $\Pr(x \geqq 20) = .92676$.

Next try $n = 140$. With $p = .10$ we find $\Pr(x \geqq 20) = .06590$, $\Pr(x \geqq 21) = .03919$. Thus the critical region is $x \geqq 21$. If $p = .20$, $\Pr(x \geqq 21) = .94766$.

166

With $n = 150$, $p = .10$ we get

$\Pr(x \geq 21) = .07209$
$\Pr(x \geq 22) = .04396$

so that the critical region is $x \geq 22$. If $p = .20$, $\Pr(x \geq 22) = .96278$.

Thus n is cornered between 140 and 150. If the Ordnance Corps table [6] were used, the exact minimum n could be found. However, for practical purposes any n between 140 and 150 could be used. Certainly $n = 150$ is on the safe side.

EXAMPLE 6-6

Find the power of the test used in Example 6-1 if $p = .40$.

Solution

We need $\Pr(x \leq 39) + \Pr(x \geq 61)$ computed with $p = .40$, and we get

$\Pr(x \leq 39) = B(39;100,.40) = .46208$
$\Pr(x \geq 61) = 1 - B(60;100,.40) = .00002$

Thus the required power is $.46208 + .00002 = .46210$.

As we might suspect, a good point estimate of p is $\hat{p} = x/n$. That is, our best guess for the population value of p is $\hat{p}$, the proportion of the sample having the characteristic in question. The estimate $\hat{p}$ is unbiased and has smaller variance than any other unbiased estimate of p based upon n independent trials.

Appendix D-15 contains graphs from which a confidence interval for p can be obtained. Specifically, we can find two numbers p_L and p_U such that

$$\Pr(p_L < p < p_U) = 1 - \alpha \qquad\qquad (6\text{-}6)$$

for $\alpha = .01, .05, .10$. Of course, the probability statement (6-6) must be interpreted in the usual way for a confidence interval. To use the graphs, we need to know $\hat{p} = x/n$, n, and α. An example follows.

EXAMPLE 6-7

Find a confidence interval with coefficient .95 for the probability of obtaining a head based upon the results of Exercise 6-1.

Solution

We had $x = 43$, $n = 100$, so that $\hat{p} = .43$. Turn to the set of graphs in Appendix D-15 headed by confidence coefficient .95. The horizontal scale is the $\hat{p}$ scale. Imagine a vertical line through $\hat{p} = .43$. This line crosses the two curves labeled 100 at points $p_L = .33$, $p_U = .53$, which are read from the vertical scale on the left. Hence $(.33,.53)$ is the desired confidence interval.

We note that the interval found in Example 6-7 covers the hypothesized value of $p = \frac{1}{2}$ of Exercise 6-1. In general, the interval given by (6-6) covers a value of p_0 if, and only if, the test of H_0: $p = p_0$ against H_1: $p \neq p_0$ leads to acceptance provided the α_0 of the test and α of the confidence interval are the same. Hence the graphs could be used in place of the tables for the two-sided hypothesis-testing problem to determine whether to accept or reject H_0.

Inferences concerning p can also be drawn by using the negative binomial. This is a topic we shall omit except for mentioning that it can be shown that $(c - 1)/(N - 1)$ is an unbiased estimate p.

EXERCISES

◆ 6-1 A seed company claims that 90 per cent of its radish seeds germinate. Fifty seeds are planted and eight fail to germinate. Test a hypothesis formulated from the company's claim. Use $\alpha_0 = .05$ and follow the six-step outline.

◆ 6-2 Find the power of test used in Exercise 6-1 if $p = .75$. If $p = .60$.

◆ 6-3 Find a confidence interval with coefficient .95 for the value of p in Exercise 6-1.

6-4 According to a genetic theory, 25 per cent of a species have a certain characteristic. A random sample of 20 of the species contains 9 having the characteristic. If $\alpha_0 = .05$, is the theory contradicted? Follow the six-step outline.

6-5 Find the power of the test used in Exercise 6-4 if 10 per cent of the species have the characteristic. If 40 per cent have the characteristic.

6-6 Find a confidence interval with coefficient .95 for the value of p in Exercise 6-4.

◆ 6-7 Parts are drawn at random from an assembly line until 6 defectives are obtained and 51 draws are required. Give an unbiased estimate of the proportion of defective parts turned out by the process.

6-8 A fruit wholesaler inspects a hundred of each large lot of grapefruit he receives. He rejects a whole lot if more than 10 per cent are bad, but he is afraid to reject wrongly more than 1 per cent of the time. On the other hand, he cannot afford to accept lots

168

with 25 per cent (or more) bad more than 10 per cent of the time. Can he meet both requirements with the sample he has?

♦ 6-9   The standard cure for tuberculosis is successful 30 per cent of the time. A new cure is tried on a group of 50 patients and is successful in 29 cases. The new cure is more expensive, and we do not want to use it unless we can prove at the .01 level of significance that it is better. Follow the six-step outline and recommend the appropriate action.

6-3 INFERENCES ABOUT THE POISSON PARAMETER μ

The hypothesis-testing situations which we shall discuss are similar to those encountered previously with other parameters. If an individual decides that he will have his telephone taken out if his average number of calls is less than 2 per day, he will be interested in testing

$$H_0\colon \mu = \mu_0 \text{ against } H_1\colon \mu < \mu_0 \tag{6-7}$$

(with $\mu_0 = 2$) and he will remove the telephone if H_0 is rejected. If an executive is willing to hire a secretary unless the secretary averages more than one error per typed page, the executive will probably test

$$H_0\colon \mu = \mu_0 \text{ against } H_1\colon \mu > \mu_0 \tag{6-8}$$

(with $\mu_0 = 1$) and hire the secretary unless H_0 is rejected. If a given small volume of blood contains on the average 5 red cells in a healthy individual, a laboratory technician may want to test

$$H_0\colon \mu = \mu_0 \text{ against } H_1\colon \mu \neq \mu_0 \tag{6-9}$$

(with $\mu_0 = 5$) if either too many or too few red cells indicate trouble.
In some problems we may prefer to replace (6-7) by

$$H_0\colon \mu \geqq \mu_0 \text{ against } H_1\colon \mu < \mu_0 \tag{6-10}$$

and (6-8) by

$$H_0\colon \mu \leqq \mu_0 \text{ against } H_1\colon \mu > \mu_0 \tag{6-11}$$

Again α has to be interpreted as the largest power under H_0.

The statistic used to test hypotheses about μ is $y = \sum\limits_{i=1}^{n} x_i$, where $x_1, \ldots, x_n$ are n observations of the random variable which has a Poisson distribution. If (a) $x_1, \ldots, x_n$ is a random sample and (b) each of the x_i has a Poisson distribution with parameter μ, then y has a Poisson distribution with parameter $n\mu$. Further, if the H_0 of (6-7), (6-8), or (6-9) is true, then y is Poisson with parameter $n\mu_0$. Again n may be chosen arbitrarily or to meet some power requirement.

When (6-7) or (6-10) is tested, small values of y support H_1 and lead to rejection of H_0. If α_0 is the significance level at which we aim, then the critical region is $y \leq y_0$, where y_0 is the largest y such that $\Pr(y \leq y_0) \leq \alpha_0$. The actual achieved significance level is $\alpha = \Pr(y \leq y_0)$. Similarly, when (6-8) or (6-11) is tested, H_0 is rejected when $y \geq y_0$, where $\Pr(y \geq y_0) = \alpha$, the significance level. If we have a predetermined α_0 in mind, y_0 should be the smallest y such that $\Pr(y \leq y_0) \leq \alpha_0$. Finally, for the two-sided situation of (6-9) both large and small y contradict H_0 and lead to rejection. If α_0 is the aimed-at significance level, the critical region usually selected is $y \leq y_1$, $y \geq y_2$, where y_1 is the largest value of y such that $\Pr(y \leq y_1) \leq \alpha_0/2$ and y_2 is the smallest value of y such that $\Pr(y \geq y_2) \leq \alpha_0/2$. The true significance level is $\alpha = \Pr(y \leq y_1) + \Pr(y \geq y_2)$.

EXAMPLE 6-8 ————————————————————————————

Suppose that an individual wants to have his telephone disconnected if his average number of calls per day is less than 2. He selects five days at random and records the following number of calls on these days: 0, 2, 1, 1, 1. Using $\alpha_0 = .05$, should he have his telephone removed?

Solution

We shall follow the six-step outline.

1 We test H_0: $\mu = 2$ against H_1: $\mu < 2$. If H_0 is rejected, the telephone will be removed.
2 The significance level we hope to achieve is $\alpha_0 = .05$. However, the critical region to be selected in step 4 will yield $\alpha < .05$.
3 The statistic we use is $y = \sum_{i=1}^{5} x_i$, where x_i is the number of calls observed on the ith randomly selected day. The random variable y has a Poisson distribution with parameter $n\mu_0 = 5\mu_0 = 10$ if (a) $x_1, \ldots, x_5$ are random observations (which is given) and (b) each x_i has a Poisson distribution with parameter $\mu = 2$. We have previously indicated that the Poisson is a reasonable model to use for telephone-call data.
4 The critical region is $y \leq y_0 = 4$. We observe that $\alpha = \Pr(y \leq 4)$ = .02925 and $\Pr(y \leq 5) = .06709$.
5 Computations: $y = 0 + 2 + 1 + 1 + 1 = 5$.
6 Since 5 does not fall in the critical region, H_0 is accepted. Consequently, on the basis of this sample, the telephone will not be removed.

EXAMPLE 6-9

During a 12-month period, the number of twin births per month recorded in a hospital are 2, 0, 1, 1, 0, 0, 3, 2, 1, 1, 0, 1. Do these results contradict the hypothesis that the average number of twin births is .5 per month? Use $\alpha_0 = .05$.

Solution

We shall follow the six-step outline.

1 We test $H_0: \mu = .5$ against $H_1: \mu \neq .5$.

2 Again we aim at a significance level of .05, but α will actually be something less than this figure.

3 The statistic we use is $y = \sum_{i=1}^{12} x_i$, where x_i is the number of twin births observed in the ith month. The random variable y has a Poisson distribution with parameter $n\mu_0 = 12(.5) = 6$ provided (*a*) the sample is randomly selected and (*b*) the number of twin births during a month has a Poisson distribution with $\mu = .5$. The assumptions seem reasonable, since events are presumably independent, the probability that an event occurs is proportional to the time interval, and the probability that two or more events occur in a small time interval is negligible.

4 The critical region is $y \leq y_1 = 1$, $y \geq y_2 = 12$. The true significance level is

$$\alpha = \Pr(y \leq 1) + \Pr(y \geq 12) = .01735 + .02009 = .03744$$

We observe $\Pr(y \leq 2) = .06197 > .025$ and $\Pr(y \geq 11) = .04262 > .025$.

5 Computations:

$$y = 2 + 0 + 1 + 1 + 0 + 0 + 3 + 2 + 1 + 1 + 0 + 1 = 12$$

6 H_0 is rejected. We will conclude that the average number of births is larger than .5.

As in the binomial case, power calculations are fairly routine if the necessary tables are available.

EXAMPLE 6-10

Find the power of the test used in Example 6-8 if $\mu = 1$.

Solution

We need $\Pr(y \leq 4)$ if $\mu = 1$, where y has a Poisson distribution with parameter $n\mu = 1(5) = 5$. Appendix D-4 yields

$$\Pr(y \leq 4) = P(4;5) = .44049$$

EXAMPLE 6-11

Find the power of test used in Example 6-9 if $\mu = .75$.

Solution

We need $\Pr(y \leq 1) + \Pr(y \geq 12)$, where y has a Poisson distribution with parameter $n\mu = 12(.75) = 9$. We get

$$\Pr(y \leq 1) = .00123 \qquad \Pr(y \geq 12) = .19699$$

Hence the required power is $.00123 + .19699 = .19822$.

A good point estimate to use for μ is

$$\hat{\mu} = \frac{\sum\limits_{i=1}^{n} x_i}{n} = \frac{y}{n} = \bar{x}$$

As in previous situations involving the mean, $\bar{x}$ is an unbiased estimate and its variance is smaller than any other unbiased estimate of μ based upon n observations.

A confidence interval for μ can be obtained with the assistance of Appendix D-7 or D-8. The numbers used are μ_L and μ_U, where

$$\Pr(\mu_L < \mu < \mu_U) = 1 - \alpha \tag{6-12}$$

$$\mu_L = \frac{\chi^2_{2y;\alpha/2}}{2n} = \frac{y}{n}\frac{\chi^2_{2y;\alpha/2}}{2y} \qquad \mu_U = \frac{\chi^2_{2y+2;1-\alpha/2}}{2n} = \frac{y+1}{n}\frac{\chi^2_{2y+2;1-\alpha/2}}{2y+2}$$

The probability statement (6-12) must be interpreted in the usual way for a confidence interval.

EXAMPLE 6-12

Find a confidence interval with coefficient .95 for the μ of Example 6-9.

Solution

We had $y = 12$, $n = 12$. Since $\alpha = .05$, $\alpha/2 = .025$, $\chi^2_{24;.025} = 12.40$, $\chi^2_{26;.975} = 41.92$, $\mu_L = \frac{12.40}{2(12)} = .52$, $\mu_U = \frac{41.92}{2(12)} = 1.75$. The required interval is $(.52,1.75)$.

172

We note that the interval found in Example 6-12 does not cover the rejected hypothesized value $\mu = .5$ of Example 6-9. As in previous situations, the interval (μ_L, μ_U) covers a value μ_0 if, and only if, $H_0: \mu = \mu_0$ is accepted when tested against $H_1: \mu \neq \mu_0$ provided the α_0 of the hypothesis-testing problem is equal to the α used for the confidence interval.

EXERCISES

6-10 An executive is willing to hire a secretary who has applied for a position unless she averages more than one error per typed page. A random sample of five pages is selected from some prepared by the secretary. The errors per page are 3, 3, 4, 1, 2. Using $\alpha_0 = .05$, what decision should be made? Follow the six-step outline.

6-11 Find the power of the test used in Exercise 6-10 if $\mu = 1.6$. If $\mu = 2$.

6-12 Find a confidence interval with coefficient .95 for the average number of errors the secretary of Exercise 6-10 makes per page.

6-13 A bakery would like to have a certain kind of cookie that they make contain two raisins on the average. A random sample of four cookies yields a total of five raisins. Test the appropriate hypothesis following the six-step outline. Use $\alpha_0 = .05$.

6-14 What is the power of the test used in Exercise 6-13 if the average number of raisins is 2.5? If the average is 1?

6-15 Find a confidence interval with coefficient .90 for the average number of raisins per cookie by using the information of Exercise 6-13.

6-4 LARGE-SAMPLE PROCEDURES FOR BINOMIAL p AND POISSON μ

When $n > 1,000$, so that existing binomial tables are of no assistance, we can use the statistic

$$Z' = \frac{\hat{p} - p_0}{\sqrt{p_0(1 - p_0)/n}} = \frac{x - np_0}{\sqrt{np_0(1 - p_0)}} \tag{6-13}$$

to test hypotheses (6-1) to (6-5). Because of the central limit theorem, the random variable Z' has approximately a standard normal distribution when x is a binomial variable and n is large. When n is larger than 1,000, we no longer need to concern ourselves with the difference between a desired significance level α_0 and an achieved level α. For all practical purposes a desired level can now be achieved.

When (6-1) or (6-4) is tested, only small values of $\hat{p}$ (or x), and hence small Z' support H_1. If the significance level is α, then the critical region is

$$\frac{\hat{p} - p_0}{\sqrt{p_0(1 - p_0)/n}} < Z_\alpha \tag{6-14}$$

Similarly, only large $\hat{p}$ and large Z' support the H_1 of (6-2) and (6-5). A test of significance level α is obtained by rejecting H_0 when

$$\frac{\hat{p} - p_0}{\sqrt{p_0(1 - p_0)/n}} > Z_{1-\alpha} \tag{6-15}$$

Finally, when (6-3) is tested, both large and small values of $\hat{p}$, and hence Z', provide support for H_1. Thus it is reasonable to reject H_0 with both small and large values of Z', and the critical region we choose to yield a test with significance level α is

$$\frac{\hat{p} - p_0}{\sqrt{p_0(1 - p_0)/n}} < Z_{\alpha/2} \quad \text{or} \quad \frac{\hat{p} - p_0}{\sqrt{p_0(1 - p_0)/n}} > Z_{1-\alpha/2} \tag{6-16}$$

EXAMPLE 6-13

Redo Example 6-2 for a sample of 2,500 bolts that produces 277 requiring rework.

Solution

1 Same as in Example 6-2.
2 The significance level is .05.
3 The statistic we use is Z' given by (6-13). Since we have decided that x has a binomial distribution, Z' has approximately a standard normal distribution.
4 The critical region is

$$\frac{x - 2,500(.10)}{\sqrt{2,500(.10)(.90)}} > 1.645$$

5 Computations: Since $x = 277$, we have

$$\frac{277 - 250}{\sqrt{2,500}\sqrt{.09}} = \frac{27}{50(.3)} = \frac{27}{15} = 1.8$$

6 We reject the hypothesis and do not purchase the machine.

174

Formulas which yield approximate power for the large-sample tests of (6-1) to (6-3) are obtained with a little algebraic manipulation. It is not too difficult to show that the power of the tests whose critical regions are given by (6-14) and (6-15) is

$$\Pr\left(Z < \frac{Z_\alpha \sqrt{p_0(1 - p_0)} + \sqrt{n}\,|p_0 - p_1|}{\sqrt{p_1(1 - p_1)}}\right) \qquad (6\text{-}17)$$

where p_1 is a value of p in the range designated under H_1. An approximate power for the test of (6-3), whose critical region is given by (6-16), can be obtained from (6-17) by replacing α by $\alpha/2$. The maximum error is approximately $\alpha/2$, and in most practical situations the error will be negligible. If a power of $1 - \beta$ is required for some p_1 in the alternative H_1 of either (6-1) or (6-2), then

$$n \geq \left[\frac{Z_\alpha \sqrt{p_0(1 - p_0)} + Z_\beta \sqrt{p_1(1 - p_1)}}{p_0 - p_1}\right]^2 \qquad (6\text{-}18)$$

guarantees that the power is achieved.

EXAMPLE 6-14

Find the power of the test used in Example 6-13 if $p = .12$.

Solution

The hypothesis and alternative are a special case of (6-2), and the critical region is given by (6-15). Thus, since $\alpha = .05$, $n = 2,500$, $p_0 = .10$, $p_1 = .12$, we get

$$\begin{aligned}
\text{Power} &= \Pr\left(Z < \frac{-1.645\sqrt{(.10)(.90)} + \sqrt{2,500}\,|.10 - .12|}{\sqrt{(.12)(.88)}}\right) \\
&= \Pr\left(Z < \frac{-1.645(.30) + 50|-.02|}{.325}\right) \\
&= \Pr(Z < 1.56) = .94
\end{aligned}$$

EXAMPLE 6-15

Find the n required to yield a power of .90 when $p = .12$ for the test of Example 6-13.

Solution

We use (6-18) with $\alpha = .05$, $\beta = .10$, $p_0 = .10$, $p_1 = .12$. We get

$$n \geq \left(\frac{-1.645\sqrt{(.10)(.90)} - 1.282\sqrt{(.12)(.88)}}{.10 - .12}\right)^2$$

$$n \geq (45.5)^2 = 2,070$$

To get a large-sample confidence interval for p, we start with

$$\Pr\left(-Z_{1-\alpha/2} < \frac{\hat{p} - p}{\sqrt{p(1-p)/n}} < Z_{1-\alpha/2}\right) = 1 - \alpha \qquad (6\text{-}19)$$

To get p in the middle of the inequalities requires that a quadratic inequality be solved. If certain small terms are then discarded, (6-19) leads to

$$\Pr\left(\hat{p} - Z_{1-\alpha/2}\sqrt{\frac{\hat{p}(1-\hat{p})}{n}} < p < \hat{p} + Z_{1-\alpha/2}\sqrt{\frac{\hat{p}(1-\hat{p})}{n}}\right)$$
$$= 1 - \alpha \qquad (6\text{-}20)$$

EXAMPLE 6-16

Find a confidence interval with coefficient .95 for p by using the information of Example 6-13.

Solution

We have $n = 2{,}500$, $\hat{p} = {}^{277}\!/_{2,500} = .1108$, $\alpha = .05$, $Z_{.975} = 1.96$. Thus

$$Z_{1-\alpha/2}\sqrt{\frac{\hat{p}(1-\hat{p})}{n}} = \frac{1.96\sqrt{(.1108)(.8892)}}{50} = .012$$

and the interval is $(.111 - .012, .111 + .012)$, which reduces to $(.099, .123)$.

Large-sample results for Poisson μ are similar to those for binomial p. If $n\mu \leq 100$, then we can proceed as in Sec. 6-3 and use the Molina tables [4]† described in Chap. 2. If $n\mu > 100$, then the statistic

$$Z' = \frac{\hat{\mu} - \mu_0}{\sqrt{\mu_0/n}} = \frac{y - n\mu_0}{\sqrt{n\mu_0}} \qquad (6\text{-}21)$$

can be used to test hypotheses (6-7) to (6-11). As in Sec. 6-3, $y = \sum_{i=1}^{n} x_i$. Because of the central limit theorem, the random variable Z' has approximately a standard normal distribution when $x_1, \ldots, x_n$ (a) constitute a random sample (b) drawn from a Poisson population with parameter μ_0.

† Numbers in brackets are those of references listed at the end of the chapter.

Critical regions are selected in the same manner as in the binomial case. For (6-7) and (6-10) reject if

$$\frac{y - n\mu_0}{\sqrt{n\mu_0}} < Z_\alpha \tag{6-22}$$

For (6-8) and (6-11) reject if

$$\frac{y - n\mu_0}{\sqrt{n\mu_0}} > Z_{1-\alpha} \tag{6-23}$$

Finally, for (6-9) the critical region is

$$\frac{y - n\mu_0}{\sqrt{n\mu_0}} < Z_{\alpha/2} \quad \text{and} \quad \frac{y - n\mu_0}{\sqrt{n\mu_0}} > Z_{1-\alpha/2} \tag{6-24}$$

The formulas and comments concerning power calculations and confidence intervals given earlier in the section apply with minor modifications. The counterparts of (6-17), (6-18), and (6-20) are

$$\Pr\left(Z < \frac{Z_\alpha \sqrt{\mu_0} + \sqrt{n} \, |\mu_0 - \mu_1|}{\sqrt{\mu_1}} \right) \tag{6-25}$$

$$n \geqq \left[\frac{Z_\alpha \sqrt{\mu_0} + Z_\beta \sqrt{\mu_1}}{\mu_0 - \mu} \right]^2 \tag{6-26}$$

and

$$\Pr\left(\hat{\mu} - Z_{1-\alpha/2} \sqrt{\frac{\hat{\mu}}{n}} < \mu < \hat{\mu} + Z_{1-\alpha/2} \sqrt{\frac{\hat{\mu}}{n}} \right) = 1 - \alpha \tag{6-27}$$

EXAMPLE 6-17

Suppose that the individual of Example 6-8 selects 200 days at random during which he received a total of 364 telephone calls. Find the new critical region and make the appropriate decision. How large does n have to be to achieve a power of .95 if $\mu = 1.8$?

Solution

The new critical region is given by (6-22) with $\alpha = .05$, $n = 200$, $\mu_0 = 2$. Hence, we now reject if

$$\frac{y - 400}{\sqrt{400}} < -1.645$$

Since $y = 364$, the statistic has the value $(364 - 400)/20 = -1.8$ and H_0: $\mu = 2$ is rejected.

To achieve a power of .95 when $\mu = 1.8$, we must have

$$n \geqq \left[\frac{-1.645 \sqrt{2} - 1.645 \sqrt{1.8}}{2 - 1.8} \right]^2 \cong 513$$

EXERCISES

6-16   Suppose that in Exercise 6-1 the seed company's claim is investigated by using 1,600 seeds, 184 of which fail to germinate. Follow the six-step outline and test the appropriate hypothesis by using $\alpha = .05$.

6-17   Find the power of the test used in Exercise 6-16 if $p = .88$. How large would n have to be to raise this to .90?

6-18   Find a confidence interval with coefficient .90 for the value of p in Exercise 6-16.

6-19   According to a genetic theory, 25 per cent of a species have a certain characteristic. A random sample of 1,200 of the species contains 324 having the characteristic. If $\alpha = .05$ is used, is the theory contradicted? Follow the six-step outline.

6-20   Find the power of the test used in Exercise 6-19 if 23 per cent have the characteristic. If 27 per cent have the characteristic.

6-21   Find a confidence interval with coefficient .95 for the value of p in Exercise 6-19. How is the confidence interval related to the test used in Exercise 6-19?

6-22   Suppose that the executive in Exercise 6-10 looks at a random sample of 225 pages of the secretary's work and finds 252 errors. Follow the six-step outline and recommend the appropriate decision. Use $\alpha = .05$.

6-23   Find the power of the test used in Exercise 6-22 if $\mu = 1.21$. How large would n have to be to raise the power to .95?

6-24   Find a confidence interval with coefficient .95 for the value of μ in Exercise 6-22.

6-5   TESTING HYPOTHESES CONCERNING $p_1, \ldots, p_k$ OF THE MULTINOMIAL DISTRIBUTION

In Sec. 2-4 we derived formula (2-9), which enables us to compute probabilities associated with a series of experiments characterized by the properties (2-8). If the parameters p_1, p_2, . . . , p_k, n are known, it is easy to write down, though tedious to evaluate, a probability associated with certain outcome x_1, x_2, . . . , x_k. We now turn our

178

attention to some hypothesis-testing problems which arise from multi-nomial-type problems with unknown p's.

In the simplest situation all the p's are specified by the hypothesis. For example, suppose we would like to know whether or not a die is true (or unbiased). A reasonable hypothesis to test is

H_0: $p_1 = \frac{1}{6}$, $p_2 = \frac{1}{6}$, $p_3 = \frac{1}{6}$, $p_4 = \frac{1}{6}$, $p_5 = \frac{1}{6}$, $p_6 = \frac{1}{6}$

against   (6-28)

H_1: not all p's are $\frac{1}{6}$

The choice presented by (6-28) is a special case of

H_0: $p_1 = p_{10}$, $p_2 = p_{20}$, . . . , $p_k = p_{k0}$

against   (6-29)

H_1: not all p's are as specified by H_0

where p_{10}, p_{20}, . . . , p_{k0} are known probabilities suggested by the problem. Of course, we must have $\sum_{i=1}^{k} p_i = \sum_{i=1}^{k} p_{i0} = 1$, since the result of each experiment must fall in one of the k categories.

It is possible to obtain an exact test for (6-29). To do so, however, is very tedious and time-consuming even for small n. A critical region of unusual values of x_1, x_2, . . . , x_n such that a known probability α is associated with the region would have to be determined. Both the enumeration of points of the critical region and computation of probabilities get rather involved. Fortunately, an approximate test that is applicable in many real-life situations is available.

If x_1, x_2, . . . , x_k are random variables arising from a set of experiments with properties (2-8), then it is known that

$$\chi'^2_{k-1} = \sum_{i=1}^{k} \frac{(x_i - np_i)^2}{np_i} \tag{6-30}$$

has approximately a chi-square distribution with $k - 1$ degrees of freedom. The quantity np_i is the average or expected number of observations for category i when the set of experiments is repeated n times. When the observed values of x_i, $i = 1, 2, . . . , k$ are close to the expected values, the statistic (6-30) will be small. The more the observed values differ from the expected values, the larger the value of (6-30). Thus it seems reasonable to reject the H_0 of (6-29) if the statistic (6-30) is large. A test with significance level equal to approximately α has for its critical region

$$\sum_{i=1}^{k} \frac{(x_i - np_{i0})^2}{np_{i0}} > \chi^2_{k-1;1-\alpha} \tag{6-31}$$

179

EXAMPLE 6-18

Suppose that a die is thrown 120 times with the following results:

Spots showing	1	2	3	4	5	6
Observed number	11	21	29	30	19	10

Does this result contradict the hypothesis of unbiasedness?

Solution

We shall follow the six-step outline.

1 The hypothesis and the alternative are given by (6-28).

2 Select $\alpha = .05$, an arbitrary choice.

3 The statistic we use is $\sum_{i=1}^{k} (x_i - np_{i0})^2/np_{i0}$ with $n = 120$, each
$p_{i0} = \frac{1}{6}$. The statistic is approximately distributed as $\chi^2_{k-1} = \chi^2_5$ if the hypothesis is true and the multinomial is the correct model to use to describe the behavior of the x_i. The multinomial seems reasonable, since (*a*) the result of each throw can be classified into one of six categories 1, 2, 3, 4, 5, 6, (*b*) the probabilities of falling into these categories are $\frac{1}{6}, \frac{1}{6}, \frac{1}{6}, \frac{1}{6}, \frac{1}{6}, \frac{1}{6}$ on each throw, (*c*) each throw is independent of all the others, and (*d*) $n = 120$ is a fixed number of throws.

4 We reject H_0 if the observed value of the statistic is larger than $\chi^2_{5;.95} = 11.07$.

5 Computations:

$$\chi'^2_5 = \frac{(11 - 20)^2}{20} + \frac{(21 - 20)^2}{20} + \frac{(29 - 20)^2}{20} + \frac{(30 - 20)^2}{20}$$
$$+ \frac{(19 - 20)^2}{20} + \frac{(10 - 20)^2}{20}$$
$$= \frac{81}{20} + \frac{1}{20} + \frac{81}{20} + \frac{100}{20} + \frac{1}{20} + \frac{100}{20} = \frac{364}{20}$$
$$= 18.2$$

6 The observed value of χ'^2_5 is larger than 11.07 and falls in the critical region. Consequently, we reject H_0 and conclude that the die is not true. Since $\chi^2_{5;.995} = 16.75$, we even reject at the .005 level of significance.

EXAMPLE 6-19

A coin is thrown 1,600 times, and 840 heads are recorded. Test the hypothesis that the coin is unbiased. Use both the normal approximation and the chi-square approximation and compare the results. Use $\alpha = .05$.

Solution

We shall follow the six-step outline.

1 In binomial notation we test $H_0: p = \frac{1}{2}$ against $H_1: p \neq \frac{1}{2}$. In multinomial notation we test $H_0: p_1 = \frac{1}{2}$, $p_2 = \frac{1}{2}$ against H_1: both p's are not $\frac{1}{2}$.
2 $\alpha = .05$ is given.
3 With the normal approximation we use $Z' = (x - np)/\sqrt{npq}$, where x is the number of heads. With the chi-square approximation we use

$$\chi'^2_1 = \frac{(x_1 - np_1)^2}{np_1} + \frac{(x_2 - np_2)^2}{np_2}$$

where x_1 and x_2 are the number of heads and tails, respectively. Of course, x must have a binomial distribution and x_1, x_2 a multinomial distribution (with $k = 2$) to use these approximations. We have already investigated the reasonableness of this assumption.
4 The critical region for the normal approximation is $Z < -1.96$, $Z > 1.96$. For the chi-square approximation the critical region is $\chi'^2_1 > \chi^2_{1;.95} = 3.84$ (note $1.96^2 = 3.84$).
5 Computations:

$$Z' = \frac{840 - 800}{\sqrt{1,600(\frac{1}{2})(\frac{1}{2})}} = \frac{40}{20} = 2$$

$$\chi'^2_1 = \frac{(840 - 800)^2}{800} + \frac{(760 - 800)^2}{800} = 2 + 2 = 4$$

since $x_1 = 840$, $x_2 = 760$ (note $Z'^2 = \chi'^2_1$).
6 Reject H_0 using either approximation.

Example 6-19 demonstrates that the chi-square approximation yields a test that is equivalent to the normal approximation when $k = 2$. The chi-square statistic is the square of the normal statistic. The two critical regions correspond to one another, since

$$\Pr(Z < -1.96) + \Pr(Z > 1.96) = \Pr(\chi^2_1 > 3.84) = .05$$

Consequently, the chi-square test can be regarded as a generalization of the normal test and (6-29) a generalization of (6-3). With two categories, either procedure can be used; but with more than two, we are forced to use chi-square.

The statistic (6-30) has a distribution that is sufficiently close to chi-square for practical purposes provided the expected number in every category is at least 5 and $n \geqq 20$. If the expected number in any category falls below 5, then two or more categories may be combined into a single larger category which satisfies the requirement.

Power considerations for the approximate chi-square test are somewhat complicated and will not be considered here.

Use the six-step outline.

◆ 6-25 Suppose that it is hypothesized that twice as many accidents occur on Saturday and Sunday as on other days of the week. That is, the probability of a Saturday accident is $\frac{2}{9}$, the probability of a Sunday accident is $\frac{2}{9}$, and the probability that an accident occurs on each of the other days of the week is $\frac{1}{9}$. From records, 90 accidents are selected independently of one another. The distribution of accidents according to the days of the week is

Sun.	Mon.	Tues.	Wed.	Thurs.	Fri.	Sat.
30	6	8	11	7	10	18

Do these results contradict the hypothesis if $\alpha = .05$?

6-26 Use the digits in the first four rows of Appendix D-2 to test the hypothesis that the digits are randomly distributed, that is, $f(x) = \frac{1}{10}$, $x = 0, 1, \ldots, 9$ is the probability function.

◆ 6-27 The number of male births in 120 families each containing three children is

Families	21	37	44	18
Male births	0	1	2	3

According to theory, the probabilities of 0, 1, 2, 3 male births are respectively $\frac{1}{8}$, $\frac{3}{8}$, $\frac{3}{8}$, $\frac{1}{8}$. Does this sample contradict the theory?

6-28 In a classical genetic experiment involving the crossing of two types of peas, Mendel found that the seeds from the plants could be classified as follows:

Round and yellow	315
Round and green	108
Wrinkled and yellow	101
Wrinkled and green	32

According to his theory, the frequencies should be in the ratio of 9:3:3:1, or the probabilities associated with the four classes should be respectively $\frac{9}{16}$, $\frac{3}{16}$, $\frac{3}{16}$, $\frac{1}{16}$. Does this sample contradict his theory?

6-6 CHI-SQUARE TEST FOR POISSON AND NORMAL DATA

In Sec. 2-7 we gave conditions (2-15) under which the Poisson can be derived. Although in given situations we can argue that the conditions seem reasonable, or unreasonable, it is desirable to have a statistical testing procedure to investigate the adequacy of the Poisson model. The tests used in Chap. 5 are derived by assuming that observations are drawn from a normal population. Although the normality assumption is not too crucial in drawing inferences about means, nonnormality of data can seriously affect inferences concerning variances. Experience has shown that many types of data do come from normal (or near normal) populations. Nevertheless, an experimenter may doubt the normality assumption and seek a statistical procedure which supports or disproves it. We shall now discuss approximate chi-square tests for these two situations.

In the Poisson case we test

$$H_0: p_1 = p(0;\mu), p_2 = p(1;\mu), \ldots , p_{k-1} = p(k-2;\mu), p_k = 1 - \sum_{i=1}^{k-1} p_i$$

against $\hspace{10cm}$ (6-32)

H_1: the p's are not given by the Poisson

where $p(x;\mu)$ is defined by (2-16). The kth category includes all observations $k-1$ or larger. The main difference between (6-29) and (6-32) is that in the latter case the p's depend upon an unknown parameter μ, whereas in the former the p's were completely specified. The statistic used to test (6-32) is

$$\chi'^2_{k-2} = \frac{\sum_{i=1}^{k} (x_i - n\hat{p}_i)^2}{n\hat{p}_i}$$

$\hspace{10cm}$ (6-33)

which is approximately distributed as χ^2_{k-2}. The loss of one degree of freedom is due to the fact that μ must be replaced by its estimate $\hat{\mu}$ before the expected numbers np_i can be estimated by $n\hat{p}_i$.

EXAMPLE 6-20

Suppose that we have some doubts concerning the adequacy of the Poisson model for Example 2-14. We examine 100 pages of the secretary's work and find the following results:

Errors	0	1	2	3	4	5	6
Pages	36	40	19	2	0	2	1

Do these data make the Poisson seem unreasonable?

Solution

We shall follow the six-step outline.

1 The hypothesis and alternative are given by (6-32).
2 Select $\alpha = .05$, an arbitrary choice.
3 The statistic we use is

$$\chi'^2_{k-2} = \sum_{i=1}^{k} \frac{(x_i - n\hat{p}_i)^2}{n\hat{p}_i}$$

which is approximately distributed as χ^2_{k-2} provided the conditions for the multinomial are satisfied and the hypothesis is true. Checking (2-8) we observe (a) the result from each page can be classified into one of seven categories: 0 errors, 1 error . . . , 5 errors, 6 or more errors, (b) according to the hypothesis, p_1, . . . , p_7 remain constant from page to page, (c) the results on one page can be regarded as independent of the results on another, and (d) a fixed number of pages, $n = 100$, is used.

4 The critical region is $\chi'^2_{k-2} > \chi^2_{k-2;.95}$. At this point we are not sure we want to use $k = 7$, since some expected numbers may be less than 5 so that one or more categories may have to be grouped together.

5 Computations:

$$\hat{\mu} = \bar{x} = \frac{0(36) + 1(40) + 2(19) + 3(2) + 4(0) + 5(2) + 6(1)}{36 + 40 + 19 + 2 + 0 + 2 + 1}$$

$$= \frac{100}{100} = 1$$

From Appendix D-4 we find under $\mu = 1$, $\hat{p}_1 = .36788$, $\hat{p}_2 = .73576 - .36788 = .36788$, $\hat{p}_3 = .91970 - .73576 = .18394$, $\hat{p}_4 = .98101 - .91970 = .01631$, $\hat{p}_5 = .99634 - .98101 = .01533$, $\hat{p}_6 = .99941 - .99634 = .00307$, $\hat{p}_7 = 1 - .99941 = .00059$. The estimates of the expected numbers are obtained by multiplying the $\hat{p}$'s by 100. Since categories 5 to 7 have estimated expected numbers less than 5, we group them with 4, making a category for three or more errors. Summarized in table form, the calculation of $\chi'^2_{k-2} = \chi'^2_2$ is

Errors	x_i	$\hat{p}_i$	$n\hat{p}_i$	$(x_i - n\hat{p}_i)^2/n\hat{p}_i$
0	36	.36788	36.788	.017
1	40	.36788	36.788	.280
2	19	.18394	18.394	.020
3 or more	5	.08030	8.030	1.143
		1.00000	100.000	$1.460 = \chi'^2_2$

6   Since the critical region is $\chi'^2_2 > \chi^2_{2;.95} = 5.99$, we conclude that the Poisson is a reasonable model for the number of errors per page.

In the normal case we test

H_0: the density function is given by (3-7)
  (the distribution is normal with mean μ, variance σ^2)

against   (6-34)

H_1: the density function is not given by (3-7)
  (the distribution is not normal)

For (6-32) the p's were specifically given by the hypothesis even though they depended upon an unknown parameter μ. For (6-34) a set of p's can be chosen in a variety of ways such that

$$p_1 + p_2 + \cdots + p_k = 1$$

All we have to do is divide the range of the normal random variable into k mutually exclusive intervals, say, $(-\infty, a_1)$, (a_1, a_2), ..., (a_{k-2}, a_{k-1}), (a_{k-1}, ∞), and let the probabilities of a normal random variable falling in these intervals be p_1, p_2, ..., p_k, respectively. To calculate the p's, we need to know μ and σ for the normal distribution. Since the parameters are usually unknown, we replace μ and σ by $\bar{x}$ and s and obtain estimates $\hat{p}_1$, $\hat{p}_2$, ..., $\hat{p}_k$. Then the statistic used for (6-34) is

$$\chi'^2_{k-3} = \sum_{i=1}^{k} \frac{(x_i - n\hat{p}_i)^2}{n\hat{p}_i}$$ (6-35)

which is approximately distributed as χ^2_{k-3} if H_0 is true. A critical region for a test with significance level α is given by $\chi'^2_{k-3} > \chi^2_{k-3;1-\alpha}$.

The degrees of freedom are two less than in the completely specified case (6-29) because two parameters, μ and σ^2, have to be estimated from the observations before probabilities can be estimated.

The number of intervals, k, and the way the intervals are selected are at the disposal of the investigator. One method of selection makes all expected numbers the same. Thus each $\hat{p}_i = 1/k$ and $n\hat{p}_i = n/k$, where k is so chosen that the estimated expected numbers are at least 5 and preferably 10. Let us illustrate by an example.

EXAMPLE 6-21

The following 40 numbers represent a random sample of corn yields per acre for a given variety: 32, 40, 93, 53, 93, 15, 92, 44, 33, 83, 61, 51, 46, 41, 100, 26, 46, 28, 88, 36, 66, 22, 82, 39, 81, 69, 78, 13, 74, 48, 61, 96, 108, 46, 74, 90, 53, 59, 79, 85. Do these results contradict the assumption that corn yields are normally distributed?

Solution

We shall follow the six-step outline.

1 The hypothesis and alternative are given by (6-34).
2 Select $\alpha = .05$, an arbitrary choice.
3 The statistic we use is $\chi'^2_{k-3} = \sum_{i=1}^{k} \dfrac{(x_i - n\hat{p}_i)^2}{n\hat{p}_i}$, which is approximately distributed as χ^2_{k-3} provided the hypothesis is true and the conditions of the multinomial are satisfied. After dividing yields into k intervals, we observe (a) each yield falls into one of the k intervals; (b) the probabilities of obtaining a yield in the various intervals $p_1, p_2, \ldots, p_k$ remain constant for each yield if yields have the same distribution and sampling is random; (c) if the yields are selected at random, they are independent; and (d) a fixed number of yields $n = 40$ is used.
4 We reject if $\chi'^2_{k-3} > \chi^2_{k-3;.95}$, where k has yet to be chosen.
5 Computations: Suppose we make each expected number equal to 10. Since $n = 40$, $n\hat{p}_i = 10$, each $\hat{p}_i = .25$. The four intervals on Z meeting this requirement are (using Appendix D-5) $(-\infty, -.675)$, $(-.675, 0)$, $(0, .675)$, $(.675, \infty)$. Now $Z = (x - \mu)/\sigma$ or $x = \sigma Z + \mu$ has to be used to convert the intervals on Z to x. Since σ and μ are unknown, we use their estimates s and $\bar{x}$. We find $\bar{x} = 60.6$, $s^2 = 658.0$, $s = 25.7$. Thus for wheat yields the four intervals become $(-\infty, 43.3)$ $(43.3, 60.6)$, $(60.6, 77.9)$, $(77.9, \infty)$. The number

of yields falling in these intervals are 11, 9, 6, 14, respectively. We get

$$\chi'^2_1 = \frac{(11-10)^2}{10} + \frac{(9-10)^2}{10} + \frac{(6-10)^2}{10} + \frac{(14-10)^2}{10} = 3.4$$

6   Since $\chi^2_{1;.95} = 3.84$, the hypothesis is not rejected.

When conducting the test illustrated by Example 6-21, it is desirable to have a larger sample. In a review-type paper published in 1952, Cochran [1] has recommended that expected numbers in each interval be about 12 with $n = 200$, 20 with $n = 400$, and 30 with $n = 1,000$.

A test competitive to chi-square (but apparently more powerful) for the situations discussed in this section is due to Kolmogorov. Examples illustrating the procedure are given on page 258 of [3] and on page 471 of [5]. The disadvantage of the test is that the distribution must be completely specified. In our examples it was not, because the parameters μ and σ^2 had to be estimated from the sample.

EXERCISES

Follow the six-step outline.

6-29   The following data concerning the number of corn borers found in various hills of corn were collected.

Number of corn borers	0	1	2	3	4	5	6
Number of hills	23	22	16	18	15	4	2

Use the approximate chi-square test to investigate the adequacy of the Poisson model. Use $\alpha = .05$.

6-30   Rework Example 6-21, making each expected number equal to 5.

6-7   THE CHI-SQUARE TESTS FOR INDEPENDENCE AND HOMOGENEITY

Some enumeration data are classified according to two characteristics into what is called a contingency table. Approximate chi-square tests can be used to test a variety of hypotheses concerning the behavior of the characteristics. In this section we shall discuss two such tests.

Table 6-1   Storks versus birthrate

Countries with	Countries with		Totals
	Few storks	Many storks	
Small birthrate	42	10	52
Large birthrate	130	18	148
Totals	172	28	200

When considering two characteristics, sometimes it is of interest to know whether or not they are independent. As an example, suppose 200 countries are classified according to the number of storks in the country and the country's birthrate, as in Table 6-1. A reasonable hypothesis to test is

H_0: birthrate and number of storks are independent

against   (6-36)

H_1: birthrate and number of storks are not independent

If we let

p_{11} = probability that a country has small birthrate and few storks
p_{12} = probability that a country has small birthrate and many storks
p_{21} = probability that a country has large birthrate and few storks
p_{22} = probability that a country has large birthrate and many storks
$p_{1\cdot} = p_{11} + p_{12}$ = probability that a country has small birthrate
$p_{2\cdot} = p_{21} + p_{22}$ = probability that a country has large birthrate
$p_{\cdot 1} = p_{11} + p_{21}$ = probability that a country has few storks
$p_{\cdot 2} = p_{12} + p_{22}$ = probability that a country has many storks

then, in terms of the p's and because of (1-12), (6-36) can be written

H_0: $p_{11} = p_{1\cdot}p_{\cdot 1}$, $p_{12} = p_{1\cdot}p_{\cdot 2}$, $p_{21} = p_{2\cdot}p_{\cdot 1}$, $p_{22} = p_{2\cdot}p_{\cdot 2}$

against   (6-37)

H_1: the equations given under H_0 are not all true

The expected number of observations in the cells are np_{11}, np_{12}, np_{21}, and np_{22}, where n is the total number of observations ($n = 200$). According to the hypothesis, the expected numbers can be written $np_{1\cdot}p_{\cdot 1}$, $np_{1\cdot}p_{\cdot 2}$, $np_{2\cdot}p_{\cdot 1}$, $np_{2\cdot}p_{\cdot 2}$. However, since none of the p's are known, the best we can do is estimate them from the observed results. A reasonable estimate for $p_{1\cdot}$, the probability of a small birthrate, is the fraction of countries in the sample having a small birthrate. Thus in place of $p_{1\cdot}$ we use $\hat{p}_{1\cdot} = {}^{52}\!/_{200}$. Similarly, $\hat{p}_{2\cdot} = {}^{148}\!/_{200}$, $\hat{p}_{\cdot 1} = {}^{172}\!/_{200}$, and $\hat{p}_{\cdot 2} = {}^{28}\!/_{200}$. The estimates of the expected numbers are

$$n\hat{p}_1.\hat{p}_{.1} = 200 \frac{52}{200} \frac{172}{200} = \frac{(52)(172)}{200} = 44.72$$

$$n\hat{p}_1.\hat{p}_{.2} = 200 \frac{52}{200} \frac{28}{200} = \frac{(52)(28)}{200} = 7.28$$

$$n\hat{p}_2.\hat{p}_{.1} = 200 \frac{148}{200} \frac{172}{200} = \frac{(148)(172)}{200} = 127.28$$

$$n\hat{p}_2.\hat{p}_{.2} = 200 \frac{148}{200} \frac{28}{200} = \frac{(148)(28)}{200} = 20.72$$

To test H_0, we use the statistic

$$\chi'^2_1 = \frac{(42 - 44.72)^2}{44.72} + \frac{(10 - 7.28)^2}{7.28} + \frac{(130 - 127.28)^2}{127.28} + \frac{(18 - 20.72)^2}{20.72}$$
$$= .17 + 1.02 + .06 + .36 = 1.61 \tag{6-38}$$

rejecting at significance level α if the statistic is larger than $\chi^2_{1;1-\alpha}$. Except for the fact that two degrees of freedom have been lost because two parameters have been estimated, the computation (6-38) is the same as (6-30). Although it appears that we have estimated four parameters $p_1.$, $p_2.$, $p_{.1}$, $p_{.2}$, actually we have estimated only two. Since $p_1. + p_2. = 1$, an estimate of $p_1.$ gives an estimate $p_2.$. Similarly, since $p_{.1} + p_{.2} = 1$, an estimate of $p_{.1}$ produces an estimate of $p_{.2}$.

Next we shall generalize the preceding discussion. Suppose that characteristic A is divided into r categories and characteristic B into c categories. Let the experiment be repeated n times with observed results appearing as in Table 6-2. Let x_{ij} be the number of objects that fall in category i of characteristic A and category j of characteristic B, p_{ij} be the probability that an object falls in category i of charac-

Table 6-2   Contingency table

Characteristic A	Characteristic B 1	2	j	c	Totals
1	x_{11}	x_{12}	x_{1j}	x_{1c}	$T_1.$
2	x_{21}	x_{22} ...	x_{2j} ...	x_{2c}	$T_2.$
...	...	...	...	...	...
i	x_{i1}	x_{i2} ...	x_{ij} ...	x_{ic}	$T_i.$
...	...	...	...	...	
r	x_{r1}	x_{r2} ...	x_{rj} ...	x_{rc}	$T_r.$
Totals	$T_{.1}$	$T_{.2}$ ...	$T_{.j}$ ...	$T_{.c}$	$T_{..} = n$

teristic A and category j of characteristic B, $p_{i.}$ be the probability that an object falls in category i of characteristic A, and $p_{.j}$ be the probability that an object falls in category j of characteristic B. Then the generalization of (6-37) is

H_0: $p_{ij} = p_{i.}p_{.j}$, $i = 1, 2, \ldots, r$, $j = 1, 2, \ldots, c$

against (6-39)

H_1: the equations given under H_0 are not all true

To test H_0, we compute

$$\chi'^2_{(r-1)(c-1)} = \sum_{i=1}^{r} \sum_{j=1}^{c} \frac{(x_{ij} - n\hat{p}_{i.}\hat{p}_{.j})^2}{n\hat{p}_{i.}\hat{p}_{.j}} \tag{6-40}$$

$$\chi'^2_{(r-1)(c-1)} = \sum_{i=1}^{r} \sum_{j=1}^{c} \frac{(x_{ij} - T_{i.}T_{.j}/n)^2}{T_{i.}T_{.j}/n} \tag{6-41}$$

a statistic which is approximately distributed as $\chi^2_{(r-1)(c-1)}$ provided H_0 is true and the observations are drawn from a multinomial distribution. To obtain a test of significance level α, reject H_0 if

$$\chi'^2_{(r-1)(c-1)} > \chi^2_{(r-1)(c-1);1-\alpha}$$

EXAMPLE 6-22

Write out the six-step outline for testing independence of number of storks and birthrate.

Solution

1   The hypothesis and the alternative are given by (6-37).
2   Select $\alpha = .05$, an arbitrary choice.
3   The statistic we use is (6-40) with $r = c = 2$, which is approximately distributed as chi-square provided H_0 is true and the observations are drawn from a multinomial distribution. Let us check those conditions. We have: (a) There are four categories. (b) The probabilities of drawing a country in the four categories are p_{11}, p_{12}, p_{21}, and p_{22} on each draw if drawing from an infinite population of existing and conceivable countries. Without an infinite population, probabilities will change on each draw. A practical way to generate an infinite population is to draw countries with replacement. (c) Unless we visualize an infinite population of countries, or draw with replacement, draws will not be independent, since the outcome of any draw will be related to succeeding draws. (d) The experiment is repeated a fixed number of times ($n = 200$).

Thus if we think in terms of a large population of countries or draw with replacement, the assumptions are fairly reasonable.

4 The critical region is $\chi_1'^2 > \chi_{1;.95}^2 = 3.84$.

5 $\chi_1'^2 = 1.61$ from (6-38).

6 Accept the hypothesis of independence. Conclude that the number of storks and birthrate are independent.

The chi-square test for homogeneity is very similar to the chi-square test of independence. As we shall see, the hypothesis is different but the statistic used for the test is the same. To illustrate the concept of homogeneity, let us consider an example. Suppose that three random samples of university students are selected. The first contains 300 lower classmen, the second 200 upper classmen, and the third 100 graduate students. Each student is then asked to select the one of the following three categories which best characterizes his feeling: (1) Professors expect too much work from their students. (2) Professors do not demand enough work from their students. (3) The amount of work professors require is about what it should be. The results of the questioning are presented in Table 6-3. A reasonable hypothesis to test is that the proportion of students falling into each of the categories is the same irrespective of their classification. In other words, the three classifications are homogeneous with respect to their opinions about work load. In terms of the notation used with Table 6-2, the hypothesis of homogeneity tests

H_0: $p_{11} = p_{21} = p_{31}$, $p_{12} = p_{22} = p_{32}$, $p_{13} = p_{23} = p_{33}$

against (6-42)

H_1: the equations given under H_0 are not all satisfied

To test (6-42), we compute the usual-type sum for the approximate chi-square test. That is, for each cell we square the difference

Table 6-3

| Classification | Professors require | | | |
	Too much work	Too little work	Right amount of work	Totals
Lower classmen	182	85	33	300
Upper classmen	68	60	72	200
Graduate	32	53	15	100
Totals	282	198	120	600

between the observed and expected numbers, then divide by the expected number, and finally add the results for all cells. The expected numbers have to be estimated. If the hypothesis is true, the best estimates for the proportions specifying too much work, too little work, right amount of work are respectively $282/600, 198/600, 120/600$. Hence of the 300 lower classmen we expect $(300)(282)/600 = 141$, $(300)(198)/600 = 99$, $(300)(120)/600 = 60$ in the three categories. Similar computations yield the estimated expected numbers in the other cells. It can be shown that (6-41) has an approximate chi-square distribution with $(r - 1)(c - 1)$ degrees of freedom provided the hypothesis of homogeneity is true and the observations in each sample (row) constitute a random sample from a multinomial population. Again H_0 is rejected if the statistic is large.

EXAMPLE 6-23

Write out the six-step outline for testing homogeneity with Table 6-3.

Solution

1 The hypothesis and the alternative are given by (6-42).

2 Select $\alpha = .05$, an arbitrary choice.

3 The statistic we use is (6-41) with $r = c = 3$, which is approximately distributed as chi-square provided H_0 is true and each of the three samples is drawn from a multinomial distribution. Let us check those conditions. We have: (*a*) Under each classification there are three categories. (*b*) In each classification it is reasonable to regard the probabilities of falling into the respective categories as constants if the population is infinite (or very large) or if the drawing is done with replacement. (*c*) If the populations are very large, draws can be regarded as independent, since probabilities will change very little from draw to draw. If the samples are drawn randomly with replacement, the independence condition is satisfied. (*d*) Each of the three experiments is repeated a fixed number of times (300, 200, 100). Thus if the populations are large or samples are drawn with replacement, the assumptions are fairly reasonable. We note that according to the assumptions the number of students holding the various opinions about workload are distributed according to the multinomial for each classification. The hypothesis implies all three multinomial distributions are the same.

4 The critical region is $\chi'^2_4 > \chi^2_{4;.95} = 9.49$.

5 Computations:

The estimated expected numbers are

$$\frac{(282)(300)}{600} = 141 \qquad \frac{(198)(300)}{600} = 99 \qquad \frac{(120)(300)}{600} = 60$$

$$\frac{(282)(200)}{600} = 94 \qquad \frac{(198)(200)}{600} = 66 \qquad \frac{(120)(200)}{600} = 40$$

$$\frac{(282)(100)}{600} = 47 \qquad \frac{(198)(100)}{600} = 33 \qquad \frac{(120)(100)}{600} = 20$$

Hence

$$\chi'^2_4 = \frac{(182 - 141)^2}{141} + \frac{(85 - 99)^2}{99} + \frac{(33 - 60)^2}{60} + \frac{(68 - 94)^2}{94}$$
$$+ \frac{(60 - 66)^2}{66} + \frac{(72 - 40)^2}{40}$$
$$+ \frac{(32 - 47)^2}{47} + \frac{(53 - 33)^2}{33} + \frac{(15 - 20)^2}{20}$$
$$= 13.90 + 1.98 + 12.15 + 7.19 + .55 + 25.60 + 4.79$$
$$+ 12.12 + 1.25 = 79.53$$

6   Reject the hypothesis of homogeneity. Since $\chi^2_{4;.995} = 14.86$, H_0 is rejected at a level far smaller than .005. We would conclude that the proportion of students falling into each of the three categories changes with classification.

The generalization of (6-42) is fairly obvious. With r rows and c columns it becomes

$$H_0: p_{1j} = p_{2j} = \cdots = p_{rj}, j = 1, 2, \ldots, c$$
against   (6-43)
H_1: the equations given under H_0 are not all satisfied

Although the same statistic is used to test the hypothesis of independence and the hypothesis of homogeneity, two main differences exist. First, as we have already noted, the hypothesis in terms of the p's is different. Second, in the former case the data consist of a sample from one population, while in the latter case one sample from each of r populations is used. Another way to distinguish between the two cases is to observe that in the independence case both row and column totals are obtained by chance, while in the homogeneity situation the row totals are chosen numbers.

As is the case with other approximate chi-square tests, power is difficult to compute and may be disappointingly low.

Follow the six-step outline and comment on the assumptions.

◆ 6-31 A random sample of 200 men is selected from each of the four undergraduate classes. Each man is asked to express his preference for blondes, brunettes, or redheads. The results are

Class	Blondes	Preference Brunettes	Redheads	Totals
Freshmen	51	110	39	200
Sophomore	74	106	20	200
Junior	25	124	51	200
Senior	90	60	50	200
Totals	240	400	160	800

Are the classes alike in their preference?

6-32 A random sample of 600 grades is selected from those turned in from the colleges of engineering, agriculture, and arts and sciences. The results are

Grades	Engineering	Colleges Agriculture	A and S	Totals
A	25	15	30	70
B	41	20	79	140
C	82	70	138	290
Below C	18	30	52	100
Totals	166	135	299	600

What conclusion can be drawn?

◆ 6-33 In a certain large city 1,000 people were selected at random and questioned about their smoking and drinking habits. The results of the survey were

Drink	Never	Smoke Occasionally	Moderately	Heavily
Never	85	23	56	36
Occasionally	153	44	128	75
Moderately	128	26	101	45
Heavily	34	7	15	44

What conclusion can be drawn concerning the smoking and drinking habits of people in the city?

6-34 In order to compare a new machining process with the standard one, 500 parts are selected from those produced by each process. The results are

Process	Defective parts	Nondefective parts
New	52	448
Old	77	423

What conclusions can be drawn?

REFERENCES

1 COCHRAN, WILLIAM G.: The χ^2 Test of Goodness of Fit, *Annals of Mathematical Statistics*, vol. 3, no. 3, pp. 315–345, 1952.

2 HARVARD UNIVERSITY COMPUTATION LABORATORY: "Tables of the Cumulative Binomial Probability Distribution," Harvard University Press, Cambridge, Mass., 1955.

3 KEEPING, E. S.: "Introduction to Statistical Inference," D. Van Nostrand Company, Inc., Princeton, N.J., 1962.

4 MOLINA, E. C.: "Poisson's Exponential Binomial Limit," D. Van Nostrand Company, Inc., Princeton, N.J., 1949.

5 OSTLE, BERNARD: "Statistics in Research," 2d ed., Iowa State University Press, Ames, Iowa, 1963.

6 U.S. ARMY ORDNANCE CORPS: Tables of Cumulative Binomial Probabilities, *Ordnance Corps Pamphlet ORDP*20-1, September, 1952.

SUMMARY OF RESULTS: DRAWING INFERENCES
CONCERNING BINOMIAL p, POISSON μ,
AND MULTINOMIAL $p_1, \ldots, p_k$

I. Inferences concerning binomial p (Secs. 6-2 and 6-4)
   A. Standard hypotheses, alternatives, statistics, and critical regions [significance level α less than or equal to an aimed-at significance level α_0 (disregard difference between α, α_0 with large samples)]

Hypothesis	Alternative	Statistic*	Critical region
$H_0: p = p_0$	$H_1: p < p_0$		All calculations performed with $p = p_0$ Small sample: reject if $x \leq x_0$, where x_0 is the largest value of x such that $\Pr(x \leq x_0) = \alpha \leq \alpha_0$. Large samples: reject if $Z' < Z_\alpha$.
$H_0: p \geq p_0$	$H_1: p < p_0$		Small sample: reject if $x \leq x_0$, where x_0 is the largest value of x such that $\Pr(x \leq x_0) = \alpha \leq \alpha_0$. Large samples: reject if $Z' < Z_\alpha$.
$H_0: p = p_0$	$H_1: p > p_0$	Small sample: $x =$ number of successes in n trials if p_0 is the probability of a success on each trial Large sample: $$Z' = \frac{x - np_0}{\sqrt{np_0(1 - p_0)}}$$	Small sample: reject if $x \geq x_0$, where x_0 is the smallest value of x such that $\Pr(x \geq x_0) = \alpha \leq \alpha_0$. Large samples: reject if $Z' > Z_{1-\alpha}$.
$H_0: p \leq p_0$	$H_1: p > p_0$		Small sample: reject if $x \geq x_0$, where x_0 is the smallest value of x such that $\Pr(x \geq x_0) = \alpha \leq \alpha_0$. Large samples: reject if $Z' > Z_{1-\alpha}$.
$H_0: p = p_0$	$H_1: p \neq p_0$		Small sample: reject if $x \leq x_1$, $x \geq x_2$, where x_1 is the largest value of x such that $\Pr(x \leq x_1) = \alpha_1 \leq \alpha_0/2$ and x_2 is the smallest value of x such that $\Pr(x \geq x_2) = \alpha_2 \leq \alpha_0/2$ (the significance level is then $\alpha_1 + \alpha_2$). Large samples: reject if $Z' < Z_{\alpha/2}$, $Z' > Z_{1-\alpha/2}$.

* Note that whenever a statistic is given in this summary, certain assumptions are made. These assumptions, giving the statistic the required distribution, may be found in the text material.

B. Power calculations
1. With small samples use binomial tables with appropriate value of p, say, p_1, and find the probability that x falls in the critical region if $p = p_1$.
2. With large samples and one-sided alternatives the power is approximately

$$\Pr\left(Z < \frac{Z_\alpha \sqrt{p_0(1 - p_0)} + \sqrt{n}\,|p_0 - p_1|}{\sqrt{p_1(1 - p_1)}}\right)$$

where p_1 is a value of p in the range designated under H_1. The n required to yield a specified power $1 - \beta$ when $p = p_1$ is

$$n \geqq \left[\frac{Z_\alpha \sqrt{p_0(1 - p_0)} + Z_\beta \sqrt{p_1(1 - p_1)}}{p_0 - p_1}\right]^2$$

C. Two-sided confidence interval with coefficient α
1. With small samples find the interval (p_L, p_U) from Appendix D-15. Entries required are α, n, $\hat{p} = x/n$.
2. With large samples the interval is

$$\left(\hat{p} - Z_{1-\alpha/2}\sqrt{\frac{\hat{p}(1 - \hat{p})}{n}},\ \hat{p} + Z_{1-\alpha/2}\sqrt{\frac{\hat{p}(1 - \hat{p})}{n}}\right)$$

II. Inferences concerning Poisson μ (Secs. 6-3 and 6-4)
A. Standard hypotheses, alternatives, statistics, and critical regions [significance level α less than or equal to an aimed-at significance level α_0 (disregard difference between α, α_0 with large samples)]

Hypothesis	Alternative	Statistic	Critical region
$H_0: \mu = \mu_0$	$H_1: \mu < \mu_0$		Small sample: reject if $y \leqq y_0$, where y_0 is the largest value of a Poisson random variable with parameter $n\mu_0$ such that $\Pr(y \leqq y_0) = \alpha \leqq \alpha_0$. Large samples: reject if $Z' < Z_\alpha$.
$H_0: \mu \geqq \mu_0$	$H_1: \mu < \mu_0$		Small sample: reject if $y \leqq y_0$, where y_0 is the largest value of a Poisson random variable with parameter $n\mu_0$ such that $\Pr(y \leqq y_0) = \alpha \leqq \alpha_0$. Large samples: reject if $Z' < Z_\alpha$.

Table continued next page

Hypothesis	Alternative	Statistic	Critical region
$H_0: \mu = \mu_0$	$H_1: \mu > \mu_0$	Small sample: $$y = \sum_{i=1}^{n} x_i$$ where $x_1, \ldots, x_n$ are the observations	Small sample: reject if $y \geqq y_0$, where y_0 is the smallest value of a Poisson random variable with parameter $n\mu_0$ such that $\Pr(y \geqq y_0) = \alpha \leqq \alpha_0$. Large samples: reject if $Z' > Z_{1-\alpha}$.
$H_0: \mu \leqq \mu_0$	$H_1: \mu > \mu_0$	Large sample: $$Z' = \frac{y - n\mu_0}{\sqrt{n\mu_0}}$$	Small sample: reject if $y \geqq y_0$, where y_0 is the smallest value of a Poisson random variable with parameter $n\mu_0$ such that $\Pr(y \geqq y_0) = \alpha \leqq \alpha_0$. Large samples: reject if $Z' > Z_{1-\alpha}$.
$H_0: \mu = \mu_0$	$H_1: \mu \neq \mu_0$		Small sample: reject if $y \leqq y_1$, $y \geqq y_2$, where y_1 is the largest value of y such that $\Pr(y \leqq y_1) = \alpha_1 < \alpha_0/2$ and y_2 is the smallest value of y such that $\Pr(y \geqq y_2) = \alpha_2 < \alpha_0/2$ (the significance level is $\alpha_1 + \alpha_2$), where y is a Poisson random variable with parameter $n\mu_0$. Large samples: reject if $Z' < Z_{\alpha/2}$, $Z' > Z_{1-\alpha/2}$.

B. Power calculations
1. With small samples use Poisson tables with parameter $n\mu_1$ and find the probability that y falls in the critical region.
2. With large samples and one-sided alternatives the power is approximately

$$\Pr\left(Z < \frac{Z_\alpha \sqrt{\mu_0} + \sqrt{n}\,|\mu_0 - \mu_1|}{\sqrt{\mu_1}} \right)$$

where μ_1 is a value of μ in the range designated under H_1. The n required to yield a specified power $1 - \beta$ when $\mu = \mu_1$ is

$$n \geqq \left[\frac{Z_\alpha \sqrt{\mu_0} + Z_\beta \sqrt{\mu_1}}{\mu_0 - \mu_1} \right]^2$$

C. Two-sided confidence interval with coefficient α
   1. With small samples compute the interval (μ_L, μ_U) by using (6-12)

$$\mu_L = \frac{\chi^2_{2y;\alpha/2}}{2n} \qquad \mu_U = \frac{\chi^2_{2y+2;1-\alpha/2}}{2n}$$

   2. With large samples the interval is

$$\left(\hat{\mu} - Z_{1-\alpha/2} \sqrt{\frac{\hat{\mu}}{n}}, \ \hat{\mu} + Z_{1-\alpha/2} \sqrt{\frac{\hat{\mu}}{n}} \right) \qquad \text{where } \hat{\mu} = \frac{y}{n}$$

III. Inferences concerning multinomial $p_1, \ldots, p_k$ (all p's specified by hypothesis) (Sec. 6-5)
   A. Standard hypotheses, alternatives, statistics, and critical regions (significance level α)

Hypothesis	Alternative	Statistic	Critical region
$H_0: p_1 = p_{10},$ $p_2 = p_{20}, \ldots$ $p_k = p_{k0}$	H_1: not all p's are as specified by H_0	χ'^2_{k-1} $= \displaystyle\sum_{i=1}^{k} \frac{(x_i - np_{i0})^2}{np_{i0}}$	$\chi'^2_{k-1} > \chi^2_{k-1;1-\alpha}$

   B. Power calculations are difficult and have been omitted.
IV. Inferences concerning multinomial p's (p's unspecified) (Sec. 6-7)
   A. Standard hypotheses, alternatives, statistics, and critical regions (significance level α)

Hypothesis	Alternative	Statistic	Critical region
Hypothesis of independence $H_0: p_{ij} = p_{i\cdot}p_{\cdot j}$ for all i and j	H_1: the equations given under H_0 are not all true	$\chi'^2_{(r-1)(c-1)}$ $= \displaystyle\sum_{i=1}^{r} \sum_{j=1}^{c} \frac{(x_{ij} - T_{i\cdot}T_{\cdot j}/n)^2}{T_{i\cdot}T_{\cdot j}/n}$	$\chi'^2_{(r-1)(c-1)} > \chi^2_{(r-1)(c-1);1-\alpha}$
Hypothesis of homogeneity $H_0: p_{1j} = p_{2j} = \cdots = p_{rj}, j = 1, 2, \ldots, c$	H_1: the equations given under H_0 are not all true		

   B. Power calculations are difficult and have been omitted.

CHAPTER SEVEN

Analysis of Variance

7-1 INTRODUCTION

In Sec. 5-9 we considered some problems associated with drawing inferences about two population means by using a random sample from each of the populations. In particular we discussed methods of testing

$$H_0: \mu_1 = \mu_2 \text{ against } H_1: \mu_1 \neq \mu_2 \tag{7-1}$$

computation of power, and confidence intervals. Now we would like to generalize those procedures so that we can draw inferences about r, $r \geqq 2$, population means based upon r random samples, one drawn from each population. The generalization of (7-1) is

$$H_0: \mu_1 = \mu_2 = \cdots = \mu_r \text{ against } H_1: \text{not all } r \text{ means are equal} \tag{7-2}$$

where $\mu_1, \mu_2, \ldots, \mu_r$ are the means of the r populations.

It is not difficult to imagine situations in which an experimenter may want to draw inferences about several means. The large corporation of Example 5-1 may have five brands of light bulbs from which to choose. The smoker discussed in Sec. 4-3 may be interested in comparing the average nicotine content of four brands of cigarettes. A wheat grower may want to obtain information about average yields for six varieties of wheat. A teacher may be interested in comparing average results achieved by three teaching methods.

The topics to be considered in this chapter are a small part of an important branch of statistics which is called *analysis of variance*. It is moderately difficult to give a good meaningful definition of analysis of variance, and one will not be presented here. Our objectives have already been listed, and for our purpose it will be sufficient to consider analysis of variance as a body of statistical techniques which is useful in drawing inferences about r population means.

7-2 SOME NOTATION

Before discussing the test procedure for (7-2), we shall define some notation which will be used throughout the chapter. The r random samples can be arranged as in Table 7-1. The first column represents a sample of size n_1 drawn from population 1; the second column represents a sample of size n_2 drawn from population 2; the jth column represents a sample of size n_j drawn from population j.

Let x_{ij} be the ith sample value drawn from population j. The totals and means are defined in the obvious way. We have

$$T._1 = \sum_{i=1}^{n_1} x_{i1} = \text{sum of the sample values drawn from population 1}$$

Table 7-1   r random samples with totals and means

	Population				
	1	2	j	r	
	x_{11}	x_{12}	x_{1j}	x_{1r}	
	x_{21}	x_{22}	x_{2j}	x_{2r}	
	. . . .				
	$x_{n_1 1}$	$x_{n_2 2}$	$x_{n_j j}$	$x_{n_r r}$	
Totals	$T._1$	$T._2$	$T._j$	$T._r$	$T_{..}$
Means	$\bar{x}._1$	$\bar{x}._2$	$\bar{x}._j$	$\bar{x}._r$	$\bar{x}_{..}$

$$T_{\cdot 2} = \sum_{i=1}^{n_2} x_{i2} = \text{sum of the sample values drawn from population 2}$$

$$T_{\cdot j} = \sum_{i=1}^{n_j} x_{ij} = \text{sum of the sample values drawn from population } j$$

$$T_{\cdot\cdot} = \sum_{j=1}^{r} \sum_{i=1}^{n_j} x_{ij} = \sum_{j=1}^{r} T_{\cdot j} = \text{total of all observations}$$

$$\bar{x}_{\cdot 1} = \frac{T_{\cdot 1}}{n_1} = \text{sample mean for population 1}$$

$$\bar{x}_{\cdot 2} = \frac{T_{\cdot 2}}{n_2} = \text{sample mean for population 2}$$

$$\bar{x}_{\cdot j} = \frac{T_{\cdot j}}{n_j} = \text{sample mean for population } j$$

$$\bar{x}_{\cdot\cdot} = \frac{T_{\cdot\cdot}}{N} = \text{mean of all observations} \left(N = \sum_{j=1}^{r} n_j \right)$$

The means of the r populations are, of course, unknown. As we have previously stated, they will be designated by $\mu_1, \mu_2, \ldots, \mu_r$. Let $\sigma_1^2, \sigma_2^2, \ldots, \sigma_r^2$ be the unknown variances.

To illustrate Table 7-i with a numerical example, suppose that final-examination scores for three statistics classes are the numbers appearing in Table 7-2. All three classes are taught by the same instructor, but each has a different text. We might be interested in testing

$H_0 \colon \mu_1 = \mu_2 = \mu_3$ against $H_1 \colon$ not all means are equal

for the populations of final-examination scores. The n's are small to make the example simple.

Table 7-2 Final-examination scores

	Textbook			
	1	2	3	
	56	77	70	
	53	73	61	
	68	63	67	
		74	62	
		68		
Totals	$T_{\cdot 1} = 177$	$T_{\cdot 2} = 355$	$T_{\cdot 3} = 260$	$T_{\cdot\cdot} = 792$
Means	$\bar{x}_{\cdot 1} = 59$	$\bar{x}_{\cdot 2} = 71$	$\bar{x}_{\cdot 3} = 65$	$\bar{x}_{\cdot\cdot} = 66$
Sample sizes	$n_1 = 3$	$n_2 = 5$	$n_3 = 4$	$N = 12$

The distribution of the statistic which we shall use to test (7-2) depends upon assumptions which are a generalization of the assumptions required for the use of (5-71). If all r means are equal and if

(a) *The r samples are drawn randomly*
(b) *The r populations are normal*   (7-3)
(c) *The r population variances are equal*

then it can be shown that

$$F_{r-1,N-r} = \frac{\sum\limits_{j=1}^{r} \sum\limits_{i=1}^{n_j} (\bar{x}_{\cdot j} - \bar{x}_{\cdot\cdot})^2 / (r-1)}{\sum\limits_{j=1}^{r} \sum\limits_{i=1}^{n_j} (x_{ij} - \bar{x}_{\cdot j})^2 / (N-r)} \qquad (7\text{-}4)$$

has an F distribution with $r-1$ and $N-r$ degrees of freedom. Further, it can be demonstrated that the statistic (7-4) is a desirable one to use for testing (7-2) and that the critical region consists only of large values of $F_{r-1,N-r}$. Hence, for a test with significance level α, reject if

$$F_{r-1,N-r} > F_{r-1,N-r;\, 1-\alpha} \qquad (7\text{-}5)$$

The critical region of (7-5) can be justified on an intuitive basis. The numerator of (7-4) contains N terms of the type $(\bar{x}_{\cdot j} - \bar{x}_{\cdot\cdot})^2$. If the sample means are equal, then each sample mean $\bar{x}_{\cdot j} = \bar{x}_{\cdot\cdot}$, every term of the type $(\bar{x}_{\cdot j} - \bar{x}_{\cdot\cdot})^2$ is zero, and $F_{r-1,N-r}$ is zero. Such an unlikely result would be strong support for the hypothesis of equal means. If the sample means are nearly equal, then $F_{r-1,N-r}$ is small. The more the sample means differ, the larger the F ratio becomes. Consequently, it seems reasonable to reject H_0 only if $F_{r-1,N-r}$ is large.

EXAMPLE 7-1 ────────────────────────────────────

Evaluate the statistic (7-4) for Table 7-2.

Solution

Consider the denominator first.

$$\sum_{j=1}^{r} \sum_{i=1}^{n_j} (x_{ij} - \bar{x}_{\cdot j})^2 / (N-r) = [(56-59)^2 + (53-59)^2 + (68-59)^2$$
$$+ (77-71)^2 + (73-71)^2 + (63-71)^2 + (74-71)^2$$
$$+ (68-71)^2 + (70-65)^2 + (61-65)^2 + (67-65)^2$$
$$+ (62-65)^2]/9$$
$$= [9 + 36 + 81 + \cdots + 4 + 9]/9$$
$$= 302/9 = 33.56$$

For the numerator we get

$$\sum_{j=1}^{r} \sum_{i=1}^{n_j} (\bar{x}._{j} - \bar{x}..)^2/(r-1) = [(59-66)^2 + (59-66)^2 + (59-66)^2$$
$$+ (71-66)^2 + (71-66)^2 + (71-66)^2 + (71-66)^2$$
$$+ (71-66)^2 + (65-66)^2 + (65-66)^2 + (65-66)^2$$
$$+ (65-66)^2]/2$$
$$= [49 + 49 + 49 + 25 + \cdots + 1 + 1]/2$$
$$= 276/2 = 138$$

Finally,

$$F_{2,9} = \frac{138}{33.56} = 4.11$$

EXAMPLE 7-2

Follow the six-step outline for testing the hypothesis of equal means with the situation of Table 7-2.

Solution

1   We test $H_0: \mu_1 = \mu_2 = \mu_3$ against H_1: not all three means are equal.
2   Choose $\alpha = .05$, an arbitrary decision.
3   The statistic we use is given by (7-4) with $r = 3$, $N = 12$, $N - r = 9$. If H_0 is true, (7-4) has an F distribution with two and nine degrees of freedom provided (*a*) the three samples are drawn randomly, (*b*) the three populations are normal, and (*c*) the three population variances are equal. Samples can be selected in a manner to make (*a*) seem reasonable. As we have seen, assumption (*b*) is not too unreasonable for many types of data.
4   The critical region is $F_{2,9} > F_{2,9;.95} = 4.26$.
5   From Example 7-1 the observed value of $F_{2,9} = 4.11$.
6   We accept H_0. If the means are not equal, the data of Table 7-2 fail to provide sufficient proof.

It is not too difficult to show that, when $r = 2$, the F test of this section and the t test of Sec. 5-9 produce the same decision. When there are only two populations, formula (7-4) is the square of the t statistic. That is, $F_{1, n_1+n_2-2} = t^2_{n_1+n_2-2}$. In addition, the observed F falls in the critical region if, and only if, the observed t falls in the critical region. Hence the F test for (7-2) can be regarded as a generalization of the t test for (7-1).

204

Consider the identity

$$\sum_{j=1}^{r} \sum_{i=1}^{n_j} (x_{ij} - \bar{x}..)^2 = \sum_{j=1}^{r} \sum_{i=1}^{n_j} [(x_{ij} - \bar{x}._j) + (\bar{x}._j - \bar{x}..)]^2 \qquad (7\text{-}6)$$

The left-hand side is obtained by subtracting the mean of all observations from each sample value, squaring each difference, and summing all of these squares. The sum is nothing more than the numerator of the sample variance if all N observations are regarded as one sample. In analysis of variance we call the left-hand side of (7-6) the total sum of squares, and we shall designate it by SS_T. Obviously the right-hand side of (7-6) reduces to the left-hand side, since $\bar{x}._j$, the column mean, has been subtracted and added to each term. If each bracket is squared, the right-hand side can be written

$$\sum_{j=1}^{r} \sum_{i=1}^{n_j} [(x_{ij} - \bar{x}._j)^2 + (\bar{x}._j - \bar{x}..)^2 + 2(x_{ij} - \bar{x}._j)(\bar{x}._j - \bar{x}..)]$$

$$= \sum_{j=1}^{r} \sum_{i=1}^{n_j} (x_{ij} - \bar{x}._j)^2 + \sum_{j=1}^{r} \sum_{i=1}^{n_j} (\bar{x}._j - \bar{x}..)^2$$

$$+ 2 \sum_{j=1}^{r} \sum_{i=1}^{n_j} (x_{ij} - \bar{x}._j)(\bar{x}._j - \bar{x}..)$$

It is fairly easy to show that

$$2 \sum_{j=1}^{r} \sum_{i=1}^{n_j} (x_{ij} - \bar{x}._j)(\bar{x}._j - \bar{x}..) = 0 \qquad (7\text{-}7)$$

The term

$$\sum_{j=1}^{r} \sum_{i=1}^{n_j} (x_{ij} - \bar{x}._j)^2$$

will be called the within-sample sum of squares, and to save writing it will be designated as SS_W. As is evident by the first calculation in Example 7-1, SS_W can serve as a measure of the variation within the samples. If the observations within each column of Table 7-1 are nearly alike, SS_W will be small. If the observations within each column differ greatly, then SS_W will be large.

The term

$$\sum_{j=1}^{r} \sum_{i=1}^{n_j} (\bar{x}._j - \bar{x}..)^2$$

will be called the among-samples sum of squares and will be designated by SS_A. The second calculation of Example 7-1 demonstrates that

205

SS_A measures the variability of the sample means. If the means of all r columns of Table 7-1 are nearly alike, then SS_A is small. The more the means differ, the larger SS_A becomes. If SS_A is large enough, we shall not believe the hypothesis of equal means.

Putting together the shorthand notation and the results of squaring the right-hand side of (7-6) yields the identity

$$SS_T = SS_A + SS_W \tag{7-8}$$

Thus (7-4) can be rewritten as

$$F_{r-1, N-r} = \frac{SS_A/(r-1)}{SS_W/(N-r)} \tag{7-9}$$

If we let $SS_A/(r-1) = MS_A$, called the mean square for among samples, and $SS_W/(N-r) = MS_W$, called the mean square for within samples, then (7-4) can be written even more simply as

$$F_{r-1, N-r} = \frac{MS_A}{MS_W} \tag{7-10}$$

EXAMPLE 7-3

Verify the identity (7-8) for the data of Table 7-2.

Solution

In Example 7-1 we found $SS_A = 276$, $SS_W = 302$. We need to show that $SS_T = 276 + 302 = 578$. We have

$$
\begin{aligned}
SS_T = \sum_{j=1}^{3} \sum_{i=1}^{n_j} (x_{ij} - \bar{x}..)^2 &= (56 - 66)^2 + (53 - 66)^2 + (68 - 66)^2 \\
&+ (77 - 66)^2 + (73 - 66)^2 + (63 - 66)^2 + (74 - 66)^2 \\
&+ (68 - 66)^2 + (70 - 66)^2 + (61 - 66)^2 + (67 - 66)^2 \\
&+ (62 - 66)^2 \\
&= 100 + 169 + 4 + 121 + 49 + 9 + 64 + 4 + 16 + 25 + 1 \\
&+ 16 \\
&= 578
\end{aligned}
$$

as required.

EXAMPLE 7-4

Verify (7-7) for the data of Table 7-2.

Solution

We have

$$\sum_{j=1}^{3} \sum_{i=1}^{n_j} (x_{ij} - \bar{x}_{\cdot j})(\bar{x}_{\cdot j} - \bar{x}_{\cdot\cdot})$$

$$= (56 - 59)(59 - 66) + (53 - 59)(59 - 66) + (68 - 59)(59 - 66)$$
$$+ (77 - 71)(71 - 66) + (73 - 71)(71 - 66) + (63 - 71)(71 - 66)$$
$$+ (74 - 71)(71 - 66) + (68 - 71)(71 - 66) + (70 - 65)(65 - 66)$$
$$+ (61 - 65)(65 - 66) + (67 - 65)(65 - 66) + (62 - 65)(65 - 66)$$

$$= (59 - 66)[56 + 53 + 68 - 3(59)]$$
$$+ (71 - 66)[77 + 73 + 63 + 74 + 68 - 5(71)]$$
$$+ (65 - 66)[70 + 61 + 67 + 62 - 4(65)]$$

$$= (-7)[0] + (5)[0] + (-1)[0] = 0$$

The proof of (7-7) follows the numerical scheme we have used in the solution.

EXERCISES

◆ 7-1   Follow the scheme of Example 7-4 to prove (7-7).

7-5   COMPUTING FORMULAS

In Example 7-1 the numerator and denominator of (7-4) were evaluated directly from the expressions that define the fraction.   As in the case of s^2, defined by (3-4), we can obtain formulas more adaptable to the hand calculator.

Consider first

$$\sum_{j=1}^{r} \sum_{i=1}^{n_j} (x_{ij} - \bar{x}_{\cdot\cdot})^2 \tag{7-11}$$

Except for the fact that we are using double-summation notation, (7-11) is exactly the same as the numerator of s^2.   By squaring out each individual term, we showed [Eq. (3-5)] that

$$\sum_{i=1}^{n} (x_i - \bar{x})^2 = \sum_{i=1}^{n} x_i^2 - n\bar{x}^2 \tag{7-12}$$

Upon conversion to the notation of this chapter, (7-12) becomes

$$\sum_{j=1}^{r} \sum_{i=1}^{n_j} (x_{ij} - \bar{x}_{\cdot\cdot})^2 = \sum_{j=1}^{r} \sum_{i=1}^{n_j} x_{ij}^2 - N\bar{x}_{\cdot\cdot}^2$$

or

$$SS_T = \sum_{j=1}^{r} \sum_{i=1}^{n_j} x_{ij}^2 - \frac{T_{..}^2}{N} \tag{7-13}$$

the desired computing formula.

Next consider

$$SS_A = \sum_{j=1}^{r} \sum_{i=1}^{n_j} (\bar{x}_{.j} - \bar{x}_{..})^2 = \sum_{j=1}^{r} n_j(\bar{x}_{.j} - \bar{x}_{..})^2$$

We get, upon squaring,

$$SS_A = \sum_{j=1}^{r} n_j(\bar{x}_{.j}^2 - 2\bar{x}_{..}\cdot\bar{x}_{.j} + \bar{x}_{..}^2)$$

$$= \sum_{j=1}^{r} n_j\bar{x}_{.j}^2 - 2\bar{x}_{..}\cdot\sum_{j=1}^{r} n_j\bar{x}_{.j} + \bar{x}_{..}^2\cdot\sum_{j=1}^{r} n_j$$

$$= \sum_{j=1}^{r} n_j\left(\frac{T_{.j}}{n_j}\right)^2 - 2\bar{x}_{..}\cdot\sum_{j=1}^{r} n_j\frac{T_{.j}}{n_j} + N\bar{x}_{..}^2$$

$$= \sum_{j=1}^{r} \frac{T_{.j}^2}{n_j} - 2\frac{T_{..}}{N}T_{..} + N\left(\frac{T_{..}}{N}\right)^2$$

$$= \sum_{j=1}^{r} \frac{T_{.j}^2}{n_j} - \frac{T_{..}^2}{N} \tag{7-14}$$

Finally, because of identity (7-8), we get

$$SS_W = SS_T - SS_A \tag{7-15}$$

EXAMPLE 7-5

Use the computing formulas on the data of Table 7-2.

Solution

We have

$$SS_T = 56^2 + 53^2 + 68^2 + 77^2 + 73^2 + 63^2 + 74^2 + 68^2 + 70^2$$
$$+ 61^2 + 67^2 + 62^2 - \frac{792^2}{12}$$
$$= 52{,}850 - 52{,}272 = 578$$

$$SS_A = \frac{177^2}{3} + \frac{355^2}{5} + \frac{260^2}{4} - \frac{792^2}{12}$$
$$= 10{,}443 + 25{,}205 + 16{,}900 - 52{,}272$$
$$= 52{,}548 - 52{,}272 = 276$$

as before.

208

The results from an analysis of variance are usually presented in a table. The form we shall use when testing (7-2) with assumptions (7-3) is given in Table 7-3. If the assumptions (7-3) are true,

$$E(MS_W) = \sigma^2$$

$$E(MS_A) = \sigma^2 + \sum_{j=1}^{r} \frac{n_j(\mu_j - \mu)^2}{r - 1}$$

where $\mu = \sum_{j=1}^{r} n_j\mu_j/N$. Note that if $\mu_1 = \mu_2 = \cdots = \mu_r$, then $\mu = \mu_1 \sum_{j=1}^{r} n_j/N = \mu_1$ and $E(MS_A) = \sigma^2$. This latter fact would perhaps suggest that it is reasonable to compare MS_A and MS_W in an F ratio to test (7-2). Although the EMS column is not useful in the simple analysis of variance problem considered in this chapter, it is of great assistance in more complicated situations.

The analysis of variance table for the data of Table 7-2 is given by Table 7-4. In the outline the table should be given under step 5.

Table 7-3   An analysis of variance table

Source of variation	SS	D.F.†	MS	EMS‡	F
Among samples	SS_A	$r - 1$	MS_A	$\sigma^2 + \sum_{j=1}^{r} \dfrac{n_j(\mu_j - \mu)^2}{r - 1}$	$\dfrac{MS_A}{MS_W}$
Within samples	SS_W	$N - r$	MS_W	σ^2	
Total	SS_T	$N - 1$			

† Degrees of freedom.   ‡ Expected mean square.

Table 7-4   Analysis of variance for Table 7-2

Source of variation	SS	D.F.†	MS	EMS‡	F
Among samples	276	2	138	$\sigma^2 + \sum_{j=1}^{3} \dfrac{n_j(\mu_j - \mu)^2}{2}$	4.11
Within samples	302	9	33.56	σ^2	
Total	578	11			

† Degrees of freedom.   ‡ Expected mean square.

Quite often the notation 4.11* or 4.11** is used to indicate that 4.11 is significant at the .05 and .01 levels, respectively. Of course, in the Table 7-4 example, it is not significant at either level.

EXERCISES

7-2 A 33-acre field is divided into acre plots. Eleven plots are selected at random and planted with variety 1 corn. Eleven more are selected at random from the remaining 22 and planted with variety 2 corn. The other 11 acres are planted with variety 3. When the corn is harvested, the yields in bushels per acre are as recorded in Table 7-5. Test the hypothesis that the average yield for each variety is the same.

7-3 A professor teaches four classes of elementary statistics. Each class is conducted in the same way except that a different text is used. Assume that students are selected at random for the four classes. After the course is over, all students take the same final examination. The scores are recorded in Table 7-6. Do the results support the hypothesis that all four populations have the same mean?

7-4 A psychologist has devised an examination in such a way that the score achieved depends almost entirely upon the ability to follow instructions. The examination is administered to 40 available students who have been divided into four groups at random. The instructions are given in the following ways: to group I, written and brief; to group II, oral and brief; to group III, written and detailed; to group IV, oral and detailed. Computations with the scores yield $SS_T = 870$, $SS_A = 150$. What conclusions are likely to be drawn?

Table 7-5   Corn yields

Variety 1	Variety 2	Variety 3
89	122	95
97	120	80
115	115	83
82	87	100
105	105	95
108	90	100
110	105	113
80	130	105
99	130	80
110	110	80
110	111	92

Table 7-6   Final-examination scores

"Statistics Cookbook"	"Statistics with Humor"	"Statistics Made Useful"	"Statistics in Story Form"
78	51	64	54
78	57	54	61
79	64	61	79
70	75	66	69
83	42	57	69
74	83	71	65
81	54	69	76
77	58	59	
85	74	51	
	64	71	
		83	

7-7   POWER OF THE F TEST

If $r = 2$, the t test can be used to test the hypothesis of equal means. Computation of power has already been discussed in Sec. 5-9. If $r \geq 3$, a different set of graphs are needed to obtain power. These graphs, which are given in Appendix D-16, will be used only if $n_1 = n_2 = \cdots = n_r = n$, that is, if all r sample sizes are equal.

In order to obtain power from the graphs, we need certain information. First we must have $\nu_1 = r - 1$ to find the correct page. This number appears in the upper left-hand corner of each graph and runs from 2 to 5. The journal article from which the graphs are taken gives curves for $\nu_1 = 1$ to $\nu_1 = 8$. Second, we need $\nu_2 = N - r$, the degrees of freedom associated with MS_W. On each page of the table there are curves for $\nu_2 = 6, 7, 8, 9, 10, 12, 15, 20, 30, 60, \infty$. For other values of ν_2 it is necessary to interpolate. Each page contains two sets of graphs, one for $\alpha = .05$ and one for $\alpha = .01$. Thus the third quantity needed is the significance level. Finally, a parameter ϕ, which is used to enter the horizontal scale, must be computed. This parameter has the value

$$\phi = \frac{\sqrt{\dfrac{n}{r} \sum_{j=1}^{r} (\mu_j - \mu)^2}}{\sigma} \tag{7-16}$$

where $\mu = \sum_{j=1}^{r} \mu_j/r$, the average of the r population means. We shall now consider some examples which illustrate the use of the graphs.

EXAMPLE 7-6

The psychologist in Exercise 7-4 would like to know the probability of rejecting the hypothesis of equal means if three means are equal and the fourth differs from the other three by σ.

Solution

Suppose that in populations corresponding to groups I, II, and III we have equal means $\mu_1 = \mu_2 = \mu_3$ and that the fourth mean is $\mu_4 = \mu_1 + \sigma$. Then

$$\mu = \frac{\mu_1 + \mu_1 + \mu_1 + \mu_1 + \sigma}{4} = \mu_1 + \frac{\sigma}{4}$$

and

$$\sum_{j=1}^{4} (\mu_j - \mu)^2 = \left(\mu_1 - \mu_1 - \frac{\sigma}{4}\right)^2 + \left(\mu_1 - \mu_1 - \frac{\sigma}{4}\right)^2 + \left(\mu_1 - \mu_1 - \frac{\sigma}{4}\right)^2$$

$$+ \left(\mu_1 + \sigma - \mu_1 - \frac{\sigma}{4}\right)^2$$

$$= \frac{\sigma^2}{16} + \frac{\sigma^2}{16} + \frac{\sigma^2}{16} + \frac{9\sigma^2}{16} = \frac{3\sigma^2}{4}$$

Since $n = 10$, $r = 4$, we have

$$\phi = \frac{\sqrt{(10/4)(3\sigma^2/4)}}{\sigma} = \sqrt{\frac{30}{16}} = \frac{\sqrt{30}}{4} = \frac{5.477}{4} = 1.37$$

For this example $\nu_1 = r - 1 = 3$, $\nu_2 = N - r = 40 - 4 = 36$. Turning to the second page of Appendix D-16, we find

Power = .58   if $\alpha = .05$
Power = .32   if $\alpha = .01$

Since some visual interpolation is necessary on both ν_2 and ϕ, others may read values for the power differing slightly from the ones given above.

EXAMPLE 7-7

For the situation described in Example 7-6 how large should n be (instead of 10) so that the power is .95 if $\alpha = .05$?

Solution

Perhaps the best way to obtain the answer by using Appendix D-16 is trial and error. Since $n = 10$ yields a power of .58, we need a larger n.

For $n = 20$

$$\phi = \frac{\sqrt{\frac{20}{4}\left(\frac{3\sigma^2}{4}\right)}}{\sigma} = \sqrt{\frac{60}{16}} = \frac{\sqrt{60}}{4} = \frac{7.746}{4} = 1.94$$

$\nu_1 = 3 \qquad \nu_2 = 80 - 4 = 76$

and the second page of Appendix D-16 yields power $\cong .91$. Next, we try $n = 30$ and get

$$\phi = \frac{\sqrt{(30/4)(3\sigma^2/4)}}{\sigma} = \sqrt{\frac{90}{16}} = \frac{\sqrt{90}}{4} = \frac{9.487}{4} = 2.37$$

$\nu_1 = 3 \qquad \nu_2 = 120 - 4 = 116 \qquad$ power $> .98$

so samples of size 30 are larger than need be. With $n = 25$

$$\phi = \sqrt{\frac{75}{16}} = 2.17 \qquad \nu_1 = 3 \qquad \nu_2 = 100 - 4 = 96 \qquad \text{power} > .95$$

and with $n = 24$

$$\phi = \sqrt{\frac{72}{16}} = 2.12 \qquad \nu_1 = 3 \qquad \nu_2 = 96 - 4 = 92 \qquad \text{power} \cong .95$$

Thus $n = 24$, which requires about $4(24) = 96$ students, is about the number required to achieve a power of .95. Since there is some difficulty in interpolating between 60 and ∞ degrees of freedom, it is possible others may arrive at $n = 23$ or $n = 25$. However, for practical purposes the difference is not too important.

Another interesting type of problem involving power calculations arises when we seek information about the power if the maximum difference between two treatment means is a given amount, say, $a\sigma$. A little reflection reveals that many different choices of the μ's will yield a maximum difference of $a\sigma$ and that a power value will be associated with each choice. It can be shown that the minimum power for all such choices is obtained by taking one μ_j, say, μ_1, equal to $\mu + a\sigma/2$, another μ_j, say, μ_2, equal to $\mu - a\sigma/2$, and all the other μ_j's equal to μ. Then

$$\sum_{j=1}^{r} (\mu_j - \mu)^2 = \left(\mu + \frac{a\sigma}{2} - \mu\right)^2 + \left(\mu - \frac{a\sigma}{2} - \mu\right)^2 + 0 + \cdots + 0$$

$$= \frac{a^2\sigma^2}{2}$$

and

$$\phi = \frac{\sqrt{(n/r)(a^2\sigma^2/2)}}{\sigma} = a\sqrt{\frac{n}{2r}} \tag{7-17}$$

EXAMPLE 7-8

Find the minimum value of the power if the maximum difference between the true means in Exercise 7-4 is σ and $\alpha = .05$.

Solution

We use ϕ as given by 7-17 with $a = 1$, $n = 10$, $r = 4$. Thus $\phi = \sqrt{10/8} = \sqrt{5/4} = 2.236/2 = 1.12$, $\nu_1 = 3$, $\nu_2 = 36$. With this ϕ the power is approximately .40.

Unfortunately ϕ, as given by (7-16), contains the unknown quantity σ. As was done previously with δ for the power calculations with t tests, the μ_j were so chosen that σ appeared in the numerator of (7-16) as well as in the denominator. That is, differences between the various means have to be expressed as multiples of σ. As an alternative we might be tempted to replace σ by its estimate s. The latter procedure can lead to large errors in power if s differs from σ by a relatively small amount.

EXERCISES

◆ 7-5 If $\alpha = .05$, find the probability of rejecting the hypothesis of equal means in Exercise 7-2 when two means are equal and the third exceeds these two by 1.2σ.

7-6 If $\alpha = .05$, how large should n be if the probability of rejecting the hypothesis of equal means in Exercise 7-2 is to be .95 when two means are equal and the third exceeds these two by 1.2σ?

◆ 7-7 If $\alpha = .05$, find the least value for the probability of rejecting the hypothesis of equal means in Exercise 7-2 if the largest difference among the three means is 1.2σ.

7-8 CONTRASTS AND THE METHOD OF SCHEFFE

If hypothesis (7-2) is rejected, all we can conclude is that the r population means are not equal. When this happens, it is logical to inquire what inferences can be drawn about the unknown means. In particular, we may like to know whether the data indicate that certain means are larger than certain other means. Investigation of further inferences about the means leads us to a study of contrasts.

If $c_1, c_2, \ldots, c_r$ are known constants such that

$$\sum_{j=1}^{r} c_j = c_1 + c_2 + \cdots + c_r = 0$$

then

$$L = c_1\mu_1 + c_2\mu_2 + \cdots + c_r\mu_r \qquad (7\text{-}18)$$

is called a contrast. Hence, if $r = 3$,

$$
\begin{aligned}
&\mu_1 - \mu_2 \text{ is a contrast with } c_1 = 1, c_2 = -1, c_3 = 0 \\
&\mu_1 - \mu_3 \text{ is a contrast with } c_1 = 1, c_2 = 0, c_3 = -1 \\
&\mu_2 - \mu_3 \text{ is a contrast with } c_1 = 0, c_2 = 1, c_3 = -1 \\
&2\mu_1 - \mu_2 - \mu_3 \text{ is a contrast with } c_1 = 2, c_2 = -1, c_3 = -1 \\
&\mu_1 - 2\mu_2 + \mu_3 \text{ is a contrast with } c_1 = 1, c_2 = -2, c_3 = 1 \\
&\mu_1 + \mu_2 - 2\mu_3 \text{ is a contrast with } c_1 = 1, c_2 = 1, c_3 = -2
\end{aligned}
\qquad (7\text{-}19)
$$

Any other possible contrast with three means would have to be a multiple of one of those given by (7-19).

We observe that if all means are equal, then every contrast is zero. Similarly, if every contrast is zero, all means are equal. If not all the means are equal, then one or more contrasts must be different from zero. Hence if H_0 of (7-2) is rejected, it makes sense to seek confidence intervals for contrasts.

A reasonable unbiased estimate of (7-18) is

$$\hat{L} = c_1\bar{x}_{.1} + c_2\bar{x}_{.2} + \cdots + c_r\bar{x}_{.r} \qquad (7\text{-}20)$$

Scheffé [2]† has shown that the probability is $1 - \alpha$ that all contrasts will be captured by the set of intervals given by

$$\hat{L} - S\hat{\sigma}_{\hat{L}} \leqq L \leqq \hat{L} + S\hat{\sigma}_{\hat{L}} \qquad (7\text{-}21)$$

where

$$S^2 = (r - 1)F_{r-1, N-r; 1-\alpha} \qquad (7\text{-}22)$$

and

$$\hat{\sigma}_{\hat{L}}^2 = MS_W \sum_{j=1}^{r} \frac{c_j^2}{n_j} \qquad (7\text{-}23)$$

When we first discussed confidence intervals for one parameter in Sec. 5-4, we pointed out that the computation of a confidence interval is somewhat analogous to throwing an interval in one-dimensional space at a point which represents the parameter. Similarly, if there are k possible contrasts, we can compare the computation of the

† Numbers in brackets are those of references listed at the end of the chapter.

k intervals of (7-21) to throwing a k-dimensional box (or parallelepiped) at a k-dimensional point whose k coordinates are the k imaginable contrasts, with the throwing procedure being such that the point is captured by the box $100(1 - \alpha)$ per cent of the time in the long run.

EXAMPLE 7-9 ───────────────────────────────

For the data of Table 7-2 compute confidence intervals for the contrasts (7-19). Use $\alpha = .05$.

Solution

We have $\bar{x}_{.1} = 59$, $\bar{x}_{.2} = 71$, $\bar{x}_{.3} = 65$, $n_1 = 3$, $n_2 = 5$, $n_3 = 4$, $r = 3$, $N - r = 9$, $F_{2,9;.95} = 4.26$, $MS_W = 33.56$. Thus $S^2 = 2F_{2,9;.95} = 2(4.26) = 8.52$, $S = 2.92$. For the contrast $\mu_1 - \mu_2$ the estimate is

$$\hat{L} = \bar{x}_{.1} - \bar{x}_{.2} = 59 - 71 = -12$$
$$\hat{\sigma}_{\hat{L}}^2 = MS_W \left(\frac{1}{n_1} + \frac{1}{n_2} \right) = 33.56(\tfrac{1}{3} + \tfrac{1}{5}) = 17.90 \qquad \hat{\sigma}_{\hat{L}} = 4.23$$
$$S\hat{\sigma}_{\hat{L}} = (2.92)(4.23) = 12.35$$

and the interval is $(-12 - 12.35, \ -12 + 12.35)$ or $(-24.35, .35)$. For the contrast $\mu_1 - \mu_3$ the estimate is

$$\hat{L} = \bar{x}_{.1} - \bar{x}_{.3} = 59 - 65 = -6$$

$\hat{\sigma}_{\hat{L}}^2 = 33.56(\tfrac{1}{3} + \tfrac{1}{4}) = 19.58$, $\hat{\sigma}_{\hat{L}} = 4.42$, $S\hat{\sigma}_{\hat{L}} = 12.91$, and the interval is $(-6 - 12.91, \ -6 + 12.91)$ or $(-18.91, 6.91)$. For the contrast $\mu_2 - \mu_3$ the estimate is

$$\hat{L} = \bar{x}_{.2} - \bar{x}_{.3} = 71 - 65 = 6$$

$\hat{\sigma}_{\hat{L}}^2 = 33.56(\tfrac{1}{5} + \tfrac{1}{4}) = 15.10$, $\hat{\sigma}_{\hat{L}} = 3.89$, $S\hat{\sigma}_{\hat{L}} = 11.36$, and the interval is $(6 - 11.36, \ 6 + 11.36)$ or $(-5.36, 17.36)$. For the contrast $2\mu_1 - \mu_2 - \mu_3$ the estimate is

$$\hat{L} = 2\bar{x}_{.1} - \bar{x}_{.2} - \bar{x}_{.3} = 2(59) - 71 - 65 = -18$$

$\hat{\sigma}_{\hat{L}}^2 = 33.56(\tfrac{4}{3} + \tfrac{1}{5} + \tfrac{1}{4}) = 59.85$, $\hat{\sigma}_{\hat{L}} = 7.74$, $S\hat{\sigma}_{\hat{L}} = 22.60$, and the interval is $(-18 - 22.60, \ -18 + 22.60)$ or $(-40.60, 4.60)$. For the contrast $\mu_1 - 2\mu_2 + \mu_3$ the estimate is

$$\hat{L} = \bar{x}_{.1} - 2\bar{x}_{.2} + \bar{x}_{.3} = 59 - 2(71) + 65 = -18$$

$\hat{\sigma}_{\hat{L}}^2 = 33.56(\tfrac{1}{3} + \tfrac{4}{5} + \tfrac{1}{4}) = 46.42$, $\hat{\sigma}_{\hat{L}} = 6.81$, $S\hat{\sigma}_{\hat{L}} = 19.89$, and the interval is $(-18 - 19.89, \ -18 + 19.89)$ or $(-37.89, 1.89)$. Finally, for the contrast $\mu_1 + \mu_2 - 2\mu_3$ the estimate is

$$\hat{L} = \bar{x}_{\cdot 1} + \bar{x}_{\cdot 2} - 2\bar{x}_{\cdot 3} = 59 + 71 - 2(65) = 0$$

$\hat{\sigma}_{\hat{L}}^2 = 33.56(\frac{1}{3} + \frac{1}{5} + \frac{4}{4}) = 51.46$, $\hat{\sigma}_{\hat{L}} = 7.17$, $S\hat{\sigma}_{\hat{L}} = 20.94$, and the interval is $(0 - 20.94, 0 + 20.94)$ or $(-20.94, 20.94)$. In the long run all six contrasts will be captured about .95 of the time by intervals computed in this manner.

We note that each of the six intervals obtained in Example 7-9 contains 0. For example, for $\mu_2 - \mu_3$ we found

$$-5.36 \leq \mu_2 - \mu_3 \leq 17.36$$

When the interval computed for a contrast L contains zero, then $\hat{L}$ is said to be not significantly different from 0. On the other hand, calculations might have given

$$6.52 \leq \mu_2 - \mu_3 \leq 17.36 \tag{7-24}$$

an interval which does not include 0. When the latter situation happens, $\hat{L}$ is said to be significantly different from zero and certain conclusions can be drawn. The interval (7-24) would lead us to believe that $\mu_2 > \mu_3$. If (7-21) yields

$$-12.34 \leq 2\mu_1 - \mu_2 - \mu_3 \leq -3.07$$

then we conclude $2\mu_1 - \mu_2 - \mu_3 < 0$ or $\mu_1 < (\mu_2 + \mu_3)/2$, which implies that the average for population 1 is less than the average for populations 2 and 3.

Probably the most important contrasts are those which contain only two means, such as the first three of (7-19). When the estimates of one or more of these simple-type contrasts are significantly different from zero, we can make statements about which population means are higher than which others. If, for example, we find

$$-3.47 \leq \mu_1 - \mu_2 \leq 8.62$$
$$4.05 \leq \mu_1 - \mu_3 \leq 11.71$$
$$6.52 \leq \mu_2 - \mu_3 \leq 17.36$$

then the conclusions are that the means for populations 1 and 2 are higher than the mean for population 3 and that no difference between the means of populations 1 and 2 has been demonstrated.

An interesting feature of Scheffé's method is that one or more of the intervals given by (7-21) will not cover 0 if, and only if, the F test rejects the hypothesis of equal means when the same α is used. Consequently, all intervals found in Example 7-9 necessarily had to cover zero, since the F test for the data of Table 7-2 accepted the hypothesis of equal means. The region given by (7-21) is related to the F test in the same way that the confidence interval obtained from (5-77) is related to the t test of (5-66). Thus (7-21) can be regarded as a generalization of the interval given in (5-77).

When conducting an analysis of variance, we first perform the F test, then look for significant contrasts only if the hypothesis of equal means is rejected. We can regard the Scheffé intervals as something thrown in free with the F test. That is, no additional assumptions are needed and no further significance levels are involved. Further, contrasts can be selected *after* the experiment is performed (contrary to usual statistical procedures), since the region given by (7-21) attempts to capture all possible contrasts at one time.

EXERCISES

7-8   Use the method of Scheffé to determine which estimated contrasts are significantly different from zero for the data of Table 7-5. Use $\alpha = .05$.

7-9   For the data of Table 7-6 make inferences about which population means are larger than which others by obtaining the intervals of (7-21) for contrasts involving two means $\left[\text{there are } \binom{4}{2} = 6 \text{ such intervals} \right]$. Use $\alpha = .05$.

7-10   Five statistics classes were taught in the following ways: class 1, by correspondence with textbook A; class 2, by Professor Jones with textbook A; class 3, by Professor Jones with textbook B; class 4, by Professor Smith with textbook A; class 5, by Professor Smith with textbook B. Fifty students were assigned randomly, 10 to each class. All classes took a standard final examination, with 150 representing a perfect score. The totals were $T._1 = 500$, $T._2 = 700$, $T._3 = 1,000$, $T._4 = 600$, $T._5 = 1,200$, and the total sum of squares was 56,500. It is easy to verify that the hypothesis of equal means is rejected. Investigate a contrast comparing textbook A and textbook B. Investigate a contrast comparing Professor Jones and Professor Smith. [*Hint:* The averages for textbook A and textbook B are the same if $(\mu_1 + \mu_2 + \mu_4)/3 = (\mu_3 + \mu_5)/2$ or if

$$2\mu_1 + 2\mu_2 - 3\mu_3 + 2\mu_4 - 3\mu_5 = 0$$

Determine whether or not the estimate of this contrast is significantly different from 0.] Use $\alpha = .01$.

One of the assumptions (7-3) required of the F test for (7-2) stated that the r population variances are equal.   Several procedures are available for testing

$$H_0: \sigma_1^2 = \sigma_2^2 = \cdots = \sigma_r^2 \text{ against } H_1: \text{not all variances are equal} \quad (7\text{-}25)$$

We shall discuss one, called Cochran's test, which requires that all sample sizes be equal.   That is, we must have $n_1 = n_2 = \cdots = n_r = n$. (For other tests, see page 20 of [1] and page 83 of [2].)

Let $s_1^2, s_2^2, \ldots, s_r^2$ be the r sample variances.   If we assume (a) the r samples are drawn randomly and (b) the r populations are normal, then the statistic

$$R_{n,r} = \frac{\text{largest sample variance}}{s_1^2 + s_2^2 + \cdots + s_r^2} \quad (7\text{-}26)$$

can be used to test (7-25).   The hypothesis is rejected with significance level α if

$$R_{n,r} > R_{n,r;1-\alpha} \quad (7\text{-}27)$$

where $R_{n,r;1-\alpha}$ is obtained from Appendix D-17 for $\alpha = .01, .05$.

EXAMPLE 7-10

Suppose that three samples of size 10 are selected randomly from three normal populations and yield $s_1^2 = 140$, $s_2^2 = 200$, $s_3^2 = 660$.   Test the hypothesis of equal variances.

Solution

We shall follow the six-step outline.

1 We test $H_0: \sigma_1^2 = \sigma_2^2 = \sigma_3^2$ against $H_1:$ not all three variances are equal.
2 Select $\alpha = .05$, an arbitrary choice.
3 The statistic we use is (7-26).   If the hypothesis of equal variances is true, then critical values for $R_{n,r}$ can be obtained from Appendix D-17 provided (a) the three samples have been selected randomly and (b) the three populations are normal.   We are given that these assumptions are satisfied.
4 The critical region is $R_{10,3} > R_{10,3;.95} = .6167$, found in Appendix. D-17.

5   Computations: The observed value of the statistic is

$$R_{10,3} = \frac{660}{140 + 200 + 660} = .66$$

6   Thus H_0 is rejected.   (Since $R_{10,3;.99} = .6912$, H_0 is accepted if $\alpha = .01$.)

When we test (7-25) as a preliminary exercise before we test the hypothesis of equal means, we create some problems that deserve comment.   First, if (7-25) is rejected, then it appears that the analysis of variance F test is no longer available.   Second, if (7-25) is accepted, the significance level to be attached to the F test is not what it would appear to be.   The probability of rejecting H_0 when true depends upon the distribution of F subject to the condition that (7-25) has already been accepted.   Computation of such probabilities is usually very involved, even for an expert.   Section 7-10 provides a partial solution to the dilemma.

EXERCISES

◆ 7-11   Suppose that we have four random samples drawn from four normal populations.   If $s_1^2 = 190$, $s_2^2 = 527$, $s_3^2 = 66.2$, $s_4^2 = 873$, $n = 8$, is the hypothesis of equal variances accepted?
   7-12   Test the hypothesis of equal variances for the situation of Exercise 7-2.

7-10   CONCLUDING REMARKS

We have implied that samples can be drawn in such a way that the randomness assumption of (7-3) seems reasonable.   Both the F test and the method of Scheffé for contrasts depend upon the further assumptions of normality and equal variances.   However, studies have indicated that failure to satisfy the latter two assumptions does not seriously affect inferences based upon either the F test or Scheffé's method if the sample sizes are equal (or nearly so).

Another good argument for choosing equal n's is that a number of procedures depend upon this requirement and are unavailable if it is not satisfied.   For example, Cochran's test cannot be performed with unequal sample sizes.

As we observed in Chap. 5, lack of normality may seriously affect inferences about variances, in this case Cochran's test.

REFERENCES

1 GUENTHER, WILLIAM C.: "Analysis of Variance," Prentice-Hall, Inc., Englewood Cliffs, N.J., 1964.
2 SCHEFFÉ, HENRY: "The Analysis of Variance," John Wiley & Sons, Inc., New York, 1959.

I. Inferences in Analysis of r means, $r \geq 2$

   A. Standard hypotheses, alternatives, statistics, and critical regions (significance level α)

Hypothesis	Alternative	Statistic†	Critical region
$H_0: \mu_1 = \mu_2$ $= \cdots = \mu_r$	H_1: not all r means are equal	$F_{r-1,N-r} = \dfrac{SS_A/(r-1)}{SS_W/(N-r)}$ where $$SS_T = \sum_{j=1}^{r} \sum_{i=1}^{n_j} x_{ij}^2 - \frac{T_{..}^2}{N}$$ $$SS_A = \sum_{j=1}^{r} \frac{T_{.j}^2}{n_j} - \frac{T_{..}^2}{N}$$ $$SS_W = SS_T - SS_A$$	$F_{r-1,N-r} > F_{r-1,N-r;1-\alpha}$

† Note that whenever a statistic is given in this summary, certain assumptions are made. These assumptions, giving the stastistic the required distribution, may be found in the text material.

   B. Power calculations
   1. When $r = 2$, use Appendix D-10 as outlined in VI-B of the Summary of Results, Chapter 5.
   2. If $r = 3, 4, 5, 6$ and the sample sizes are equal, use Appendix D-16 with entries α, $\nu_1 = r - 1$, $\nu_2 = N - r$ and

$$\phi = \frac{\sqrt{\dfrac{n}{r} \sum_{j=1}^{r} (\mu_j - \mu)^2}}{\sigma}$$

   where $\mu = \sum_{j=1}^{r} \mu_j/r$, the average of the r population means.
   3. The sample size n required to guarantee a given power at a specified alternative can be found from Appendix D-16 by trial and error.
   C. Confidence region with coefficient α for all possible contrasts: The intervals determining the boundaries of the region are given by $\hat{L} - S\hat{\sigma}_{\hat{L}} \leq L \leq \hat{L} + S\hat{\sigma}_{\hat{L}}$, where

$$\hat{L} = c_1 \bar{x}_{\cdot 1} + \cdots + c_r \bar{x}_{\cdot r}$$
$$S^2 = (r-1)F_{r-1, N-r; 1-\alpha}$$
$$\hat{\sigma}_{\hat{L}}^2 = MS_W \sum_{j=1}^{r} \frac{c_j^2}{n_j}$$

II. Inferences in analysis of r variances, $r > 2$ (equal sample sizes)
   A. Standard hypotheses, alternatives, statistics, and critical regions (significance level α)

Hypothesis	Alternative	Statistic	Critical region
$H_0: \sigma_1^2 = \sigma_2^2$ $= \cdots = \sigma_r^2$	H_1: not all variances are equal	$R_{n,r} = \dfrac{\text{largest sample variance}}{s_1^2 + s_2^2 + \cdots + s_r^2}$	$R_{n,r} > R_{n,r;1-\alpha}$

CHAPTER EIGHT

Regression and Correlation

8-1 INTRODUCTION

In Sec. 5-10 we encountered situations in which the observations occur in pairs. One of the examples considered involved the weights of 20 adults before and after a strenuous physical training program. Thus each individual furnishes two related measurements: his weight before being subjected to the course and his weight after completing the course. It might occur to us that we could use the results associated with individuals who have completed the program to help predict final weights of others who are about to start. One of the objectives of this chapter will be to study some techniques which utilize the information furnished by one variable to help draw inferences about a related variable.

As a second example, suppose we have records that give the grade-point averages from both high school and college for a number of students. We might seek methods which utilize these data to give a reasonable prediction of the expected grade point for an incoming college freshman whose high school grade point is available. That is, by using high school grade point we would like to be able to predict college grade point. Again we have two related variables and want to use the information furnished by one to help describe the behavior of the other.

In some types of two-variable data we may be interested in obtaining a measure of the relationships between the variables for some useful purpose. For example, let us suppose we know how to control the height of a cornstalk. If we can next establish that there is a high degree of relationship between the height of a cornstalk and the weight of its yield in corn, then we may also know therefore how to control yield.

If we have a choice between two types of entrance examinations to be administered to prospective college freshmen, we may be interested in obtaining a measure of relationship between scores on the two examinations. Suppose one of the examinations, moderately difficult to give, has been used with some success in predicting how applicants will perform in their college work. The second examination is far easier to administer, and we might be tempted to substitute it for the first if scores indicate a high degree of relationship. To make a decision, a group of students would be given both examinations, which would yield a pair of scores for each student. These pairs would then be studied for relationship.

Let us consider one more situation in which we might look for some measure of relationship. Suppose that IQ is used successfully to predict scholastic achievement. Since shoe size is far easier to obtain, we may prefer to attempt to use the latter measurement in place of IQ if we can establish some degree of relationship. Probably the most sensible hypothesis to test in a case of this kind is that there is no relationship at all.

Problems involving two variables in which we are primarily interested in predicting behavior of one variable by using another are known as *regression problems*. When a measure of the degree of relationship is the prime consideration, then the two-variable investigation is referred to as a *correlation problem*. It is not always easy to draw a clear line of distinction between the two.

To introduce the subject of regression, let us return to the example concerning the prediction of college grade point from high school grade point. Suppose that the A, B, C, D, F grading system is used with letters being replaced by 4, 3, 2, 1, 0, respectively, to compute averages. Hence two numbers are associated with each student: his high school grade point x_i and his college grade point y_i. Assume that no student with a high school average of less than 2 is admitted to college, so that x_i can range from 2 to 4 and y_i from 0 to 4. From available records we select five students whose high school grade points were $x_1 = 2.0$, $x_2 = 2.5$, $x_3 = 3.0$, $x_4 = 3.5$, $x_5 = 4.0$ and find that their college grade points were $y_1 = 2.30$, $y_2 = 1.86$, $y_3 = 2.59$, $y_4 = 2.96$, $y_5 = 3.54$. The x_i's are chosen nonrandomly in order to cover the range of interest followed by a random selection of y_i for each x_i.

Let us imagine that for every given value of x, $2 \leq x \leq 4$, there exists a continuous population of y's with $0 \leq y \leq 4$. Each of these populations will have an unknown mean and an unknown variance. Let the mean be $\mu_{y|x}$, called the *mean of y given x*, and the variance be $\sigma^2_{y|x}$, called the *variance of y given x*. It is not unreasonable to assume that all the means lie on a continuous curve, called the *curve of regression*. In this chapter we shall consider only the simplest type of regression curve, namely, the straight line (actually only a line segment in our example). If we assume that all the unknown means lie on a line, this implies

$$\mu_{y|x} = A + Bx \tag{8-1}$$

where A and B are unknown constants. If A and B were known, then for any given x we could readily compute the average of the y's for that x. For example, suppose that $A = .1$ and $B = .9$ for the grade-point problem. Then with $x = 2.4$ we could calculate

$$\mu_{y|2.4} = .1 + (.9)(2.4) = 2.26$$

which would be our best guess for the college grade point of a person selected at random from the population of students whose high school grade point was 2.4. Unfortunately, we can only estimate $\mu_{y|x}$ by using estimates for A and B. Thus in place of (8-1) we shall use an estimated value given by

$$\hat{\mu}_{y|x} = a + bx \tag{8-2}$$

where a is an estimate of A, b is an estimate of B. For the grade-point situation the true but unknown regression line and its estimate might appear as in Fig. 8-1.

226

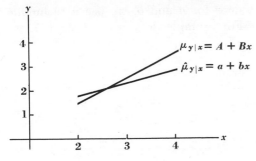

Figure 8-1 *A true regres-*
sion line and its estimate.

A procedure which yields estimates a and b with good statistical properties is known as the *method of least squares*. To follow the explanation of this concept, consider Fig. 8-2. The five dots represent the grade points associated with the five students. The d_i's represent the vertical distances from the points to the estimated regression line. Thus

$$d_1 = 2.30 - (a + 2b)$$
$$d_2 = 1.86 - (a + 2.5b)$$
$$d_3 = 2.59 - (a + 3b)$$
$$d_4 = 2.96 - (a + 3.5b)$$
$$d_5 = 3.54 - (a + 4b)$$

In general,

$$d_i = y_i - (a + bx_i)$$

The least-squares regression line is the one obtained by so choosing a and b that

$$d_1^2 + d_2^2 + d_3^2 + d_4^2 + d_5^2 = \sum_{i=1}^{5} d_i^2$$

is a minimum.

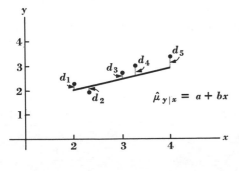

Figure 8-2 *A regression line*
estimated from five points by
least squares.

227

To find the least-squares values for a and b, we use a technique called *completing the square*. For example, if $u = 2v^2 + 3v + 7$, we can write

$$u = 2\left(v^2 + \frac{3v}{2}\right) + 7$$

$$= 2\left(v^2 + \frac{3v}{2} + \frac{9}{16} - \frac{9}{16}\right) + 7$$

$$= 2\left(v^2 + \frac{3v}{2} + \frac{9}{16}\right) - \frac{9}{8} + 7$$

$$= 2\left(v + \frac{3}{4}\right)^2 + \frac{47}{8}$$

The latter form of u makes it obvious that $v = -\frac{3}{4}$ gives a minimum value for u of $\frac{47}{8}$, since with any other choice of v, u is $\frac{47}{8}$ plus something. Now, in general, the sum of vertical distances squared is

$$\sum_{i=1}^{n} d_i^2 = \sum_{i=1}^{n} [y_i - (a + bx_i)]^2 = \sum_{i=1}^{n} (y_i - a - bx_i)^2$$

$$= \sum_{i=1}^{n} (y_i^2 + a^2 + b^2x_i^2 - 2ay_i - 2bx_iy_i + 2abx_i)$$

$$= \sum_{i=1}^{n} y_i^2 + na^2 + b^2 \sum_{i=1}^{n} x_i^2 - 2a \sum_{i=1}^{n} y_i - 2b \sum_{i=1}^{n} x_iy_i + 2ab \sum_{i=1}^{n} x_i$$

If we complete the square, first on a, then on b, we get, after a few lines of algebra,

$$\sum_{i=1}^{n} d_i^2 = n[a - (\bar{y} - b\bar{x})]^2 + \left(\sum_{i=1}^{n} x_i^2 - n\bar{x}^2\right)\left[b - \frac{\sum_{i=1}^{n} x_iy_i - n\bar{x}\bar{y}}{\sum_{i=1}^{n} x_i^2 - n\bar{x}^2}\right]^2$$

$$+ \sum_{i=1}^{n} y_i^2 - n\bar{y}^2 - \frac{\left(\sum_{i=1}^{n} x_iy_i - n\bar{x}\bar{y}\right)^2}{\sum_{i=1}^{n} x_i^2 - n\bar{x}^2} \qquad (8\text{-}3)$$

where $\bar{x}$ and $\bar{y}$ are the sample means of the x's and y's. Obviously, $\sum_{i=1}^{n} d_i^2$ is minimized if

$$b = \frac{\sum_{i=1}^{n} x_iy_i - n\bar{x}\bar{y}}{\sum_{i=1}^{n} x_i^2 - n\bar{x}^2} \qquad a = \bar{y} - b\bar{x} \qquad (8\text{-}4)$$

228

and the minimum value is

$$(n - 2)s_{y|x}^2 = \sum_{i=1}^{n} y_i^2 - n\bar{y}^2 - \frac{\left(\sum_{i=1}^{n} x_i y_i - n\bar{x}\bar{y}\right)^2}{\sum_{i=1}^{n} x_i^2 - n\bar{x}^2} \qquad (8\text{-}5)$$

If we assume that the least-squares procedure is a reasonable one to use, then the only additional assumption we need to find a and b is that the regression curve of y for given x is linear, that is, (8-1) is satisfied.   The estimated regression line we have obtained is the best in the sense of least squares whether or not we look upon the x's as values selected by the experimenter.

If we assume

(a) $\mu_{y|x} = A + Bx$, that is, the regression of y on x is linear
(b) $x_1, x_2, \ldots, x_n$ are selected nonrandomly
(c) $y_1, \ldots, y_n$ are selected randomly $\qquad\qquad\qquad (8\text{-}6)$
(d) $\sigma_{y|x}^2 = \sigma^2$, that is, the variance of each y population is the same

then it can be shown that

1   a and b are unbiased estimates of A and B; that is, $E(a) = A$, $E(b) = B$, so that $\hat{\mu}_{y|x}$ is an unbiased estimate of $\mu_{y|x}$.
2   $s_{y|x}^2$ is an unbiased estimate of $\sigma_{y|x}^2$.
3   Of all linear unbiased estimates of A and B, a and b have the smallest variances, thus making the variance of $\hat{\mu}_{y|x}$ less than for any other line whose parameters A, B are estimated by linear unbiased estimates.

(We call a and b linear estimates because we can write each of them in the form $c_1 y_1 + c_2 y_2 + \cdots + c_n y_n$, where the c_i are functions only of x_i.)

EXAMPLE 8-1

Find the least-squares regression line for the grade-point problem and use it to estimate the average college grade point for students with a high school average of 2.4.   If assumption (d) of (8-6) is satisfied, estimate σ^2 and σ.

Solution

We need

$$\sum_{i=1}^{5} x_i = 2.0 + 2.5 + 3.0 + 3.5 + 4.0 = 15.0 \qquad \bar{x} = 3.0$$

$$\sum_{i=1}^{5} y_i = 2.30 + 1.86 + 2.59 + 2.96 + 3.54 = 13.25 \qquad \bar{y} = 2.65$$

$$\sum_{i=1}^{5} x_i^2 = (2.0)^2 + (2.5)^2 + (3.0)^2 + (3.5)^2 + (4.0)^2 = 47.50$$

$$\sum_{i=1}^{5} y_i^2 = (2.30)^2 + (1.86)^2 + (2.59)^2 + (2.96)^2 + (3.54)^2 = 36.75$$

$$\sum_{i=1}^{5} x_i y_i = (2.0)(2.30) + (2.5)(1.86) + (3.0)(2.59) + (3.5)(2.96)$$
$$+ (4.0)(3.54) = 41.54$$

Thus

$$b = \frac{41.54 - 5(3.0)(2.65)}{47.50 - 5(3.0)^2} = \frac{1.79}{2.50} = .72$$
$$a = 2.65 - (.72)(3.0) = .49$$

and

$$\hat{\mu}_{y|x} = .49 + .72x$$

If $x = 2.4$, then

$$\hat{\mu}_{y|2.4} = .49 + (.72)(2.4) = .49 + 1.73 = 2.22$$

is the estimated average college grade point. Finally, the estimate of σ^2 is obtained from (8-5) by dividing by $n - 2$:

$$s_{y|x}^2 = \frac{1}{3}\left(36.75 - 5 \times 2.65^2 - \frac{1.79^2}{2.50}\right)$$
$$= \frac{1}{3}(36.75 - 35.11 - 1.28) = .12$$

The estimate of σ is $\sqrt{.12} = .35$.

EXERCISES

♦ 8-1 Suppose that in the grade-point problem we select for our x's, $x_1 = 2.0$, $x_2 = 2.1$, $x_3 = 2.2$, . . . , $x_{20} = 3.9$, $x_{21} = 4.0$. Then we draw a random sample of size 2 (so that $n = 42$) from each of the 21 y populations. Computations yield $\sum_{i=1}^{42} x_i = 126$,

$$\sum_{i=1}^{42} x_i^2 = 393.4, \quad \sum_{i=1}^{42} y_i = 105.00, \quad \sum_{i=1}^{42} y_i^2 = 284.30, \quad \sum_{i=1}^{42} x_i y_i = 330.4.$$

Table 8-1

Weight of mail on hand at 7 A.M. (in hundreds of pounds)	Man-hours required to fill orders (in thousands of hours)
5.21	12.6
7.16	17.3
6.34	15.2
8.41	18.5
6.94	15.8
6.52	15.0
7.33	16.8
5.87	13.8
6.61	14.9
8.03	18.0

Find (*a*) the estimated regression line, (*b*) the estimated average college grade point for students whose high school average is 3.0, (*c*) the estimate of σ^2 assuming a common variance for each population of y's, (*d*) the estimate of σ.

8-2 A large mail-order house uses the weight of incoming mail to determine how many of their employees are to be assigned to filling orders on a given day. Suppose that the data in Table 8-1 are taken from the company's records of 10 different days. Assuming linear regression, find the estimated regression line. Use it to predict the average number of man-hours needed to fill orders if the mail on hand at 7 A.M. weighs 673 pounds. Assume that each man works an 8-hour day and estimate the number of men required.

8-3 THE BIVARIATE NORMAL DISTRIBUTION

In Sec. 5-9 we considered situations in which random samples were drawn from two populations, each assumed to be normal. Observations coming from one distribution were not related in any way to those coming from the other. In Sec. 5-10 we encountered random samples of pairs such that the two random variables of a pair were related to each other. In seeking a model to describe the behavior of a related pair, it might occur to us that for some problems a generalization of the normal distribution would be useful. This generalization is called the bivariate normal distribution.

Let x and y be continuous random variables with means μ_x, μ_y and variances σ_x^2, σ_y^2. If x and y have a bivariate normal distribution, then the density function is given by

$$f(x,y) = \frac{1}{2\pi\sigma_x\sigma_y\sqrt{1-\rho^2}} \exp\left\{ \frac{1}{2(1-\rho^2)} \left[\frac{(x-\mu_x)^2}{\sigma_x^2} \right.\right.$$
$$\left.\left. - \frac{2\rho(x-\mu_x)(y-\mu_y)}{\sigma_x\sigma_y} + \frac{(y-\mu_y)^2}{\sigma_y^2} \right]\right\} \qquad (8\text{-}7)$$

where exp $(u) = e^{-u}$. Of course, we need not remember this complicated formula, but we should know some properties of the bivariate normal distribution. The important properties are:

(a) *The random variable x, when considered by itself, has a normal distribution with mean μ_x and variance σ_x^2.*
(b) *The random variable y, when considered by itself, has a normal distribution with mean μ_y and variance σ_y^2.*
(c) *The parameter ρ, called the correlation coefficient, can be considered as a measure of the relationship between x and y. We shall pursue this topic further in Sec. 8-5.*
(d) *The means $E(y|x) = \mu_{y|x}$ lie on a straight line. The estimated regression line is the same as the one obtained by least squares even though estimates of a and b are derived by using another procedure and by assuming x and y have a bivariate normal distribution.* $\qquad (8\text{-}8)$
(e) *The means $E(x|y) = \mu_{x|y}$ lie on a straight line. It is not necessary to consider this line separately if we want to predict x from y, since we can interchange the roles of x and y and use the line for $E(y|x)$.*
(f) *The variance of y given x, $\sigma_{y|x}^2$, is the same for all x (and $\sigma_{x|y}^2$ is the same for all y).*
(g) *Geometrically, (8-7) represents a bell-shaped surface.*

Thus we see that assumptions (a) and (d) of (8-6) are satisfied if x and y have a bivariate normal distribution.

It is possible to construct two variable distributions other than the bivariate normal which have properties (a) and (b) of (8-8). However, in most practical situations it is safe to assume that x and y have a bivariate normal distribution if we believe that each of the random variables x and y is normally distributed.

As we have already observed, the regression line can be used to predict $\mu_{y|x}$ without making any assumptions as to the form of the y distribution for given x.   However, if we want to test hypotheses about, or obtain confidence intervals for, $\mu_{y|x}$, A, B, or $\sigma_{y|x}^2$, then it is necessary to make normality assumptions.   We can assume either

(a) $\mu_{y|x} = A + Bx$
(b) $x_1, x_2, \ldots, x_n$ *are known numbers (nonrandom variables)*
(c) $y_1, y_2, \ldots, y_n$ *are selected randomly* $\qquad$ (8-9)
(d) $\sigma_{y|x}^2 = \sigma^2$
(e) *Each y population is normal*

[which is (8-6) plus normality] or

(a) (x_1,y_1), (x_2,y_2), $\ldots$, (x_n,y_n) *are n randomly selected
    pairs* $\qquad$ (8-10)
(b) *x and y have a bivariate normal distribution*

Tests of hypotheses and confidence intervals are the same for both (8-9) and (8-10).

Perhaps the most interesting tests concern $\mu_{y|x}$, the quantity that we have been estimating.   As in previous situations involving means, we can investigate hypotheses with one-sided and two-sided alternates. To test

H_0: $\mu_{y|x} = \mu_0$ against H_1: $\mu_{y|x} < \mu_0$ $\qquad$ (8-11)
H_0: $\mu_{y|x} = \mu_0$ against H_1: $\mu_{y|x} > \mu_0$ $\qquad$ (8-12)

or

H_0: $\mu_{y|x} = \mu_0$ against H_1: $\mu_{y|x} \neq \mu_0$ $\qquad$ (8-13)

for a given x, say x_0, we use

$$t_{n-2} = \frac{a + bx_0 - \mu_0}{s_{y|x} \sqrt{\dfrac{1}{n} + \dfrac{(x_0 - \bar{x})^2}{\displaystyle\sum_{i=1}^{n} x_i^2 - n\bar{x}^2}}} \qquad (8\text{-}14)$$

and reject when t_{n-2} is small with (8-11) or large with (8-12) and when t_{n-2} is either small or large with (8-13), the latter critical region being chosen symmetrically as is usual with t tests.   Thus, for tests with significance level α, reject when $t_{n-2} < t_{n-2;\alpha}$, $t_{n-2} > t_{n-2;1-\alpha}$, and $t_{n-2} < t_{n-2;\alpha/2}$ or $t_{n-2} > t_{n-2;1-\alpha/2}$, respectively, for the three situations. The statistic given by (8-14) has a t distribution with $n-2$ degrees of freedom if either (8-9) or (8-10) is satisfied and H_0 is true. Power calculations are performed in the usual manner with t tests by using

$$\delta = \frac{|\mu_0 - \mu_1|}{\sigma \sqrt{1/n + \dfrac{(x_0 - \bar{x})^2}{\displaystyle\sum_{i=1}^{n} x_i^2 - n\bar{x}^2}}} \tag{8-15}$$

when we seek the probability of rejecting H_0 if $\mu_{y|x} = \mu_1$, where μ_1 falls in the range of the alternative H_1. Thus we see that power depends on the given (or selected) set of x's, $x_1, \ldots, x_n$ unless we make $x_0 = \bar{x}$ (which we can do if we select the x's). In addition, $x_0 = \bar{x}$ produces the largest δ, and hence the largest power, since the denominator of δ is then smaller than for any other choice of x_0.

To obtain a confidence interval with coefficient $1 - \alpha$ for $\mu_{y|x}$ when $x = x_0$, we start with

$$\Pr\left(-t_{n-2;\,1-\alpha/2} < \frac{a + bx_0 - \mu_{y|x}}{s_{y|x}\sqrt{\dfrac{1}{n} + \dfrac{(x_0 - \bar{x})^2}{\displaystyle\sum_{i=1}^{n} x_i^2 - n\bar{x}^2}}} < t_{n-2;\,1-\alpha/2}\right) = 1 - \alpha \tag{8-16}$$

The usual manipulation with the inequalities converts (8-16) to

$$\Pr\left(a + bx_0 - t_{n-2;\,1-\alpha/2}s_{y|x}\sqrt{\dfrac{1}{n} + \dfrac{(x_0 - \bar{x})^2}{\displaystyle\sum_{i=1}^{n} x_i^2 - n\bar{x}^2}} < \mu_{y|x}\right.$$
$$\left. < a + bx_0 + t_{n-2;\,1-\alpha/2}s_{y|x}\sqrt{\dfrac{1}{n} + \dfrac{(x_0 - \bar{x})^2}{\displaystyle\sum_{i=1}^{n} x_i^2 - n\bar{x}^2}}\right) = 1 - \alpha \tag{8-17}$$

The probability statement (8-17) has to be interpreted in the usual way for confidence intervals. The interval of (8-17) covers a value $\mu_{y|x} = \mu_0$ if, and only if, the test of (8-13) accepts H_0 when the same α is used.

EXAMPLE 8-2

Suppose that a 2.0 college grade point is required for graduation. Using the grade-point data of Example 8-1, test a hypothesis which, if rejected, would indicate that the average college grade point is less than 2.0 for students whose high school grade point is 2.0.

234

Solution

We shall follow the six-step outline.

1 We test H_0: $\mu_{y|x} = 2.0$ against H_1: $\mu_{y|x} < 2.0$ with $x = 2.0$.
2 Select $\alpha = .05$, an arbitrary choice.
3 The statistic we use is (8-14) with $n = 5$, $x_0 = 2.0$. If H_0 is true, then (8-14) has a t distribution with three degrees of freedom provided (*a*) the regression curve is linear, (*b*) the x's are selected numbers (which they were), (*c*) the y's are selected randomly (which they were), (*d*) the variance of each y population is the same for each selected x, and (*e*) each y population is normal. Of course, we cannot be sure that (*a*), (*d*), and (*e*) are satisfied, but the assumptions are not too unreasonable.
4 The critical region is $t_3 < t_{3;.05} = -2.353$.
5 Computations: From Example 8-1 we have $a = .49$, $b = .72$, $s_{y|x} = .35$, $\sum_{i=1}^{5} x_i^2 - 5\bar{x}^2 = 2.50$, $\bar{x} = 3.0$. Thus

$$a + bx_0 = .49 + .72(2.0) = 1.93$$

and the observed value of statistic is

$$t_3 = \frac{1.93 - 2.0}{.35\sqrt{\tfrac{1}{5} + (2.0 - 3.0)^2/2.50}}$$
$$= \frac{-.07}{.35\sqrt{.60}} = \frac{-.07}{(.35)(.77)} = \frac{-.07}{.27} = -.26$$

6 We do not reject H_0. Thus this small sample does not indicate that the average college point is less than 2.0 for students whose high school average is 2.0.

EXAMPLE 8-3

In Example 8-2 find the power of the test if the true average college point is σ units below 2.0 when $x_0 = 2.0$.

Solution

$\mu_0 = 2.0$, $\mu_1 = 2.0 - \sigma$, $|\mu_0 - \mu_1| = \sigma$. Thus $\delta = \sigma/\sigma(.77) = 1.30$. Turning to Appendix D-10 with $\alpha = .05$, $f = 3$, we find that the power is .26. Of course, we expect to get low power with small n.

EXAMPLE 8-4

Using the grade-point data of Example 8-1, find a confidence interval with coefficient .95 for $\mu_{y|x}$ if $x = 3.5$.

Solution

We have $a + bx_0 = .49 + .72(3.5) = 3.01$,

$$s_{y|x} \sqrt{\frac{1}{n} + \frac{(x_0 - \bar{x})^2}{\sum\limits_{i=1}^{n} x_i^2 - n\bar{x}^2}} = .35 \sqrt{\frac{1}{5} + \frac{(3.5 - 3.0)^2}{2.50}} = .35 \sqrt{.3} = .19$$

$t_{3;.975} = 3.182$. Therefore the interval is $[3.01 - 3.182(.19), 3.01 + 3.182(.19)] = (3.01 - .60, 3.01 + .60)$ or $(2.41, 3.61)$.

Sometimes inferences concerning B are of interest. This parameter is the slope of the regression line or the rate of increase of $\mu_{y|x}$ divided by the rate of increase of x. Although we can test

$$H_0: B = B_0 \text{ against } H_1: B < B_0 \tag{8-18}$$
$$H_0: B = B_0 \text{ against } H_1: B > B_0 \tag{8-19}$$

or

$$H_0: B = B_0 \text{ against } H_1: B \neq B_0 \tag{8-20}$$

for any value B_0, the most useful case is (8-20) with $B_0 = 0$. If B is zero, this implies that $\mu_{y|x}$ is the same for all x or that the x variable is of no assistance in predicting the y variable. If $B = 2$, then $\mu_{y|x}$ increases 2 units when x is increased 1 unit. The statistic to use for testing hypotheses (8-18) to (8-20) is

$$t_{n-2} = \frac{b - B_0}{s_{y|x}} \sqrt{\sum_{i=1}^{n} x_i^2 - n\bar{x}^2} \tag{8-21}$$

rejecting when t_{n-2} is small in the first situation, large in the second, and either small or large in the third. For power calculations we use

$$\delta = \frac{|B_0 - B_1| \sqrt{\sum\limits_{i=1}^{n} x_i^2 - n\bar{x}^2}}{\sigma} \tag{8-22}$$

when we seek the probability of rejecting H_0 if $B = B_1$.

A confidence interval with coefficient $1 - \alpha$ for B is obtained by converting

$$\Pr\left(-t_{n-2;1-\alpha/2} < \frac{b - B}{s_{y|x}} \sqrt{\sum_{i=1}^{n} x_i^2 - n\bar{x}^2} < t_{n-2;1-\alpha/2}\right) = 1 - \alpha \tag{8-23}$$

236

to

$$\text{Pr}\left(b - \frac{t_{n-2;\,1-\alpha/2}S_{y|x}}{\sqrt{\sum\limits_{i=1}^{n} x_i^2 - n\bar{x}^2}} < B < b + \frac{t_{n-2;\,1-\alpha/2}S_{y|x}}{\sqrt{\sum\limits_{i=1}^{n} x_i^2 - n\bar{x}^2}}\right) = 1 - \alpha \quad (8\text{-}24)$$

The usual comments about interpretation of a statement like (8-24) and relation to the test of (8-20) still apply.

EXAMPLE 8-5

For the data of Example 8-1 test the hypothesis $B = 0$ against $B \neq 0$.

Solution

We shall follow the six-step outline.

1   We test H_0: $B = 0$ against H_1: $B \neq 0$.
2   Select $\alpha = .05$, an arbitrary choice.
3   The statistic we use is (8-21) with $n = 5$, $B = 0$.   If the hypothesis is true, then (8-21) has a t distribution with three degrees of freedom provided the five conditions discussed in step 3 of Example 8-2 are satisfied.
4   The critical region is $t_3 < t_{3;\,.025} = -3.182$, and $t_3 > t_{3;\,.975} = 3.182$.
5   Computations: From Example 8-1 we have $b = .72$, $s_{y|x} = .35$, $\sum\limits_{i=1}^{n} x_i^2 - n\bar{x}^2 = 2.50$.   Thus the observed value of the statistic is

$$t_3 = \frac{.72 - 0}{.35}\sqrt{2.50} = (2.06)(1.58) = 3.25$$

6   We reject the hypothesis that the slope of the regression line is 0 and conclude that the x variable helps to predict $\mu_{y|x}$.

EXAMPLE 8-6

Find the power of the test used in Example 8-5 if $B = 2\sigma$.

Solution

$$\delta = \frac{|0 - 2\sigma|\sqrt{2.50}}{\sigma} = 2\sqrt{2.50} = 2(1.58) = 3.16$$

Since the alternative was two-sided, we enter Appendix D-10 with $\alpha = .025$.   With $f = 3$ we find a power of approximately .56.

EXAMPLE 8-7

Using the grade-point data of Example 8-1, find a confidence interval with coefficient .95 for B.

Solution

Since $b = .72$, $t_{3;.975} = 3.182$, $s_{y|x} = .35$, $\sum_{i=1}^{5} x_i^2 - 5\bar{x}^2 = 2.50$, the interval is

$$\left(.72 - \frac{(3.182)(.35)}{\sqrt{2.50}}, .72 + \frac{(3.182)(.35)}{\sqrt{2.50}}\right)$$

or $(.72 - .70, .72 + .70)$, which reduces to $(.02, 1.42)$. Thus we infer that $\mu_{y|x}$ increases somewhere between .02 and 1.42 units when x increases 1 unit.

Another useful t random variable is

$$t_{n-2} = \frac{y - (a + bx_0)}{s_{y|x}\sqrt{1 + \frac{1}{n} + \frac{(x_0 - \bar{x})^2}{\sum_{i=1}^{n} x_i^2 - n\bar{x}^2}}} \tag{8-25}$$

which can be used to make probability statements about or obtain confidence intervals for a randomly drawn y associated with the population corresponding to $x = x_0$. If either conditions (8-9) or (8-10) are satisfied, then (8-25) has a t distribution with $n - 2$ degrees of freedom. Since

$$\Pr\left(-t_{n-2;\,1-\alpha/2} < \frac{y - (a + bx_0)}{s_{y|x}\sqrt{1 + \frac{1}{n} + \frac{(x_0 - \bar{x})^2}{\sum_{i=1}^{n} x_i^2 - n\bar{x}^2}}} < t_{n-2;\,1-\alpha/2}\right)$$

$$= 1 - \alpha \tag{8-26}$$

is equivalent to

$$\Pr\left(a + bx_0 - t_{n-2;\,1-\alpha/2}s_{y|x}\sqrt{1 + \frac{1}{n} + \frac{(x_0 - \bar{x})^2}{\sum_{i=1}^{n} x_i^2 - n\bar{x}^2}}\right.$$

$$\left. < y < a + bx_0 + t_{n-2;\,1-\alpha/2}s_{y|x}\sqrt{1 + \frac{1}{n} + \frac{(x_0 - \bar{x})^2}{\sum_{i=1}^{n} x_i^2 - n\bar{x}^2}}\right)$$

$$= 1 - \alpha \tag{8-27}$$

(8-27) provides a confidence interval for y.

238

EXAMPLE 8-8

Use the grade-point data of Example 8-1 to find the probability that a randomly selected student from the population whose high school grade point was 2.4 maintains a college grade point above 2.00.

Solution

We want $\Pr(y > 2.00)$, where y comes from the population with $x_0 = 2.4$. To evaluate the probability, we must convert $\Pr(y > 2.00)$ to the form of (8-25). From Example 8-1 we have $a + bx_0 = 2.22$, $s_{y|x} = .35$, $\bar{x} = 3.0$, $\sum_{i=1}^{n} x_i^2 - 5\bar{x}^2 = 2.50$. We need

$$\sqrt{1 + \frac{1}{n} + \frac{(x_0 - \bar{x})^2}{\sum_{i=1}^{n} x_i^2 - n\bar{x}^2}} = \sqrt{1 + \frac{1}{5} + \frac{(2.4 - 3.0)^2}{2.50}} = \sqrt{1.344} = 1.16$$

Thus

$$\Pr(y > 2.00) = \Pr\left(\frac{y - 2.22}{.35(1.16)} > \frac{2.00 - 2.22}{.35(1.16)}\right)$$
$$= \Pr(t_3 > -.54)$$

Appendix D-6 yields

$$\Pr(t_3 > -.277) = .60 \qquad \Pr(t_3 > -.584) = .70$$

Thus $\Pr(t_3 > -.54)$ is between .60 and .70. Crude interpolation gives about .69. Hence, about 69 per cent of the students whose high school average is 2.4 will maintain a 2.00 average or above in college.

EXAMPLE 8-9

Use the data of Example 8-1 to find a confidence interval with coefficient .95 for an individual grade drawn at random from the population whose high school average is 2.4.

Solution

We have $t_{3;.975} = 3.182$, $a + bx_0 = 2.22$, $s_{y|x} = .35$, and

$$\sqrt{1 + \frac{1}{5} + \frac{(2.4 - 3.0)^2}{2.50}} = 1.16$$

Thus, the interval from (8-27) is $[2.22 - (3.182)(.35)(1.16), 2.22 + (3.182)(.35)(1.16)]$, which reduces to $(2.22 - 1.29, 2.22 + 1.29)$ or $(.93, 3.51)$. The interval is wide because n is small.

Inferences concerning A, which is the value of $\mu_{y|x}$ if $x = 0$, can be handled as a special case of problems associated with (8-14). Inferences about $\sigma_{y|x}^2$ are handled according to the procedures of Sec. 5-7 after replacing (5-35) by

$$\chi_{n-2}^2 = \frac{(n-2)s_{y|x}^2}{\sigma_{y|x}^2} \tag{8-28}$$

The random variable (8-28) has a chi-square distribution with $n - 2$ degrees of freedom if the true value of $\sigma_{y|x}^2$ is used in the denominator and either conditions (8-9) or (8-10) are satisfied.

EXERCISES

8-3 Rework Example 8-2 with the data of Exercise 8-1 (instead of Example 8-1).

8-4 Use the grade-point data of Exercise 8-1 to find a confidence interval with coefficient .95 for $\mu_{y|x}$ if $x = 3.5$.

8-5 Find the power of the test used in Exercise 8-3 if the true average college grade point is σ units below 2.0 when $x_0 = 2.0$.

8-6 Use the data of Exercise 8-1 to test the hypothesis $B = 0$ against $B \neq 0$.

8-7 Find the power of the test used in Exercise 8-6 if $B = .5\sigma$.

8-8 Use the grade-point data of Exercise 8-1 to find a confidence interval with coefficient .95 for B.

8-9 Use the grade-point data of Exercise 8-1 to find the probability that a randomly selected student from the population whose high school grade point was 2.4 maintains a college grade point of above 2.00.

8-10 Use the grade-point data of Exercise 8-1 to find a confidence interval with coefficient .95 for an individual grade drawn at random from the population whose high school grade average is 2.4.

8-11 With $\alpha = .05$ and the data of Exercise 8-1 test $H_0: \sigma_{y|x}^2 = .25$ against $H_1: \sigma_{y|x}^2 < .25$.

8-12 With the data of Exercise 8-2 find the probability that more than 17,000 man-hours will be required to fill orders arriving if the mail on hand at 7 A.M. is 700 pounds.

In Sec. 8-3 we observed that the density function of the bivariate normal distribution contains a parameter ρ, called the correlation coefficient, which can be considered as a measure of relationship between x and y. It can be shown

1 $-1 \leqq \rho \leqq 1$, that is, ρ must be between -1 and $+1$.

2   When x and y have a bivariate normal distribution, x and y are independent if, and only if, $\rho = 0$.

3   If $\rho = -1$ or $\rho = +1$, then all points (x,y) lie on the regression line.

4   The distribution of y for any given x is closely concentrated about the regression line (that is, y has small variance) if ρ is close to -1 or $+1$. The variance $\sigma_{y|x}^2$ is largest if $\rho = 0$. The further ρ is from 0, the smaller the variance of y for a given x. When $\rho = +1$ or -1, the variance $\sigma_{y|x}^2$ is zero.

5   If ρ is positive, then the regression line upon which the $\mu_{y|x}$ lies has a positive slope. Thus, as x is increased, so is $\mu_{y|x}$; and the larger the value of x, the larger an individual y tends to be. If ρ is negative, then the regression line has a negative slope and $\mu_{y|x}$ decreases as x increases. Of course, similar statements can be made concerning the line containing the $\mu_{x|y}$.

Thus in the bivariate normal situation ρ can be regarded as a measure of relationship in the sense that it is an indicator of the closeness of concentration about the regression line for the distribution of y given x. When $\rho = 0$, we regard x and y as being completely unrelated. Knowledge of one of the variables is of no help in describing the behavior of the other. On the other hand, when $\rho = +1$ or -1, we regard x and y as being perfectly related. How one looks upon other values of ρ depends upon the field of application and the accumulated experience of many research workers in that field.

    The parameter ρ, like other parameters we have considered, can be given in the form of an expected value. It can be shown with (8-7) that

$$\rho = E\left(\frac{x - \mu_x}{\sigma_x}\right)\left(\frac{y - \mu_y}{\sigma_y}\right) \tag{8-29}$$

If (x_1,y_1), (x_2,y_2), . . . , (x_n,y_n) is a random sample of pairs drawn from a bivariate normal population, then ρ is estimated by

$$r = \frac{1}{n-1} \sum_{i=1}^{n} \left(\frac{x_i - \bar{x}}{s_x}\right)\left(\frac{y_i - \bar{y}}{s_y}\right) \tag{8-30}$$

which easily reduces to the computational form

$$r = \frac{\sum\limits_{i=1}^{n} x_i y_i - n\bar{x}\bar{y}}{\sqrt{\left(\sum\limits_{i=1}^{n} x_i^2 - n\bar{x}^2\right)\left(\sum\limits_{i=1}^{n} y_i^2 - n\bar{y}^2\right)}} \qquad (8\text{-}31)$$

The quantities s_x and s_y are the sample standard deviations of the x's and y's, respectively. Like ρ, r must be between -1 and $+1$.

The most useful hypothesis-testing situation arises from consideration of

$$H_0: \rho = 0 \text{ against } H_1: \rho \neq 0 \qquad (8\text{-}32)$$

The statistic used is

$$t_{n-2} = \frac{r\sqrt{n-2}}{\sqrt{1-r^2}} \qquad (8\text{-}33)$$

which has a t distribution with $n-2$ degrees of freedom when the hypothesis is true and (a) (x_1,y_1), (x_2,y_2), . . . , (x_n,y_n) is a random sample of n pairs and (b) the pairs are drawn from a bivariate normal distribution. A test with significance level α is obtained by rejecting when

$$\frac{r\sqrt{n-2}}{\sqrt{1-r^2}} < t_{n-2;\alpha/2} \quad \text{and} \quad \frac{r\sqrt{n-2}}{\sqrt{1-r^2}} > t_{n-2;1-\alpha/2} \qquad (8\text{-}34)$$

Special tables or graphs would be needed to compute the power of the test. The actual numerical calculations in terms of the x_i's and the y_i's using (8-33) and (8-34) for testing (8-32) are exactly the same as the ones performed when testing $H_0: B = 0$ against $H_1: B \neq 0$. We would, of course, expect that there would be no relationship between x and y if knowledge of one variable is of no help for drawing inferences about the other.

The random variable (8-33) can also be used for testing

$$H_0: \rho = 0 \text{ against } H_1: \rho < 0 \qquad (8\text{-}35)$$

and

$$H_0: \rho = 0 \text{ against } H_1: \rho > 0 \qquad (8\text{-}36)$$

rejecting when t_{n-2} is small in the first case, large in the second.

242

EXAMPLE 8-10

Eleven students are selected at random from those who have completed both the first course in English and the first course in physical education. Their final grades (in percentages) are (67,92), (81,65), (65,81), (42,75), (53,85), (40,78), (71,77), (64,79), (60,81), (68,82), (49,85), where the first number in each pair is the English grade and the second the physical education grade, both grades in a pair belonging to the same student. Assuming that the pairs of grades are drawn from a bivariate normal population, test the hypothesis that a student's English grade is independent of his physical education grade.

Solution

We shall follow the six-step outline.

1 To test independence, or no relationship, for data drawn from a bivariate normal distribution, we choose between H_0: $\rho = 0$ and H_1: $\rho \neq 0$.

2 Select $\alpha = .05$, an arbitrary choice.

3 The statistic we use is given by (8-33). This random variable has a t distribution with $n - 2 = 9$ degrees of freedom when H_0 is true provided (a) the pairs are drawn randomly and (b) the pairs come from a bivariate normal distribution. We are given that both assumptions are satisfied. The second assumption is reasonable in the case of grade data.

4 The critical region is $t_9 < t_{9;.025} = -2.262$, $t_9 > t_{9;.975} = 2.262$.

5 Computations: First we need r and r^2. Letting the English grade be the x_i's and the physical education grades be the y_i's, we have

$$\bar{x} = \frac{67 + 81 + \cdots + 49}{11} = 60$$

$$\bar{y} = \frac{92 + 65 + \cdots + 85}{11} = 80$$

$$\sum_{i=1}^{11} x_i^2 = 67^2 + 81^2 + \cdots + 49^2 = 41{,}210$$

$$\sum_{i=1}^{11} y_i^2 = 92^2 + 65^2 + \cdots + 85^2 = 70{,}864$$

$$\sum_{i=1}^{11} x_i y_i = (67)(92) + (81)(65) + \cdots + (49)(85) = 52{,}593$$

$$r = \frac{52{,}593 - 11(60)(80)}{\sqrt{[41{,}210 - 11(60)^2][70{,}864 - 11(80)^2]}}$$

$$= \frac{-207}{\sqrt{(1610)(464)}} = \frac{-207}{\sqrt{747{,}040}} = \frac{-207}{864.5} = -.239$$

$$r^2 = .057, \quad \sqrt{1 - r^2} = \sqrt{.943} = .971$$

The observed value of t is

$$t_9 = \frac{(-.239)(3)}{.971} = -.74$$

6   We accept the hypothesis of independence and conclude that there is no relationship between English and physical education grades.

Sometimes an experimenter may wish to test hypotheses about ρ other than ones specifying $\rho = 0$. The three situations corresponding to (8-32), (8-35), and (8-36) are respectively

$H_0: \rho = \rho_0$ against $H_1: \rho \neq \rho_0$ (8-37)
$H_0: \rho = \rho_0$ against $H_1: \rho < \rho_0$ (8-38)

and

$H_0: \rho = \rho_0$ against $H_1: \rho > \rho_0$ (8-39)

When $3 \leq n \leq 25$, special tables prepared by David [1]† can be used to obtain critical regions and evaluate power. If n is at least 25, the approximate procedure which we are about to describe will be adequate in most practical situations.

It is known that

$$Z' = (z_r - z_\rho) \sqrt{n - 3} \qquad\qquad\qquad (8\text{-}40)$$

where z_r and z_ρ are read from Appendix D-18, is approximately normally distributed if r is computed from a random sample of pairs drawn from a bivariate normal population with correlation coefficient ρ. If r (or ρ) is negative, $z_r = -z_{-r}$. Thus, for example,

$$z_{-.50} = -z_{.50} = -.5493$$

The critical regions associated with (8-37) to (8-39) are respectively

$Z' < Z_{\alpha/2}$ and $Z' > Z_{1-\alpha/2}$ (8-41)
$Z' < Z_\alpha$ (8-42)

and

$$Z' > Z_{1-\alpha} \qquad\qquad\qquad\qquad\qquad (8\text{-}43)$$

for tests with significance level α. Approximate power can be calculated in the usual way for tests based upon the Z distribution. We use

† Numbers in brackets are those of references listed at the end of the chapter.

the $f = \infty$ curves of Appendix D-10 with

$$\delta = |z_{\rho_0} - z_{\rho_1}| \sqrt{n - 3} \tag{8-44}$$

where ρ_0 is specified by H_0 and ρ_1 is some value of ρ in the range of the alternative.

EXAMPLE 8-11

College entrance examinations include a section which supposedly tests mathematical ability. After students enroll in freshman mathematics, the mathematics department gives another examination to determine which of several levels is the proper one for each individual student. Suppose that testing experts have decided that if it can be proved that $\rho > .5$, then it is a waste of time to give the second examination. That is, results from the entrance examination might just as well be used for the determination of levels. From past records of students who have taken both examinations, a random sample of 103 is selected and it found that $r = .63$. What conclusion can be drawn?

Solution

We shall follow the six-step outline.

1 We shall test H_0: $\rho = .50$ against H_1: $\rho > .50$. If H_0 is rejected, this will be regarded as "proof" that $\rho > .50$.
2 Select $\alpha = .05$, an arbitrary choice.
3 The statistic we shall use is (8-40) with $\rho = .50$. If H_0 is true, Z' is approximately normally distributed provided (*a*) the students are selected randomly (which is given) and (*b*) the pairs of scores have a bivariate normal distribution (which is fairly reasonable).
4 The critical region is $Z' > Z_{.95} = 1.645$.
5 Computations: With $r = .63$, $\rho = .50$ we find, in Appendix D-18, $z_r = z_{.63} = .7414$, $z_\rho = z_{.50} = .5493$. Thus the observed value of Z' is $Z' = (.7414 - .5493) \sqrt{103 - 3} = 1.921$.
6 We reject H_0 and conclude that the extra test is unnecessary.

EXAMPLE 8-12

Find the power of test used in Example 8-11 if the actual value of ρ is .60. If the actual value of ρ is .70.

Solution

In the first case

$$\delta = |z_{.50} - z_{.60}|(10) = |.5493 - .6931|(10)$$
$$= 1.438$$

Turning to the page of Appendix D-10 headed by $\alpha = .05$ we read a power of about .43 from the $f = \infty$ curve.

In the second case

$$\delta = |z_{.50} - z_{.70}|(10) = |.5493 - .8673|(10) = 3.180$$

and the power is approximately .94.

Appendix D-19 contains graphs from which a confidence interval for ρ can be obtained. Specifically, we can find two numbers ρ_L and ρ_U such that

$$\Pr(\rho_L < \rho < \rho_U) = 1 - \alpha \tag{8-45}$$

for $\alpha = .05, .10$. The publication [1] from which these graphs were taken also includes curves for $\alpha = .02, .01$. The probability statement (8-45) must be interpreted in the usual way for a confidence interval. To use the graphs, we need to know r, n, and α. Let us illustrate by an example.

EXAMPLE 8-13

Find a confidence interval with coefficient .95 for the correlation coefficient in the bivariate normal situation encountered in Example 8-10.

Solution

We had $n = 11$, $r = -.24$ (rounded to two significant figures). Turn to the set of graphs in Appendix D-19 headed by confidence coefficient .95. The horizontal scale is the r scale. Imagine a vertical line through $r = -.24$ and two curves labeled 11 about halfway between the ones labeled 10 and 12. The imaginary line crosses the two imaginary curves at $\rho_L = -.71$, $\rho_U = .40$ (approximately), which are read from the vertical scale on the left. Hence $(-.71, .40)$ is the desired interval.

EXAMPLE 8-14

Find a confidence interval with coefficient .95 for the correlation coefficient in the bivariate normal situation encountered in Example 8-11.

Solution

We had $n = 103$, $r = .63$. Again we turn to the set of graphs in Appendix D-19 headed by confidence coefficient .95. Since there is

246

no curve for $n = 103$, we shall use the curve for $n = 100$, the difference being so slight that interpolation is unnecessary. The vertical line through $r = .63$ crosses the two $n = 100$ curves at $\rho_L = .49$, $\rho_U = .73$ (approximately). Hence the desired interval is $(.49, .73)$.

The graphs of Appendix D-19 can be used to obtain critical regions (but not power) for two-sided tests with significance level $\alpha = .05, .10$ and one-sided tests with significance levels $\alpha = .025, .05$. We enter the vertical scale with the value of ρ specified by the hypothesis and read off the r's which form the boundaries of the critical region on the horizontal scale. Let us illustrate by examples.

EXAMPLE 8-15

Use Appendix D-19 to find the critical region in terms of r for Example 8-10.

Solution

Since the hypothesis specifies that $\rho = 0$, we use the t test and find that for $\alpha = .05$, H_0 is rejected if $t_9 < -2.262$, $t_9 > 2.262$. The critical region can also be given in terms of r. Turning to the graphs of Appendix D-19 headed by $\alpha = .05$, we find that the horizontal line through $\rho = 0$ crosses the imaginary curves for $n = 11$ at approximately $r = -.60$ and $r = .60$. Thus the critical region in terms of r is $r < -.60$ and $r > .60$. That is, if $\rho = 0$, $n = 11$,

$$\Pr(r < -.60) + \Pr(r > .60) = .025 + .025 = .05$$

Since $r = -.239$, H_0 is accepted.

EXAMPLE 8-16

Use Appendix D-19 to find the critical region for Example 8-11 in terms of r.

Solution

Turning to the graph of Appendix D-19 headed by $\alpha = .10$ (double the significance level of the test for one-sided critical regions), we find that the curves for $n = 100$ (used in place of $n = 103$) cross $\rho = .5$ above $r = .37$ and $r = .62$. The critical region for testing $H_0: \rho = .5$ against $H_1: \rho > .5$ is $r > .62$ and $\Pr(r > .62) = .05$ if $\rho = .5$, $n = 100$. [The critical region $r < .37$ is used for testing $H_0: \rho = .5$ against $H_1: \rho < .5$ and $\Pr(r < .37) = .05$ if $\rho = .5$, $n = 100$.]

Since n is large, the approximate procedure is better because power can be readily calculated.

♦ 8-13   Eighteen students are selected at random from those who have completed elementary statistics. The first number in each of the following pairs is a midterm grade, and the second is the final-examination grade for the same student: (54,48), (44,64), (31,38), (32,33), (36,29). (34,41), (53,59), (34,45), (12,17), (48,28), (36,40), (51,44), (50,63), (44,38), (39,49), (44,57), (52,49), (39,34). Assuming that the pairs of grades have a bivariate normal distribution, test the hypothesis that midterm and final-examination grades are independent. Use the t test and follow the six-step outline with $\alpha = .05$.

♦ 8-14   Use the graphs of Appendix D-19 to find the critical region in Exercise 8-13 in terms of r.

♦ 8-15   Find a confidence interval with coefficient .95 for the correlation coefficient in the bivariate normal situation encountered in Exercise 8-13. What is the relation between the confidence interval and the test of Exercise 8-13?

8-16   An instructor claims that the correlation coefficient between his midterm and final-examination grades is at least .6. A random sample of 403 past records yields $r = .54$. With $\alpha = .05$ and by following the six-step outline, test the appropriate hypothesis.

8-17   With the test used in Exercise 8-16, what is the power if $\rho = .50$?

8-18   Based upon the sample result of Exercise 8-16, find a confidence interval with coefficient .95 for the correlation coefficient.

REFERENCES

1   DAVID, F. N.: "Tables of the Ordinates and Probability Integral of the Distribution of the Correlation Coefficient in Small Samples," The Biometrika Office, London, 1938.

SUMMARY OF RESULTS: DRAWING INFERENCES IN CORRELATION AND REGRESSION

I. Inferences concerning the mean of y for a given x, $\mu_{y|x}$

   A. Standard hypotheses, alternatives, statistics, and critical regions (significance level α)

Hypothesis	Alternative	Statistic*	Critical region
$H_0: \mu_{y\|x} = \mu_0$	$H_1: \mu_{y\|x} < \mu_0$	t_{n-2}	$t_{n-2} < t_{n-2;\,\alpha}$
$H_0: \mu_{y\|x} \geqq \mu_0$	$H_1: \mu_{y\|x} < \mu_0$	$= \dfrac{a + bx_0 - \mu_0}{s_{y\|x}\sqrt{\dfrac{1}{n} + \dfrac{(x_0 - \bar{x})^2}{\displaystyle\sum_{i=1}^{n} x_i^2 - n\bar{x}^2}}}$	$t_{n-2} < t_{n-2;\,\alpha}$
$H_0: \mu_{y\|x} = \mu_0$	$H_1: \mu_{y\|x} > \mu_0$		$t_{n-2} > t_{n-2;\,1-\alpha}$
$H_0: \mu_{y\|x} \leqq \mu_0$	$H_1: \mu_{y\|x} > \mu_0$		$t_{n-2} > t_{n-2;\,1-\alpha}$
$H_0: \mu_{y\|x} = \mu_0$	$H_1: \mu_{y\|x} \neq \mu_0$		$t_{n-2} < t_{n-2;\,\alpha/2}$, $t_{n-2} > t_{n-2;\,1-\alpha/2}$

* Note that whenever a statistic is given in this summary, certain assumptions are made. These assumptions, giving the statistic the required distribution, may be found in the text material.

   B. Power calculations

      1. Use Appendix D-10 in the usual way with entries α ($\alpha/2$ for two-sided alternatives), $f = n - 2$,

$$\delta = \frac{|\mu_0 - \mu_1|}{\sigma\sqrt{\dfrac{1}{n} + \dfrac{(x_0 - \bar{x})^2}{\displaystyle\sum_{i=1}^{n} x_i^2 - n\bar{x}^2}}}$$

   C. Two-sided confidence interval with coefficient α

$$\left(a + bx_0 - t_{n-2;\,1-\alpha/2}s_{y|x}\sqrt{\frac{1}{n} + \frac{(x_0 - \bar{x})^2}{\displaystyle\sum_{i=1}^{n} x_i^2 - n\bar{x}^2}}, \right.$$

$$\left. a + bx_0 + t_{n-2;\,1-\alpha/2}s_{y|x}\sqrt{\frac{1}{n} + \frac{(x_0 - \bar{x})^2}{\displaystyle\sum_{i=1}^{n} x_i^2 - n\bar{x}^2}} \right)$$

II. Inferences concerning the slope of the regression line B

   A. Standard hypotheses, alternatives, statistics, and critical regions (significance level α)

Hypothesis	Alternative	Statistic	Critical regions
$H_0: B = B_0$	$H_1: B < B_0$	t_{n-2}	$t_{n-2} < t_{n-2;\alpha}$
$H_0: B \geqq B_0$	$H_1: B < B_0$	$= \dfrac{b - B_0}{s_{y\|x}}\sqrt{\displaystyle\sum_{i=1}^{n} x_i^2 - n\bar{x}^2}$	$t_{n-2} < t_{n-2;\alpha}$
$H_0: B = B_0$	$H_1: B > B_0$		$t_{n-2} > t_{n-2;1-\alpha}$
$H_0: B \leqq B_0$	$H_1: B > B_0$		$t_{n-2} > t_{n-2;1-\alpha}$
$H_0: B = B_0$	$H_1: B \neq B_0$		$t_{n-2} < t_{n-2;\alpha/2}$, $t_{n-2} > t_{n-2;1-\alpha/2}$

B. Power calculations
   1. Use Appendix D-10 in the usual way with entries α ($\alpha/2$ for two-sided alternatives), $f = n - 2$,

$$\delta = \frac{|B_0 - B_1|}{\sigma} \sqrt{\sum_{i=1}^{n} x_i^2 - n\bar{x}^2}$$

C. Two-sided confidence coefficient with coefficient α

$$\left(b - \frac{t_{n-2;1-\alpha/2} s_{y|x}}{\sqrt{\sum_{i=1}^{n} x_i^2 - n\bar{x}^2}}, \; b + \frac{t_{n-2;1-\alpha/2} s_{y|x}}{\sqrt{\sum_{i=1}^{n} x_i^2 - n\bar{x}^2}} \right)$$

III. Inferences concerning an individual y for a given x, say, x_0
   A. Standard hypotheses, alternatives, statistics, and critical regions (significance level α)

Hypothesis	Alternative	Statistic	Critical region
Hypotheses are inappropriate		$t_{n-2} = \dfrac{y - (a + bx_0)}{s_{y|x} \sqrt{1 + \dfrac{1}{n} + \dfrac{(x_0 - \bar{x})^2}{\sum_{i=1}^{n} x_i^2 - n\bar{x}^2}}}$	

B. Power calculations
   1. Since there are no tests, there are no power calculations.
C. Two-sided confidence interval with coefficient α

$$\left(a + bx_0 - t_{n-2;1-\alpha/2} s_{y|x} \sqrt{1 + \frac{1}{n} + \frac{(x_0 - \bar{x})^2}{\sum_{i=1}^{n} x_i^2 - n\bar{x}^2}}, \right.$$

$$\left. a + bx_0 + t_{n-2;1-\alpha/2} s_{y|x} \sqrt{1 + \frac{1}{n} + \frac{(x_0 - \bar{x})^2}{\sum_{i=1}^{n} x^2 - n\bar{x}^2}} \right)$$

IV. Inferences concerning the variance of y given x, $\sigma_{y|x}^2$. The outline IV of Chap. 5 applies if $n - 1$ is replaced by $n - 2$, s^2 by $s_{y|x}^2$, and σ^2 by $\sigma_{y|x}^2$. The assumptions for the use of the statistic become (8-9) or (8-10).
V. Inferences concerning the correlation coefficient ρ
   A. Standard hypotheses, alternatives, statistics, and critical regions (significance level α)

Hypothesis	Alternative	Statistic	Critical region
$H_0: \rho = \rho_0$	$H_1: \rho < \rho_0$	$t_{n-2} = \dfrac{r\sqrt{n-2}}{\sqrt{1-r^2}}$ if $\rho_0 = 0$	Reject if the appropriate statistic is small (for example, $Z' < Z_\alpha$)
$H_0: \rho \geqq \rho_0$	$H_1: \rho < \rho_0$	$Z' = (z_r - z_\rho)\sqrt{n-3}$ $n > 25$ or	Reject if the appropriate statistic is small (for example, $Z' < Z_\alpha$)
$H_0: \rho = \rho_0$	$H_1: \rho > \rho_0$	r if $\rho_0 \neq 0$ $n \leqq 25$ (and the special tables of David [1] or the graphs of Appendix D-19)	Reject if the appropriate statistic is large (for example, $Z' > Z_{1-\alpha}$)
$H_0: \rho \leqq \rho_0$	$H_1: \rho > \rho_0$		Reject if the appropriate statistic is large (for example, $Z' > Z_{1-\alpha}$)
$H_0: \rho = \rho_0$	$H_1: \rho \neq \rho_0$		Reject if the appropriate statistic is either large or small (for example, $Z' < Z_{\alpha/2}$, $Z' > Z_{1-\alpha/2}$)

B. Power calculations
1. Omitted for first statistic listed in V-A.
2. For the second statistic listed in V-A use Appendix D-10 with entries α ($\alpha/2$ for two-sided alternatives), $f = \infty$, $\delta = |z_{\rho_0} - z_{\rho_1}|\sqrt{n-3}$, where ρ_1 is in the range of ρ specified by the alternative.
3. Omitted for the third statistic listed in V-A but can be found from [1].

C. Two-sided confidence interval with coefficient α
1. Find the (ρ_L, ρ_U) from Appendix D-19. Entries required are α, n, r.

APPENDIXES

Summation Notation

A-1 SINGLE SUMMATION

Summation signs are used to help abbreviate lengthy mathematical expressions.   By definition we have

$$\sum_{i=1}^{n} x_i = x_1 + x_2 + \cdots + x_n \tag{A-1}$$

which is read as "the sum of the x_i, i going from 1 to n."   Each x_i represents a number which may or may not be specifically known later in the discussion.   If n is moderately large, it is obviously much easier to write the left-hand side of (A-1) than to write out the right-hand side, even with the missing x_i's being denoted by $\cdots$.

Write out $\sum_{i=1}^{6} y_i^2$.

Solution

By (A-1) we get a sum of six terms with i taking on the values 1, 2, 3, 4, 5, 6. Thus

$$\sum_{i=1}^{6} y_i^2 = y_1^2 + y_2^2 + y_3^2 + y_4^2 + y_5^2 + y_6^2$$

EXAMPLE A-2

If $x_1 = 3$, $x_2 = 5$, $x_3 = 11$, find $\sum_{i=1}^{3} x_i$, $\left(\sum_{i=1}^{3} x_i \right)^2$, $\sum_{i=1}^{3} x_i^2$.

Solution

$$\sum_{i=1}^{3} x_i = 3 + 5 + 11 = 19 \qquad \left(\sum_{i=1}^{3} x_i \right)^2 = 19^2 = 361$$

$$\sum_{i=1}^{3} x_i^2 = 3^2 + 5^2 + 11^2 = 9 + 25 + 121 = 155$$

Thus, the x_i being known numbers, the summations can be evaluated and yield specific numbers.

EXAMPLE A-3

Write out $\sum_{i=1}^{5} (x_i + y_i)$ and show that it is equivalent to

$$\sum_{i=1}^{5} x_i + \sum_{i=1}^{5} y_i$$

Solution

The definition yields

$$\sum_{i=1}^{5} (x_i + y_i) = (x_1 + y_1) + (x_2 + y_2) + (x_3 + y_3) + (x_4 + y_4)$$
$$+ (x_5 + y_5)$$

But the right-hand side can be rewritten as

$$(x_1 + x_2 + x_3 + x_4 + x_5) + (y_1 + y_2 + y_3 + y_4 + y_5)$$
$$= \sum_{i=1}^{5} x_i + \sum_{i=1}^{5} y_i$$

256

EXAMPLE A-4

Write out $\displaystyle\sum_{i=1}^{4} C$.

Solution

By definition (A-1), we get four terms in the sum. Since there is no subscript to change from term to term, each term is C. Thus

$$\sum_{i=1}^{4} C = C + C + C + C = 4C$$

EXAMPLE A-5

Write out $\displaystyle\sum_{i=1}^{5} x_i y_i$.

Solution

By definition (A-1) we get

$$\sum_{i=1}^{5} x_i y_i = x_1 y_1 + x_2 y_2 + x_3 y_3 + x_4 y_4 + x_5 y_5$$

EXAMPLE A-6

Write out $\displaystyle\sum_{i=1}^{3} (x_i + y_i)^2$.

Solution

Definition (A-1) yields

$$\sum_{i=1}^{3} (x_i + y_i)^2 = (x_1 + y_1)^2 + (x_2 + y_2)^2 + (x_3 + y_3)^2$$

If we so desire, each of three binomial terms can be expanded, giving

$$x_1^2 + 2x_1y_1 + y_1^2 + x_2^2 + 2x_2y_2 + y_2^2 + x_3^2 + 2x_3y_3 + y_3^2$$
$$= (x_1^2 + x_2^2 + x_3^2) + 2(x_1y_1 + x_2y_2 + x_3y_3) + (y_1^2 + y_2^2 + y_3^2)$$
$$= \sum_{i=1}^{3} x_i^2 + 2 \sum_{i=1}^{3} x_i y_i + \sum_{i=1}^{3} y_i^2$$

EXAMPLE A-7

Show that $\displaystyle\sum_{i=1}^{4} 3x_i = 3 \sum_{i=1}^{4} x_i$.

Solution

Definition (A-1) yields

$$\sum_{i=1}^{4} 3x_i = 3x_1 + 3x_2 + 3x_3 + 3x_4$$

$$= 3(x_1 + x_2 + x_3 + x_4)$$

$$= 3 \sum_{i=1}^{4} x_i$$

The preceding examples illustrate three useful theorems. All are proved by using definition (A-1). They are:

THEOREM I

$\sum_{i=1}^{n} C = nC$, where C is any quantity that does not have a summation subscript.

Proof

By definition

$$\sum_{i=1}^{n} C = \underbrace{C + C + \cdots + C}_{n \text{ terms}} = nC$$

THEOREM II

$$\sum_{i=1}^{n} Cx_i = C \sum_{i=1}^{n} x_i$$

Proof

By definition

$$\sum_{i=1}^{n} Cx_i = Cx_1 + Cx_2 + Cx_3 + \cdots + Cx_n$$

$$= C(x_1 + x_2 + \cdots + x_n)$$

$$= C \sum_{i=1}^{n} x_i$$

258

$$\sum_{i=1}^{n} (x_i + y_i - z_i) = \sum_{i=1}^{n} x_i + \sum_{i=1}^{n} y_i - \sum_{i=1}^{n} z_i$$

Proof

By definition

$$\sum_{i=1}^{n} (x_i + y_i - z_i) = (x_1 + y_1 - z_1) + (x_2 + y_2 - z_2)$$
$$+ \cdots + (x_n + y_n - z_n)$$
$$= (x_1 + x_2 + \cdots + x_n) + (y_1 + y_2 + \cdots + y_n)$$
$$- (z_1 + z_2 + \cdots + z_n)$$
$$= \sum_{i=1}^{n} x_i + \sum_{i=1}^{n} y_i - \sum_{i=1}^{n} z_i$$

Theorem III generalizes in the obvious way.

A-2 DOUBLE SUMMATION

Double summation does not require any new concepts. It can be regarded as a single summation on one subscript followed by a single summation on a second subscript. Double, rather than single, summation is used for convenience when working with a two-way table (such as Table 6-2 or Table 7-1).

We can evaluate $\sum_{j=1}^{r} \sum_{i=1}^{n_j} x_{ij}$ by applying definition (A-1) twice. We get

$$\sum_{j=1}^{r} \sum_{i=1}^{n_j} x_{ij} = \sum_{j=1}^{r} (x_{1j} + x_{2j} + x_{3j} + \cdots + x_{n_j j})$$
$$= (x_{11} + x_{21} + \cdots + x_{n_1 1})$$
$$+ (x_{12} + x_{22} + \cdots + x_{n_2 2}) + \cdots$$
$$+ (x_{1r} + x_{2r} + \cdots + x_{n_r r}) \quad (\text{A-2})$$

Thus to evaluate the double sum, we can first sum each column and then sum the r column totals.

EXAMPLE A-8

Evaluate $\sum_{j=1}^{2} \sum_{i=1}^{3} x_{ij}$ and $\sum_{i=1}^{3} \sum_{j=1}^{2} x_{ij}$.

Solution

Using definition (A-1) twice, we get

$$\sum_{j=1}^{2} \sum_{i=1}^{3} x_{ij} = \sum_{j=1}^{2} (x_{1j} + x_{2j} + x_{3j})$$

$$= (x_{11} + x_{21} + x_{31}) + (x_{12} + x_{22} + x_{32})$$

$$\sum_{i=1}^{3} \sum_{j=1}^{2} x_{ij} = \sum_{i=1}^{3} (x_{i1} + x_{i2})$$

$$= (x_{11} + x_{12}) + (x_{21} + x_{22}) + (x_{31} + x_{32})$$

We note

$$\sum_{j=1}^{2} \sum_{i=1}^{3} x_{ij} = \sum_{i=1}^{3} \sum_{j=1}^{2} x_{ij}$$

Example A-8 illustrates the following theorem:

THEOREM IV

$$\sum_{j=1}^{b} \sum_{i=1}^{a} x_{ij} = \sum_{i=1}^{a} \sum_{j=1}^{b} x_{ij}$$

That is, if both limits on the summation signs are constants, then the order of summation may be interchanged.

Proof

The theorem can be proved by following the scheme outlined in Example A-8.

Corresponding to Theorem I, we have

THEOREM V

$$\sum_{j=1}^{r} \sum_{i=1}^{n_j} C = C \sum_{j=1}^{r} n_j = CN$$

Proof

By Theorem I, $\sum_{i=1}^{n_j} C = n_j C$.   Hence

$$\sum_{j=1}^{r} \sum_{i=1}^{n_j} C = \sum_{j=1}^{r} Cn_j$$

$$= C \sum_{j=1}^{r} n_j \qquad \text{by Theorem II}$$

$$= CN \qquad \text{by definition of } N$$

The counterpart of Theorem II is

THEOREM VI

$$\sum_{j=1}^{r} \sum_{i=1}^{n_j} Cx_{ij} = C \sum_{j=1}^{r} \sum_{i=1}^{n_j} x_{ij}$$

a result which follows easily, since C will appear in every term of the sum and can be factored out.

Similar to Theorem II is

THEOREM VII

$$\sum_{j=1}^{r} \sum_{i=1}^{n_j} y_j x_{ij} = \sum_{j=1}^{r} y_j \sum_{j=1}^{n_j} x_{ij}$$

Thus if part of a product which is being summed involves only the outside index of summation, this part can be factored out of the inside summation sign.

Proof

By Theorem II

$$\sum_{i=1}^{n_j} y_j x_{ij} = y_j \sum_{i=1}^{n_j} x_{ij}. \quad \text{Hence the result.}$$

The counterpart of Theorem III is

THEOREM VIII

$$\sum_{j=1}^{r} \sum_{i=1}^{n_j} (x_{ij} + y_{ij} - z_{ij}) = \sum_{j=1}^{r} \sum_{i=1}^{n_j} x_{ij} + \sum_{j=1}^{r} \sum_{i=1}^{n_j} y_{ij} - \sum_{j=1}^{r} \sum_{i=1}^{n_j} z_{ij}$$

Proof

The proof follows easily by expanding the sum as in formula (A-2) followed by regrouping terms.

EXAMPLE A-9

Prove $\sum_{j=1}^{r} \sum_{i=1}^{n_j} (x_{ij} - \bar{x}_{\cdot j}) = 0$, where $\bar{x}_{\cdot j} = \sum_{i=1}^{n_j} x_{ij}/n_j$ as defined in Sec. 7-2.

Solution

$$\sum_{j=1}^{r} \sum_{i=1}^{n_j} (x_{ij} - \bar{x}_{\cdot j}) = \sum_{j=1}^{r} \sum_{i=1}^{n_j} x_{ij} - \sum_{j=1}^{r} \sum_{i=1}^{n_j} \bar{x}_{\cdot j} \qquad \text{by Theorem VIII}$$

and

$$\sum_{j=1}^{r} \sum_{i=1}^{n_j} \bar{x}_{\cdot j} = \sum_{j=1}^{r} n_j \bar{x}_{\cdot j} \qquad \text{by Theorem I}$$

$$= \sum_{j=1}^{r} \sum_{i=1}^{n_j} x_{ij} \qquad \text{by the definition of } \bar{x}_{\cdot j}$$

Consequently

$$\sum_{j=1}^{r} \sum_{i=1}^{n_j} (x_{ij} - \bar{x}_{\cdot j}) = \sum_{j=1}^{r} \sum_{i=1}^{n_j} x_{ij} - \sum_{j=1}^{r} \sum_{i=1}^{n_j} x_{ij} = 0$$

EXAMPLE A-10

Prove

$$\sum_{j=1}^{r} \sum_{i=1}^{n_j} (x_{ij} - \bar{x}_{\cdot\cdot})^2 = \sum_{j=1}^{r} \sum_{i=1}^{n_j} x_{ij}^2 - \frac{T_{\cdot\cdot}^2}{N}$$

where all symbols are as defined in Sec. 7-2.

Solution

$$\sum_{j=1}^{r} \sum_{i=1}^{n_j} (x_{ij} - \bar{x}_{\cdot\cdot})^2 = \sum_{j=1}^{r} \sum_{i=1}^{n_j} (x_{ij}^2 - 2\bar{x}_{\cdot\cdot} x_{ij} + \bar{x}_{\cdot\cdot}^2)$$

$$= \sum_{j=1}^{r} \sum_{i=1}^{n_j} x_{ij}^2 - \sum_{j=1}^{r} \sum_{i=1}^{n_j} 2\bar{x}_{\cdot\cdot} x_{ij} + \sum_{j=1}^{r} \sum_{i=1}^{n_j} \bar{x}_{\cdot\cdot}^2$$

$$\text{by Theorem VIII}$$

But

$$-\sum_{j=1}^{r} \sum_{i=1}^{n_j} 2\bar{x}_{\cdot\cdot} x_{ij} = -2\bar{x}_{\cdot\cdot} \sum_{j=1}^{r} \sum_{i=1}^{n_j} x_{ij} \qquad \text{by Theorem VI}$$

$$= -2 \frac{T_{\cdot\cdot}}{N} T_{\cdot\cdot} = -2 \frac{T_{\cdot\cdot}^2}{N} \qquad \text{by definition of } T_{\cdot\cdot} \text{ and } \bar{x}_{\cdot\cdot}$$

and

$$\sum_{j=1}^{r} \sum_{i=1}^{n_j} \bar{x}_{\cdot\cdot}^2 = N\bar{x}_{\cdot\cdot}^2 \qquad \text{by Theorem V}$$

$$= N \left(\frac{T_{\cdot\cdot}}{N} \right)^2 \qquad \text{by definition of } \bar{x}_{\cdot\cdot}$$

$$= \frac{T_{\cdot\cdot}^2}{N}$$

262

Hence we have

$$\sum_{j=1}^{r} \sum_{i=1}^{n_j} (x_{ij} - \bar{x}..)^2 = \sum_{j=1}^{r} \sum_{i=1}^{n_j} x_{ij}^2 - 2\frac{T_{..}^2}{N} + \frac{T_{..}^2}{N}$$

$$= \sum_{j=1}^{r} \sum_{i=1}^{n_j} x_{ij}^2 - \frac{T_{..}^2}{N}$$

Interpolation

B-1 LINEAR INTERPOLATION

Frequently we try to enter a table or a graph with a number x_1 and hope to read a corresponding entry y_1. Instead of finding x_1, however, we find x_0 and x_2 (with corresponding y_0 and y_2), the two closest entries, where $x_0 < x_1$ and $x_2 > x_1$. The most frequently used method for approximating y_1 (by y_1') is called linear interpolation. The name arises from the assumption that y can be approximately represented by a straight line in a small interval as indicated in Fig. B-1. We take for our estimate $y_1' = y_0 + BE$, where BE can be found by using properties of similar triangles. That is,

$$\frac{BE}{AB} = \frac{CD}{AC}$$

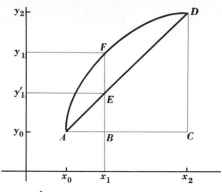

Figure B-1   *Linear interpola-*
tion.

so that

$$\frac{y_1' - y_0}{x_1 - x_0} = \frac{y_2 - y_0}{x_2 - x_0} \tag{B-1}$$

Solving for y_1' yields

$$y_1' = y_0 + \frac{x_1 - x_0}{x_2 - x_0}(y_2 - y_0) \tag{B-2}$$

EXAMPLE B-1

Approximate $t_{33,.975}$.

Solution

Appendix D-6 yields

$x_0 = 30$ $y_0 = t_{30,.975} = 2.042$
$x_1 = 33$ y_1 not given
$x_2 = 40$ $y_2 = t_{40,.975} = 2.021$

Thus

$$y_1' = 2.042 + \frac{33 - 30}{40 - 30}(2.021 - 2.042)$$

$$= 2.042 + \frac{3}{10}(-.021)$$

$$= 2.042 - .006$$

$$= 2.036$$

That is, since x_1 is three-tenths of the way between x_0 and x_2, we take y_1' to be three-tenths of the way between y_0 and y_2.

EXAMPLE B-2

Approximate $\Pr(\chi_{20}^2 < 22.8)$ by using Appendix D-7 and linear interpolation.

265

Solution

Appendix D-7 yields

$x_0 = 12.44$ $y_0 = \Pr(\chi^2_{20} < 12.44) = .10$
$x_1 = 22.8$ y_1 not given
$x_2 = 28.41$ $y_2 = \Pr(\chi^2_{20} < 28.41) = .90$

Thus

$$y_1' = .10 + \frac{22.8 - 12.44}{28.41 - 12.44}\,(.90 - .10)$$

$$= .10 + \frac{10.36}{15.97}\,(.80) = .10 + (.65)(.80)$$

$$= .10 + .52 = .62$$

Since we are interpolating over a relatively long interval, we might expect the approximation to be poor. In fact

$$\Pr(\chi^2_{20} < 22.8) = \Pr(\chi^2_{20}/20 < 1.14)$$
$$= .70 \quad \textit{from Appendix D-8}$$

EXAMPLE B-3

Approximate $F_{4,18;.95}$ by using linear interpolation.

Solution

Appendix D-9 yields

$x_0 = 15$ $y_0 = F_{4,15;.95} = 3.06$
$x_1 = 18$ y_1 not given
$x_2 = 20$ $y_2 = F_{4,20;.95} = 2.87$

Thus

$$y_1' = 3.06 + \frac{18 - 15}{20 - 15}\,(2.87 - 3.06)$$

$$= 3.06 + \tfrac{3}{5}(-.19)$$

$$= 3.06 - .11 = 2.95$$

EXAMPLE B-4

Read the power (entry on vertical scale) from the graphs of Appendix D-10 headed by $\alpha = .01$ if $\delta = 4, f = 15$.

Solution

From the set of graphs we read

$x_0 = 12$ $y_0 = $ power $ = .875$
$x_1 = 15$ y_1 not given
$x_2 = 24$ $y_2 = $ power $ = .925$

Thus

$$y_1' = .875 + \frac{15 - 12}{24 - 12}(.925 - .875)$$
$$= .875 + \tfrac{1}{4}(.050) = .888 \text{ (or .89)}$$

If points E and F in Fig. B-1 are close together, then the approximation will be very good. Of course, the closer the y curve (as represented by arc AFD) is to a straight line, the better the approximation. In most situations which we encounter, the approximation is quite good from a practical point of view, as demonstrated by Examples B-1, B-3, B-4.

B-2 INVERSE LINEAR INTERPOLATION

If $x_2 = \infty$, then Fig. B-1 does not make sense and formulas (B-1) and (B-2) are of no assistance. When this happens, we can invert the x's and proceed with linear interpolation as before, except for using the reciprocals.

EXAMPLE B-5

Approximate the power in Example B-4 if $f = 50$.

Solution

The graphs of Appendix D-10 yield

$x_0 = 24$ $y_0 = \text{power} = .925$
$x_1 = 50$ $y_1 \text{ not given}$
$x_2 = \infty$ $y_2 = \text{power} = .95$

In a practical situation we would probably be satisfied to know that the power is between .925 and .95. However, we shall use inverse linear interpolation to demonstrate the procedure. We have

$$\frac{1}{x_0} = \frac{1}{24} = .042 \qquad y_0 = \text{power} = .925$$

$$\frac{1}{x_1} = \frac{1}{50} = .02 \qquad y_1 \text{ not given}$$

$$\frac{1}{x_2} = 0 \qquad y_2 = \text{power} = .95$$

We use as our estimate

$$y_1' = .925 + \frac{.02 - .042}{0 - .042}(.95 - .925)$$

$$= .925 + \frac{.022}{.042}(.025) = .925 + .52(.025)$$

$$= .925 + .013 \cong .94$$

B-3 DOUBLE LINEAR INTERPOLATION

Linear interpolation can be used on both entries of a double entry table. We shall demonstrate by an example.

EXAMPLE B-6

Approximate $F_{35,52;.95}$ by using linear interpolation.

Solution

Appendix D-9 yields

$$F_{30,40;.95} = 1.74 \qquad F_{30,60;.95} = 1.65$$
$$F_{40,40;.95} = 1.69 \qquad F_{40,60;.95} = 1.59$$

In a practical situation we would probably be satisfied to know that $F_{35,52;.95}$ is between 1.59 and 1.74. However, we shall demonstrate double linear interpolation. First we shall estimate $F_{35,40;.95}$ and $F_{35,60;.95}$. For the former we write

$$x_0 = 30 \qquad y_0 = F_{30,40;.95} = 1.74$$
$$x_1 = 35 \qquad y_1 \text{ not given}$$
$$x_2 = 40 \qquad y_2 = F_{40,40;.95} = 1.69$$

and

$$y_1' = 1.74 + \frac{35 - 30}{40 - 30}(1.69 - 1.74)$$
$$= 1.74 + \tfrac{1}{2}(-.05) = 1.72$$

For the latter we get

$$x_0 = 30 \qquad y_0 = F_{30,60;.95} = 1.65$$
$$x_1 = 35 \qquad y_1 \text{ not given}$$
$$x_2 = 40 \qquad y_2 = F_{40,60;.95} = 1.59$$

and

$$y_1' = 1.65 + \frac{35 - 30}{40 - 30}(1.59 - 1.65)$$
$$= 1.65 + \tfrac{1}{2}(-.06) = 1.62$$

Finally, using the above estimates, we shall estimate $F_{35,52;.95}$. We have

$x_0 = 40 \qquad y_0 = F_{35,40;.95} = 1.72$ approximately
$x_1 = 52 \qquad y_1$ unknown
$x_2 = 60 \qquad y_2 = F_{35,60;.95} = 1.62$ approximately

and

$$y_1' = 1.72 + \frac{52 - 40}{60 - 40}(1.62 - 1.72)$$
$$= 1.72 + (.6)(-.10) = 1.66$$

Hence our estimate of $F_{35,52;.95}$ is 1.66. If we interpolate first between 40 and 60 and then between 35 and 40, we still get 1.66 as our estimate. However, in some situations slightly different estimates will be obtained from the two orders of interpolation. If this happens, use the average of the two estimates.

Square Root

The easiest way to determine a square root is to read it out of a table. Since the exercises in Chaps. 1 to 8 require very few square roots (which can be found rather quickly by the procedure described in Sec. C-2) and good square root tables are quite lengthy, none is given in the table appendix.

Square-root tables are available in a number of mathematical and statistical books. A good 40-page table is found in a reasonably priced paper bound edition of Herbert Arkin and Raymond Colton, "Tables for Statisticians" (Barnes & Noble, Inc., New York, 1950). The table gives $\sqrt{N}$ and $\sqrt{10N}$ to four decimal places for

$$N = 1,000(1)10,000$$

Square roots of other numbers are obtained from the table by locating the decimal point properly.

EXAMPLE C-1

From tables find $\sqrt{338.7}$.

Solution

The Arkin and Colton Tables yield 58.1979 and 184.0380 when entered with 3387. We have to select the correct one and locate the decimal point. Since $18^2 = 324$ and $19^2 = 361$, the answer is 18.40380. Of course, this is far greater accuracy than is needed for most statistical problems.

EXAMPLE C-2

From tables find $\sqrt{.12}$.

Solution

The Arkin and Colton Tables yield 34.6410 and 109.5445 when entered with 1200. Since $(.3)^2 = .09$ and $(.4)^2 = .16$, the correct answer is .346410.

EXAMPLE C-3

From tables find $\sqrt{2}$.

Solution

The Arkin and Colton Tables yield 44.7214 and 141.4214 when entered with 2000. Since $1^2 = 1$, $2^2 = 4$, the answer is 1.414214.

EXAMPLE C-4

From tables find $\sqrt{42.678}$.

Solution

The Arkin and Colton Tables yield 65.3223 and 206.5672 when entered with 4267 and 65.3299 and 206.5914 when entered with 4268. Since $6^2 = 36$, $7^2 = 49$, we have

$x_0 = 42.67$ $y_0 = 6.53223$
$x_1 = 42.678$ y_1 not given
$x_2 = 42.68$ $y_2 = 6.53299$

and by linear interpolation

$$y_1' = 6.53223 + \frac{42.678 - 42.67}{42.68 - 42.67}(6.53299 - 6.53223)$$
$$= 6.53223 + \frac{8}{10}(.00076)$$
$$= 6.53223 + .00061$$
$$= 6.53284$$

In a practical application we would probably be content to round off 42.678 to 42.68 and use 6.53 for the square root.

C-2 HAND CALCULATION

If only one square root is needed, the result can be calculated in less time than it takes to locate a table. The numerical process, which is similar to long division, is best illustrated by examples.

EXAMPLE C-5

Find $\sqrt{2}$.

Solution

The calculation is

```
            1. 4  1  4        answer
     1 | 2.00'00'00
         1
         ‾‾‾
    24 | 100
          96
         ‾‾‾‾
   281 |  400
         281
         ‾‾‾‾
  2824 | 11900
         11296
         ‾‾‾‾‾
           604 etc.
```

We start at the decimal point and mark off digits two at a time with the primes moving in each direction. Then we examine the pair

272

farthest to the left (in this case 02) and inquire which is the largest
number, when squared, that is smaller than 2. The answer is 1, and a
1 is written above 2, below 2, and to the left of 2. Then we subtract as
in long division except that two numbers are brought down (instead of
one). Next the number on top of the horizontal line is doubled, a
zero is added temporarily (giving 20), and the result is written to the
left of 100. We inquire the number of times 20 goes into 100, which is,
of course, 5. The temporary zero is replaced by a 5, another 5 is
written behind the 1 above the horizontal line, and the product
$5(25) = 125$ is written below 100. Since 125 is larger than 100, we
try the calculation again with 4, writing $4(24) = 96$ below 100. Now
we can subtract with a positive result, getting 4. The next two digits
are brought down, as in the preceding step, and the process is repeated.
Thus 14 is doubled and a zero is added temporarily, giving 280, which
is written to the left of 400. Since 280 goes into 400 one time, the 0 is
replaced by a 1, a 1 is written behind the 4 above the horizontal line,
and 281 is written to the left of 400 and below 400. The process can
be repeated indefinitely depending upon the number of places we seek
in our answer (which is the number being formed above the horizontal
line). The decimal point above the horizontal line is located above
the decimal point below that line.

EXAMPLE C-6

Find $\sqrt{338.7}$.

Solution

The calculation is

```
              1 8. 4  0  3        answer
       1 |  3'38'.70'00'00'
         |  1
      28 |  238
         |  224
     364 |   1470
         |   1456
    3680 |    1400
   36803 |    140000
         |    110409
         |         etc.
```

EXAMPLE C-7

Find $\sqrt{.12}$.

Solution

The calculation is

```
         . 3   4   6   4      answer
   3  |  .12'00'00'00'
      |    9
  64  |   300
      |   256
 686  |   4400
      |   4116
6924  |   28400
      |   27696
      |     etc.
```

EXAMPLE C-8

Find $\sqrt{42.678}$.

Solution

The calculation is

```
         6.  5   3   2      answer
    6  |  '42'67'80'00'
       |    36
  125  |   667
       |   625
 1303  |   4280
       |   3909
13062  |   37100
       |   26124
       |     etc.
```

Tables and Graphs

n	r	p = .10	p = .20	p = .25	p = .30	p = .40	p = .50
5	0	.59049	.32768	.23730	.16807	.07776	.03125
	1	.91854	.73728	.63281	.52822	.33696	.18750
	2	.99144	.94208	.89648	.83692	.68256	.50000
	3	.99954	.99328	.98437	.96922	.91296	.81250
	4	.99999	.99968	.99902	.99757	.98976	.96875
	5	1.00000	1.00000	1.00000	1.00000	1.00000	1.00000
10	0	.34868	.10737	.05631	.02825	.00605	.00098
	1	.73610	.37581	.24403	.14931	.04636	.01074
	2	.92981	.67780	.52559	.38278	.16729	.05469
	3	.98720	.87913	.77588	.64961	.38228	.17187
	4	.99837	.96721	.92187	.84973	.63310	.37695
	5	.99985	.99363	.98027	.95265	.83376	.62305
	6	.99999	.99914	.99649	.98941	.94524	.82812
	7	1.00000	.99992	.99958	.99841	.98771	.94531
	8		1.00000	.99997	.99986	.99832	.98926
	9			1.00000	.99999	.99990	.99902
	10				1.00000	1.00000	1.00000
15	0	.20589	.03518	.01336	.00475	.00047	.00003
	1	.54904	.16713	.08018	.03527	.00517	.00049
	2	.81594	.39802	.23609	.12683	.02711	.00369
	3	.94444	.64816	.46129	.29687	.09050	.01758
	4	.98728	.83577	.68649	.51549	.21728	.05923
	5	.99775	.93895	.85163	.72162	.40322	.15088
	6	.99969	.98194	.94338	.86886	.60981	.30362
	7	.99997	.99576	.98270	.94999	.78690	.50000
	8	1.00000	.99921	.99581	.98476	.90495	.69638
	9		.99989	.99921	.99635	.96617	.84912
	10		.99999	.99988	.99933	.99065	.94077
	11		1.00000	.99999	.99991	.99807	.98242
	12			1.00000	.99999	.99972	.99631
	13				1.00000	.99997	.99951
	14					1.00000	.99997
	15						1.00000
20	0	.12158	.01153	.00317	.00080	.00004	.00000
	1	.39175	.06918	.02431	.00764	.00052	.00002
	2	.67693	.20608	.09126	.03548	.00361	.00020
	3	.86705	.41145	.22516	.10709	.01596	.00129
	4	.95683	.62965	.41484	.23751	.05095	.00591
	5	.98875	.80421	.61717	.41637	.12560	.02069
	6	.99761	.91331	.78578	.60801	.25001	.05766

n	r	p = .10	p = .20	p = .25	p = .30	p = .40	p = .50
20	7	.99958	.96786	.89819	.77227	.41589	.13159
	8	.99994	.99002	.95907	.88667	.59560	.25172
	9	.99999	.99741	.98614	.95204	.75534	.41190
	10	1.00000	.99944	.99606	.98286	.87248	.58810
	11		.99990	.99906	.99486	.94347	.74828
	12		.99998	.99982	.99872	.97897	.86841
	13		1.00000	.99997	.99974	.99353	.94234
	14			1.00000	.99996	.99839	.97931
	15				.99999	.99968	.99409
	16				1.00000	.99995	.99871
	17					.99999	.99980
	18					1.00000	.99998
	19						1.00000
25	0	.07179	.00378	.00075	.00013	.00000	.00000
	1	.27121	.02739	.00702	.00157	.00005	.00000
	2	.53709	.09823	.03211	.00896	.00043	.00001
	3	.76359	.23399	.09621	.03324	.00237	.00008
	4	.90201	.42067	.21374	.09047	.00947	.00046
	5	.96660	.61669	.37828	.19349	.02936	.00204
	6	.99052	.78004	.56110	.34065	.07357	.00732
	7	.99774	.89088	.72651	.51185	.15355	.02164
	8	.99954	.95323	.85056	.67693	.27353	.05388
	9	.99992	.98267	.92867	.81056	.42462	.11476
	10	.99999	.99445	.97033	.90220	.58577	.21218
	11	1.00000	.99846	.98027	.95575	.73228	.34502
	12		.99963	.99663	.98253	.84623	.50000
	13		.99992	.99908	.99401	.92220	.65498
	14		.99999	.99979	.99822	.96561	.78782
	15		1.00000	.99996	.99955	.98683	.88524
	16			.99999	.99990	.99567	.94612
	17			1.00000	.99998	.99879	.97836
	18				1.00000	.99972	.99268
	19					.99995	.99796
	20					.99999	.99954
	21					1.00000	.99992
	22						.99999
	23						1.00000
50	0	.00515	.00001	.00000	.00000		
	1	.03379	.00019	.00001	.00000		
	2	.11173	.00129	.00009	.00000		
	3	.25029	.00566	.00050	.00003		

n	r	p = .10	p = .20	p = .25	p = .30	p = .40	p = .50
50	4	.43120	.01850	.00211	.00017		
	5	.61612	.04803	.00705	.00072	.00000	
	6	.77023	.10340	.01939	.00249	.00001	
	7	.87785	.19041	.04526	.00726	.00006	
	8	.94213	.30733	.09160	.01825	.00023	
	9	.97546	.44374	.16368	.04023	.00076	.00000
	10	.99065	.58356	.26220	.07885	.00220	.00001
	11	.99678	.71067	.38162	.13904	.00569	.00005
	12	.99900	.81394	.51099	.22287	.01325	.00015
	13	.99971	.88941	.63704	.32788	.02799	.00047
	14	.99993	.93928	.74808	.44683	.05396	.00130
	15	.99998	.96920	.83692	.56918	.09550	.00330
	16	1.00000	.98556	.90169	.68388	.15609	.00767
	17		.99374	.94488	.78219	.23688	.01642
	18		.99749	.97127	.85944	.33561	.03245
	19		.99907	.98608	.91520	.44648	.05946
	20		.99968	.99374	.95224	.56103	.10132
	21		.99990	.99738	.97491	.67014	.16112
	22		.99997	.99898	.98772	.76602	.23994
	23		.99999	.99963	.99441	.84383	.33591
	24		1.00000	.99988	.99763	.90219	.44386
	25			.99996	.99907	.94266	.55614
	26			.99999	.99966	.96859	.66409
	27			1.00000	.99988	.98397	.76006
	28				.99996	.99238	.83888
	29				.99999	.99664	.89868
	30				1.00000	.99863	.94054
	31					.99948	.96755
	32					.99982	.98358
	33					.99994	.99233
	34					.99998	.99670
	35					1.00000	.99870
	36						.99953
	37						.99985
	38						.99995
	39						.99999
	40						1.00000
100	0	.00003					
	1	.00032					
	2	.00194					
	3	.00784					
	4	.02371	.00000				

n	r	p = .10	p = .20	p = .25	p = .30	p = .40	p = .50
100	5	.05758	.00002				
	6	.11716	.00008				
	7	.20605	.00028	.00000			
	8	.32087	.00086	.00001			
	9	.45129	.00233	.00004			
	10	.58316	.00570	.00014	.00000		
	11	.70303	.01257	.00039	.00001		
	12	.80182	.02533	.00103	.00002		
	13	.87612	.04691	.00246	.00006		
	14	.92743	.08044	.00542	.00016		
	15	.96011	.12851	.01108	.00040		
	16	.97940	.19234	.02111	.00097		
	17	.98999	.27119	.03763	.00216		
	18	.99542	.36209	.06301	.00452	.00000	
	19	.99802	.46016	.09953	.00889	.00001	
	20	.99919	.55946	.14883	.01646	.00002	
	21	.99969	.65403	.21144	.02883	.00004	
	22	.99989	.73893	.28637	.04787	.00011	
	23	.99996	.81091	.37018	.07553	.00025	
	24	.99999	.86865	.46167	.11357	.00056	
	25	1.00000	.91252	.55347	.16313	.00119	
	26		.94417	.64174	.22440	.00240	
	27		.96585	.72238	.29637	.00460	.00000
	28		.97998	.79246	.37678	.00843	.00001
	29		.98875	.85046	.46234	.01478	.00002
	30		.99394	.89621	.54912	.02478	.00004
	31		.99687	.93065	.63311	.03985	.00009
	32		.99845	.95540	.71072	.06150	.00020
	33		.99926	.97241	.77926	.09125	.00044
	34		.99966	.98357	.83714	.13034	.00089
	35		.99985	.99059	.88392	.17947	.00176
	36		.99994	.99482	.92012	.23861	.00332
	37		.99998	.99725	.94695	.30681	.00602
	38		.99999	.99860	.96602	.38219	.01049
	39		1.00000	.99931	.97901	.46208	.01760
	40			.99968	.98750	.54329	.02844
	41			.99985	.99283	.62253	.04431
	42			.99994	.99603	.69674	.06661
	43			.99997	.99789	.76347	.09667
	44			.99999	.99891	.82110	.13563
	45			1.00000	.99946	.86891	.18410
	46				.99974	.90702	.24206
	47				.99988	.93621	.30865

n	r	p = .10	p = .20	p = .25	p = .30	p = .40	p = .50
100	48				.99995	.95770	.38218
	49				.99998	.97290	.46021
	50				.99999	.98324	.53979
	51				1.00000	.98999	.61782
	52					.99424	.69135
	53					.99680	.79794
	54					.99829	.81590
	55					.99912	.86437
	56					.99956	.90333
	57					.99979	.93339
	58					.99990	.95569
	59					.99996	.97156
	60					.99998	.98240
	61					.99999	.98951
	62					1.00000	.99398
	63						.99668
	64						.99824
	65						.99911
	66						.99956
	67						.99980
	68						.99991
	69						.99996
	70						.99998
	71						.99999
	72						1.00000

Appendix D-2   Table of random digits†

Row
number

00000	10097	32533	76520	13586	34673	54876	80959	09117	39292	74945
00001	37542	04805	64894	74296	24805	24037	20636	10402	00822	91665
00002	08422	68953	19645	09303	23209	02560	15953	34764	35080	33606
00003	99019	02529	09376	70715	38311	31165	88676	74397	04436	27659
00004	12807	99970	80157	36147	64032	36653	98951	16877	12171	76833
00005	66065	74717	34072	76850	36697	36170	65813	39885	11199	29170
00006	31060	10805	45571	82406	35303	42614	86799	07439	23403	09732
00007	85269	77602	02051	65692	68665	74818	73053	85247	18623	88579
00008	63573	32135	05325	47048	90553	57548	28468	28709	83491	25624
00009	73796	45753	03529	64778	35808	34282	60935	20344	35273	88435
00010	98520	17767	14905	68607	22109	40558	60970	93433	50500	73998
00011	11805	05431	39808	27732	50725	68248	29405	24201	52775	67851
00012	83452	99634	06288	98033	13746	70078	18475	40610	68711	77817
00013	88685	40200	86507	58401	36766	67951	90364	76493	29609	11062
00014	99594	67348	87517	64969	91826	08928	93785	61368	23478	34113
00015	65481	17674	17468	50950	58047	76974	73039	57186	40218	16544
00016	80124	35635	17727	08015	45318	22374	21115	78253	14385	53763
00017	74350	99817	77402	77214	43236	00210	45521	64237	96286	02655
00018	69916	26803	66252	29148	36936	87203	76621	13990	94400	56418
00019	09893	20505	14225	68514	46427	56788	96297	78822	54382	14598
00020	91499	14523	68479	27686	46162	83554	94750	89923	37089	20048
00021	80336	94598	26940	36858	70297	34135	53140	33340	42050	82341
00022	44104	81949	85157	47954	32979	26575	57600	40881	22222	06413
00023	12550	73742	11100	02040	12860	74697	96644	89439	28707	25815
00024	63606	49329	16505	34484	40219	52563	43651	77082	07207	31790
00025	61196	90446	26457	47774	51924	33729	65394	59593	42582	60527
00026	15474	45266	95270	79953	59367	83848	82396	10118	33211	59466
00027	94557	28573	67897	54387	54622	44431	91190	42592	92927	45973
00028	42481	16213	97344	08721	16868	48767	03071	12059	25701	46670
00029	23523	78317	73208	89837	68935	91416	26252	29663	05522	82562
00030	04493	52494	75246	33824	45862	51025	61962	79335	65337	12472
00031	00549	97654	64051	88159	96119	63896	54692	82391	23287	29529
00032	35963	15307	26898	09354	33351	35462	77974	50024	90103	39333
00033	59808	08391	45427	26842	83609	49700	13021	24892	78565	20106
00034	46058	85236	01390	92286	77281	44077	93910	83647	70617	42941

† Extracted with permission from the Rand Corporation publication "A Million Random Digits," The Free Press of Glencoe, New York, 1955.

**Row
number**

00035	32179	00597	87379	25241	05567	07007	86743	17157	85394	11838
00036	69234	61406	20117	45204	15956	60000	18743	92423	97118	96338
00037	19565	41430	01758	75379	40419	21585	66674	36806	84962	85207
00038	45155	14938	19476	07246	43667	94543	59047	90033	20826	69541
00039	94864	31994	36168	10851	34888	81553	01540	35456	05014	51176
00040	98086	24826	45240	28404	44999	08896	39094	73407	35441	31880
00041	33185	16232	41941	50949	89435	48581	88695	41994	37548	73043
00042	80951	00406	96382	70774	20151	23387	25016	25298	94624	61171
00043	79752	49140	71961	28296	69861	02591	74852	20539	00387	59579
00044	18633	32537	98145	06571	31010	24674	05455	61427	77938	91936
00045	74029	43902	77557	32270	97790	17119	52527	58021	80814	51748
00046	54178	45611	80993	37143	05335	12969	56127	19255	36040	90324
00047	11664	49883	52079	84827	59381	71539	09973	33440	88461	23356
00048	48324	77928	31249	64710	02295	36870	32307	57546	15020	09994
00049	69074	94138	87637	91976	35584	04401	10518	21615	01848	76938
00050	09188	20097	32825	39527	04220	86304	83389	87374	64278	58044
00051	90045	85497	51981	50654	94938	81997	91870	76150	68476	64659
00052	73189	50207	47677	26269	62290	64464	27124	67018	41361	82760
00053	75768	76490	20971	87749	90429	12272	95375	05871	93823	43178
00054	54016	44056	66281	31003	00682	27398	20714	53295	07706	17813
00055	08358	69910	78542	42785	13661	58873	04618	97553	31223	08420
00056	28306	03264	81333	10591	40510	07893	32604	60475	94119	01840
00057	53840	86233	81594	13628	51215	90290	28466	68795	77762	20791
00058	91757	53741	61613	62269	50263	90212	55781	76514	83483	47055
00059	89415	92694	00397	58391	12607	17646	48949	72306	94541	37408
00060	77513	03820	86864	29901	68414	82774	51908	13980	72893	55507
00061	19502	37174	69979	20288	55210	29773	74287	75251	65344	67415
00062	21818	59313	93278	81757	05686	73156	07082	85046	31853	38452
00063	51474	66499	68107	23621	94049	91345	42836	09191	08007	45449
00064	99559	68331	62535	24170	69777	12830	74819	78142	43860	72834
00065	33713	48007	93584	72869	51926	64721	58303	29822	93174	93972
00066	85274	86893	11303	22970	28834	34137	73515	90400	71148	43643
00067	84133	89640	44035	52166	73852	70091	61222	60561	62327	18423
00068	56732	16234	17395	96131	10123	91622	85496	57560	81604	18880
00069	65138	56806	87648	85261	34313	65861	45875	21069	85644	47277

Row
number

00070	38001 02176	81719 11711	71602 92937	74219 64049	65584 49698
00071	37402 96397	01304 77586	56271 10086	47324 62605	40030 37438
00072	97125 40348	87083 31417	21815 39250	75237 62047	15501 29578
00073	21826 41134	47143 34072	64638 85902	49139 06441	03856 54552
00074	73135 42742	95719 09035	85794 74296	08789 88156	64691 19202
00075	07638 77929	03061 18072	96207 44156	23821 99538	04713 66994
00076	60528 83441	07954 19814	59175 20695	05533 52139	61212 06455
00077	83596 35655	06958 92983	05128 09719	77433 53783	92301 50498
00078	10850 62746	99599 10507	13499 06319	53075 71839	06410 19362
00079	39820 98952	43622 63147	64421 80814	43800 09351	31024 73167
00080	59580 06478	75569 78800	88835 54486	23768 06156	04111 08408
00081	38508 07341	23793 48763	90822 97022	17719 04207	95954 49953
00082	30692 70668	94688 16127	56196 80091	82067 63400	05462 69200
00083	65443 95659	18238 27437	49632 24041	08337 65676	96299 90836
00084	27267 50264	13192 72294	07477 44606	17985 48911	97341 30358
00085	91307 06991	19072 24210	36699 53728	28825 35793	28976 66252
00086	68434 94688	84473 13622	62126 98408	12843 82590	09815 93146
00087	48908 15877	54745 24591	35700 04754	83824 52692	54130 55160
00088	06913 45197	42672 78601	11883 09528	63011 98901	14974 40344
00089	10455 16019	14210 33712	91342 37821	88325 80851	43667 70883
00090	12883 97343	65027 61184	04285 01392	17974 15077	90712 26769
00091	21778 30976	38807 36961	31649 42096	63281 02023	08816 47449
00092	19523 59515	65122 59659	86283 68258	69572 13798	16435 91529
00093	67245 52670	35583 16563	79246 86686	76463 34222	26655 90802
00094	60584 47377	07500 37992	45134 26529	26760 83637	41326 44344
00095	53853 41377	36066 94850	58838 73859	49364 73331	96240 43642
00096	24637 38736	74384 89342	52623 07992	12369 18601	03742 83873
00097	83080 12451	38992 22815	07759 51777	97377 27585	51972 37867
00098	16444 24334	36151 99073	27493 70939	85130 32552	54846 54759
00099	60790 18157	57178 65762	11161 78576	45819 52979	65130 04860
00100	03991 10461	93716 16894	66083 24653	84609 58232	88618 19161
00101	38555 95554	32886 59780	08355 60860	29735 47762	71299 23853
00102	17546 73704	92052 46215	55121 29281	59076 07936	27954 58909
00103	32643 52861	95819 06831	00911 98936	76355 93779	80863 00514
00104	69572 68777	39510 35905	14060 40619	29549 69616	33564 60780

Row number

00105	24122	66591	27699	06494	14845	46672	61958	77100	90899	75754
00106	61196	30231	92962	61773	41839	55382	17267	70943	78038	70267
00107	30532	21704	10274	12202	39685	23309	10061	68829	55986	66485
00108	03788	97599	75867	20717	74416	53166	35208	33374	87539	08823
00109	48228	63379	85783	47619	53152	67433	35663	52972	16818	60311
00110	60365	94653	35075	33949	42614	29297	01918	28316	98953	73231
00111	83799	42402	56623	34442	34994	41374	70071	14736	09958	18065
00112	32960	07405	36409	83232	99385	41600	11133	07586	15917	06253
00113	19322	53845	57620	52606	66497	68646	78138	66559	19640	99413
00114	11220	94747	07399	37408	48509	23929	27482	45476	85244	35159
00115	31751	57260	68980	05339	15470	48355	88651	22596	03152	19121
00116	88492	99382	14454	04504	20094	98977	74843	93413	22109	78508
00117	30934	47744	07481	83828	73788	06533	28597	20405	94205	20380
00118	22888	48893	27499	98748	60530	45128	74022	84617	82037	10268
00119	78212	16993	35902	91386	44372	15486	65741	14014	87481	37220
00120	41849	84547	46850	52326	34677	58300	74910	64345	19325	81549
00121	46352	33049	69248	93460	45305	07521	61318	31855	14413	70951
00122	11087	96294	14013	31792	59747	67277	76503	34513	39663	77544
00123	52701	08337	56303	87315	16520	69676	11654	99893	02181	68161
00124	57275	36898	81304	48585	68652	27376	92852	55866	88448	03584
00125	20857	73156	70284	24326	79375	95220	01159	63267	10622	48391
00126	15633	84924	90415	93614	33521	26665	55823	47641	86225	31704
00127	92694	48297	39904	02115	59589	49067	66821	41575	49767	04037
00128	77613	19019	88152	00080	20554	91409	96277	48257	50816	97616
00129	38688	32486	45134	63545	59404	72059	43947	51680	43852	59693
00130	25163	01889	70014	15021	41290	67312	71857	15957	68971	11403
00131	65251	07629	37239	33295	05870	01119	92784	26340	18477	65622
00132	36815	43625	18637	37509	82444	99005	04921	73701	14707	93997
00133	64397	11692	05327	82162	20247	81759	45197	25332	83745	22567
00134	04515	25624	95096	67946	48460	85558	15191	18782	16930	33361
00135	83761	60873	43253	84145	60833	25983	01291	41349	20368	07126
00136	14387	06345	80854	09279	43529	06318	38384	74761	41196	37480
00137	51321	92246	80088	77074	88722	56736	66164	49431	66919	31678
00138	72472	00008	80890	18002	94813	31900	54155	83436	35352	54131
00139	05466	55306	93128	18464	74457	90561	72848	11834	79982	68416

**Row
number**

00140	39528 72484	82474 25593	48545 35247	18619 13674	18611 19241
00141	81616 18711	53342 44276	75122 11724	74627 73707	58319 15997
00142	07586 16120	82641 22820	92904 13141	32392 19763	61199 67940
00143	90767 04235	13574 17200	69902 63742	78464 22501	18627 90872
00144	40188 28193	29593 88627	94972 11598	62095 36787	00441 58997
00145	34414 82157	86887 55087	19152 00023	12302 80783	32624 68691
00146	63439 75363	44989 16822	36024 00867	76378 41605	65961 73488
00147	67049 09070	93399 45547	94458 74284	05041 49807	20288 34060
00148	79495 04146	52162 90286	54158 34243	46978 35482	59362 95938
00149	91704 30552	04737 21031	75051 93029	47665 64382	99782 93478
00150	94015 46874	32444 48277	59820 96163	64654 25843	41145 42820
00151	74108 88222	88570 74015	25704 91035	01755 14750	48968 38603
00152	62880 87873	95160 59221	22304 90314	72877 17334	39283 04149
00153	11748 12102	80580 41867	17710 59621	06554 07850	73950 79552
00154	17944 05600	60478 03343	25852 58905	57216 39618	49856 99326
00155	66067 42792	95043 52680	46780 56487	09971 59481	37006 22186
00156	54244 91030	45547 70818	59849 96169	61459 21647	87417 17198
00157	30945 57589	31732 57260	47670 07654	46376 25366	94746 49580
00158	69170 37403	86995 90307	94304 71803	26825 05511	12459 91314
00159	08345 88975	35841 85771	08105 59987	87112 21476	14713 71181
00160	27767 43584	85301 88977	29490 69714	73035 41207	74699 09310
00161	13025 14338	54066 15243	47724 66733	47431 43905	31048 56699
00162	80217 36292	98525 24335	24432 24896	43277 58874	11466 16082
00163	10875 62004	90391 61105	57411 06368	53856 30743	08670 84741
00164	54127 57326	26629 19087	24472 88779	30540 27886	61732 75454
00165	60311 42824	37301 42678	45990 43242	17374 52003	70707 70214
00166	49739 71484	92003 98086	76668 73209	59202 11973	02902 33250
00167	78626 51594	16453 94614	39014 97066	83012 09832	25571 77628
00168	66692 13986	99837 00582	81232 44987	09504 96412	90193 79568
00169	44071 28091	07362 97703	76447 42537	98524 97831	65704 09514
00170	41468 85149	49554 17994	14924 39650	95294 00556	70481 06905
00171	94559 37559	49678 53119	70312 05682	66986 34099	74474 20740
00172	41615 70360	64114 58660	90850 64618	80620 51790	11436 38072
00173	50273 93113	41794 86861	24781 89683	55411 85667	77535 99892
00174	41396 80504	90670 08289	40902 05069	95083 06783	28102 57816

Row
number

00175	25807 24260	71529 78920	72682 07385	90726 57166	98884 08583
00176	06170 97965	88302 98041	21443 41808	68984 83620	89747 98882
00177	60808 54444	74412 81105	01176 28838	36421 16489	18059 51061
00178	80940 44893	10408 36222	80582 71944	92638 40333	67054 16067
00179	19516 90120	46759 71643	13177 55292	21036 82808	77501 97427
00180	49386 54480	23604 23554	21785 41101	91178 10174	29420 90438
00181	06312 88940	15995 69321	47458 64809	98189 81851	29651 84215
00182	60942 00307	11897 92674	40405 68032	96717 54244	10701 41393
00183	92329 98932	78284 46347	71209 92061	39448 93136	25722 08564
00184	77936 63574	31384 51924	85561 29671	58137 17820	22751 36518
00185	38101 77756	11657 13897	95889 57067	47648 13885	70669 93406
00186	39641 69457	91339 22502	92613 89719	11947 56203	19324 20504
00187	84054 40455	99396 63680	67667 60631	69181 96845	38525 11600
00188	47468 03577	57649 63266	24700 71594	14004 23153	69249 05747
00189	43321 31370	28977 23896	76479 68562	62342 07589	08899 05985
00190	64281 61826	18555 64937	13173 33365	78851 16499	87064 13075
00191	66847 70495	32350 02985	86716 38746	26313 77463	55387 72681
00192	72461 33230	21529 53424	92581 02262	78438 66276	18396 73538
00193	21032 91050	13058 16218	12470 56500	15292 76139	59526 52113
00194	95362 67011	06651 16136	01016 00857	55018 56374	35824 71708
00195	49712 97380	10404 55452	34030 60726	75211 10271	36633 68424
00196	58275 61764	97586 54716	50259 46345	87195 46092	26787 60939
00197	89514 11788	68224 23417	73959 76145	30342 40277	11049 72049
00198	15472 50669	48139 36732	46874 37088	73465 09819	58869 35220
00199	12120 86124	51247 44302	60883 52109	21437 36786	49226 77837

Appendix D-3   The hypergeometric distribution†

N	n	k	r or x	P(r)	p(x)	N	n	k	r or x	P(r)	p(x)
10	1	1	0	0.900000	0.900000	10	5	3	0	0.083333	0.083333
10	1	1	1	1.000000	0.100000	10	5	3	1	0.500000	0.416667
10	2	1	0	0.800000	0.800000	10	5	3	2	0.916667	0.416667
10	2	1	1	1.000000	0.200000	10	5	3	3	1.000000	0.083333
10	2	2	0	0.622222	0.622222	10	5	4	0	0.023810	0.023810
10	2	2	1	0.977778	0.355556	10	5	4	1	0.261905	0.238095
10	2	2	2	1.000000	0.022222	10	5	4	2	0.738095	0.476190
10	3	1	0	0.700000	0.700000	10	5	4	3	0.976190	0.238095
10	3	2	1	1.000000	0.300000	10	5	4	4	1.000000	0.023810
10	3	2	0	0.466667	0.466667	10	5	5	0	0.003968	0.003968
10	3	2	1	0.933333	0.466667	10	5	5	1	0.103175	0.099206
10	3	2	2	1.000000	0.066667	10	5	5	2	0.500000	0.396825
10	3	3	0	0.291667	0.291667	10	5	5	3	0.896825	0.396825
10	3	3	1	0.816667	0.525000	10	5	5	4	0.996032	0.099206
10	3	3	2	0.991667	0.175000	10	5	5	5	1.000000	0.003968
10	3	3	3	1.000000	0.008333	10	6	1	0	0.400000	0.400000
10	4	1	0	0.600000	0.600000	10	6	1	1	1.000000	0.600000
10	4	1	1	1.000000	0.400000	10	6	2	0	0.133333	0.133333
10	4	2	0	0.333333	0.333333	10	6	2	1	0.666667	0.533333
10	4	2	1	0.866667	0.533333	10	6	2	2	1.000000	0.333333
10	4	2	2	1.000000	0.133333	10	6	3	0	0.033333	0.033333
10	4	3	0	0.166667	0.166667	10	6	3	1	0.333333	0.300000
10	4	3	1	0.666667	0.500000	10	6	3	2	0.833333	0.500000
10	4	3	2	0.966667	0.300000	10	6	3	3	1.000000	0.166667
10	4	3	3	1.000000	0.033333	10	6	4	0	0.004762	0.004762
10	4	4	0	0.071429	0.071429	10	6	4	1	0.119048	0.114286
10	4	4	1	0.452381	0.380952	10	6	4	2	0.547619	0.428571
10	4	4	2	0.880952	0.428571	10	6	4	3	0.928571	0.380952
10	4	4	3	0.995238	0.114286	10	6	4	4	1.000000	0.071429
10	4	4	4	1.000000	0.004762	10	6	5	1	0.023810	0.023810
10	5	1	0	0.500000	0.500000	10	6	5	2	0.261905	0.238095
10	5	1	1	1.000000	0.500000	10	6	5	3	0.738095	0.476190
10	5	2	0	0.222222	0.222222	10	6	5	4	0.976190	0.238095
10	5	2	1	0.777778	0.555556	10	6	5	5	1.000000	0.023810
10	5	2	2	1.000000	0.222222	10	6	6	2	0.071429	0.071429

N	n	k	r or x	P(r)	p(x)	N	n	k	r or x	P(r)	p(x)
10	6	6	3	0.452381	0.380952	10	8	3	2	0.533333	0.466667
10	6	6	4	0.880952	0.428571	10	8	3	3	1.000000	0.466667
10	6	6	5	0.995238	0.114286	10	8	4	2	0.133333	0.133333
10	6	6	6	1.000000	0.004762	10	8	4	3	0.666667	0.533333
10	7	1	0	0.300000	0.300000	10	8	4	4	1.000000	0.333333
10	7	1	1	1.000000	0.700000	10	8	5	3	0.222222	0.222222
10	7	2	0	0.066667	0.066667	10	8	5	4	0.777778	0.555556
10	7	2	1	0.533333	0.466667	10	8	5	5	1.000000	0.222222
10	7	2	2	1.000000	0.466667	10	8	6	4	0.333333	0.333333
10	7	3	0	0.008333	0.008333	10	8	6	5	0.866667	0.533333
10	7	3	1	0.183333	0.175000	10	8	6	6	1.000000	0.133333
10	7	3	2	0.708333	0.525000	10	8	7	5	0.466667	0.466667
10	7	3	3	1.000000	0.291667	10	8	7	6	0.933333	0.466667
10	7	4	1	0.033333	0.033333	10	8	7	7	1.000000	0.066667
10	7	4	2	0.333333	0.300000	10	8	8	6	0.622222	0.622222
10	7	4	3	0.833333	0.500000	10	8	8	7	0.977778	0.355556
10	7	4	4	1.000000	0.166667	10	8	8	8	1.000000	0.022222
10	7	5	2	0.083333	0.083333	10	9	1	0	0.100000	0.100000
10	7	5	3	0.500000	0.416667	10	9	1	1	1.000000	0.900000
10	7	5	4	0.916667	0.416667	10	9	2	1	0.200000	0.200000
10	7	5	5	1.000000	0.083333	10	9	2	2	1.000000	0.800000
10	7	6	3	0.166667	0.166667	10	9	3	2	0.300000	0.300000
10	7	6	4	0.666667	0.500000	10	9	3	3	1.000000	0.700000
10	7	6	5	0.966667	0.300000	10	9	4	3	0.400000	0.400000
10	7	6	6	1.000000	0.033333	10	9	4	4	1.000000	0.600000
10	7	7	4	0.291667	0.291667	10	9	5	4	0.500000	0.500000
10	7	7	5	0.816667	0.525000	10	9	5	5	1.000000	0.500000
10	7	7	6	0.991667	0.175000	10	9	6	5	0.600000	0.600000
10	7	7	7	1.000000	0.008333	10	9	6	6	1.000000	0.400000
10	8	1	0	0.200000	0.200000	10	9	7	6	0.700000	0.700000
10	8	1	1	1.000000	0.800000	10	9	7	7	1.000000	0.300000
10	8	2	0	0.022222	0.022222	10	9	8	7	0.800000	0.800000
10	8	2	1	0.377778	0.355556	10	9	8	8	1.000000	0.200000
10	8	2	2	1.000000	0.622222	10	9	9	8	0.900000	0.900000
10	8	3	1	0.066667	0.066667	10	9	9	9	1.000000	0.100000

† Extracted with permission from Gerald J. Lieberman and Donald B. Owen, "Tables of the Hypergeometric Probability Distribution," Stanford University Press, Stanford, Calif., 1961.

Appendix D-4   The cumulative Poisson distribution†

r	$\mu = .1$	$\mu = .2$	$\mu = .3$	$\mu = .4$	$\mu = .5$
0	.90484	.81873	.74082	.67302	.60653
1	.99532	.98248	.96306	.93845	.90980
2	.99985	.99885	.99640	.99207	.98561
3	1.00000	.99994	.99973	.99922	.99825
4		1.00000	.99998	.99994	.99983
5			1.00000	1.00000	.99999
6					1.00000

r	$\mu = .6$	$\mu = .7$	$\mu = .8$	$\mu = .9$	$\mu = 1.0$
0	.54881	.49658	.44933	.40657	.36788
1	.87810	.84419	.80879	.77248	.73576
2	.97688	.96586	.95258	.93714	.91970
3	.99664	.99425	.99092	.98654	.98101
4	.99961	.99921	.99859	.99766	.99634
5	.99996	.99991	.99982	.99966	.99941
6	1.00000	.99999	.99998	.99996	.99992
7		1.00000	1.00000	1.00000	.99999
8					1000000

r	$\mu = 2$	$\mu = 3$	$\mu = 4$	$\mu = 5$	$\mu = 6$
0	.13534	.04979	.01832	.00674	.00248
1	.40601	.19915	.09158	.04043	.01735
2	.67668	.42319	.23810	.12465	.06197
3	.85712	.64723	.43347	.26503	.15120
4	.94735	.81526	.62884	.44049	.28506
5	.98344	.91608	.78513	.61596	.44568
6	.99547	.96649	.88933	.76218	.60630
7	.99890	.98810	.94887	.86663	.74398
8	.99976	.99620	.97864	.93191	.84724
9	.99995	.99890	.99187	.96817	.91608
10	.99999	.99971	.99716	.98630	.95738
11	1.00000	.99993	.99908	.99455	.97991
12		.99998	.99973	.99798	.99117
13		1.00000	.99992	.99930	.99637
14			.99998	.99977	.99860
15			1.00000	.99993	.99949
16				.99998	.99982
17				1.00000	.99994
18					.99998
19					1.00000

r	$\mu = 7$	$\mu = 8$	$\mu = 9$	$\mu = 10$
0	.00091	.00033	.00012	.00004
1	.00730	.00302	.00123	.00050
2	.02964	.01375	.00623	.00277
3	.08176	.04238	.02123	.01034
4	.17299	.09963	.05496	.02925
5	.30071	.19124	.11569	.06709
6	.44971	.31337	.20678	.13014
7	.59871	.45296	.32390	.22022
8	.72909	.59255	.45565	.33282
9	.83050	.71662	.58741	.45793
10	.90148	.81589	.70599	.58304
11	.94665	.88808	.80301	.69678
12	.97300	.93620	.87577	.79156
13	.98719	.96582	.92615	.86446
14	.99428	.98274	.95853	.91654
15	.99759	.99177	.97796	.95126
16	.99904	.99628	.98889	.97296
17	.99964	.99841	.99468	.98572
18	.99987	.99935	.99757	.99281
19	.99996	.99975	.99894	.99655
20	.99999	.99991	.99956	.99841
21	1.00000	.99997	.99982	.99930
22		.99999	.99993	.99970
23		1.00000	.99998	.99988
24			.99999	.99995
25			1.00000	.99998
26				.99999
27				1.00000

† Extracted with permission from E. C. Molina, "Poisson's Binomial Exponential Limit," D. Van Nostrand Company, Inc., Princeton, N.J., 1949.

Appendix D-5 The cumulative standardized normal distribution function† (Entry = $\Pr[Z < Z_p] = p$)

Z_p	.00	.01	.02	.03	.04	.05	.06	.07	.08	.09
− .0	.5000	.4960	.4920	.4880	.4840	.4801	.4761	.4721	.4681	.4641
− .1	.4602	.4562	.4522	.4483	.4443	.4404	.4364	.4325	.4286	.4247
− .2	.4207	.4168	.4129	.4090	.4052	.4013	.3974	.3936	.3897	.3859
− .3	.3821	.3783	.3745	.3707	.3669	.3632	.3594	.3557	.3520	.3483
− .4	.3446	.3409	.3372	.3336	.3300	.3264	.3228	.3192	.3156	.3121
− .5	.3085	.3050	.3015	.2981	.2946	.2912	.2877	.2843	.2810	.2776
− .6	.2743	.2709	.2676	.2643	.2611	.2578	.2546	.2514	.2483	.2451
− .7	.2420	.2389	.2358	.2327	.2297	.2266	.2236	.2206	.2177	.2148
− .8	.2119	.2090	.2061	.2063	.2005	.1977	.1949	.1922	.1894	.1867
− .9	.1841	.1814	.1788	.1762	.1736	.1711	.1685	.1660	.1635	.1611
− 1.0	.1587	.1562	.1539	.1515	.1492	.1469	.1446	.1423	.1401	.1379
− 1.1	.1357	.1335	.1314	.1292	.1271	.1251	.1230	.1210	.1190	.1170
− 1.2	.1151	.1131	.1112	.1093	.1075	.1056	.1038	.1020	.1003	.09853
− 1.3	.09680	.09510	.09342	.09176	.09012	.08851	.08691	.08534	.08379	.08226
− 1.4	.08076	.07927	.07780	.07636	.07493	.07353	.07215	.07078	.06944	.06811
− 1.5	.06681	.06552	.06426	.06301	.06178	.06057	.05938	.05821	.05705	.05592
− 1.6	.05480	.05370	.05262	.05155	.05050	.04947	.04846	.04746	.04648	.04551
− 1.7	.04457	.04363	.04272	.04182	.04093	.04006	.03920	.03836	.03754	.03673
− 1.8	.03593	.03515	.03438	.03362	.03288	.03216	.03144	.03074	.03005	.02938
− 1.9	.02872	.02807	.02743	.02680	.02619	.02559	.02500	.02442	.02385	.02330
− 2.0	.02275	.02222	.02169	.02118	.02068	.02018	.01970	.01923	.01876	.01831
− 2.1	.01786	.01743	.01700	.01659	.01616	.01578	.01539	.01500	.01463	.01426
− 2.2	.01390	.01355	.01321	.01287	.01255	.01222	.01191	.01160	.01130	.01101
− 2.3	.01072	.01044	.01017	$.0^2 9903$	$.0^2 9642$	$.0^2 9387$	$.0^2 9137$	$.0^2 8894$	$.0^2 8656$	$.0^2 8424$
− 2.4	$.0^2 8198$	$.0^2 7976$	$.0^2 7760$	$.0^2 7549$	$.0^2 7344$	$.0^2 7143$	$.0^2 6947$	$.0^2 6756$	$.0^2 6569$	$.0^2 6387$
− 2.5	$.0^2 6210$	$.0^2 6037$	$.0^2 5868$	$.0^2 5703$	$.0^2 5543$	$.0^2 5386$	$.0^2 5234$	$.0^2 5085$	$.0^2 4940$	$.0^2 4799$
− 2.6	$.0^2 4661$	$.0^2 4527$	$.0^2 4396$	$.0^2 4269$	$.0^2 4145$	$.0^2 4025$	$.0^2 3907$	$.0^2 3793$	$.0^2 3681$	$.0^2 3573$
− 2.7	$.0^2 3467$	$.0^2 3364$	$.0^2 3264$	$.0^2 3167$	$.0^2 3072$	$.0^2 2980$	$.0^2 2890$	$.0^2 2803$	$.0^2 2718$	$.0^2 2635$
− 2.8	$.0^2 2555$	$.0^2 2477$	$.0^2 2401$	$.0^2 2327$	$.0^2 2256$	$.0^2 2186$	$.0^2 2118$	$.0^2 2052$	$.0^2 1988$	$.0^2 1926$
− 2.9	$.0^2 1866$	$.0^2 1807$	$.0^2 1750$	$.0^2 1695$	$.0^2 1641$	$.0^2 1589$	$.0^2 1538$	$.0^2 1490$	$.0^2 1441$	$.0^2 1395$

z	.00	.01	.02	.03	.04	.05	.06	.07	.08	.09
.1	.5398	.5438	.5478	.5517	.5557	.5596	.5636	.5675	.5714	.5753
.2	.5793	.5832	.5871	.5910	.5948	.5987	.6026	.6064	.6103	.6141
.3	.6179	.6217	.6255	.6293	.6331	.6368	.6406	.6443	.6480	.6517
.4	.6554	.6591	.6628	.6664	.6700	.6736	.6772	.6808	.6844	.6879
.5	.6915	.6950	.6985	.7019	.7054	.7088	.7123	.7157	.7190	.7224
.6	.7257	.7291	.7324	.7357	.7389	.7422	.7454	.7486	.7517	.7549
.7	.7580	.7611	.7642	.7673	.7703	.7734	.7764	.7794	.7823	.7852
.8	.7881	.7910	.7939	.7967	.7995	.8023	.8051	.8078	.8106	.8133
.9	.8159	.8186	.8212	.8238	.8264	.8289	.8315	.8340	.8365	.8389
1.0	.8413	.8438	.8461	.8485	.8508	.8531	.8554	.8577	.8599	.8621
1.1	.8643	.8665	.8686	.8708	.8729	.8749	.8770	.8790	.8810	.8830
1.2	.8849	.8869	.8888	.8907	.8925	.8944	.8962	.8980	.8997	.90147
1.3	.90320	.90490	.90658	.90824	.90988	.91149	.91309	.91466	.91621	.91774
1.4	.91924	.92073	.92220	.92364	.92507	.92647	.92785	.92922	.93056	.93189
1.5	.93319	.93448	.93574	.93669	.93822	.93943	.94062	.94179	.94295	.94408
1.6	.94520	.94630	.94738	.94845	.94950	.95053	.95154	.95254	.95352	.95449
1.7	.95543	.95637	.95728	.95818	.95907	.95994	.96080	.96164	.96246	.96327
1.8	.96407	.96485	.96562	.96638	.96712	.96784	.96856	.96926	.96995	.97062
1.9	.97128	.97193	.97257	.97320	.97381	.97441	.97500	.97558	.97615	.97670
2.0	.97725	.97778	.97831	.97882	.97932	.97982	.98030	.98077	.98124	.98169
2.1	.98214	.98257	.98300	.98341	.98382	.98422	.98461	.98500	.98537	.98574
2.2	.98610	.98645	.98679	.98713	.98745	.98778	.98809	.98840	.98870	.98899
2.3	.98928	.98956	.98983	$.9^20097$	$.9^20358$	$.9^20613$	$.9^20863$	$.9^21106$	$.9^21344$	$.9^21576$
2.4	$.9^21802$	$.9^22024$	$.9^22240$	$.9^22451$	$.9^22656$	$.9^22857$	$.9^23053$	$.9^23244$	$.9^23431$	$.9^23613$
2.5	$.9^23790$	$.9^23963$	$.9^24132$	$.9^24297$	$.9^24457$	$.9^24614$	$.9^24766$	$.9^24915$	$.9^25060$	$.9^25201$
2.6	$.9^25339$	$.9^25473$	$.9^25604$	$.9^25731$	$.9^25855$	$.9^25975$	$.9^26093$	$.9^26207$	$.9^26319$	$.9^26427$
2.7	$.9^26533$	$.9^26636$	$.9^26736$	$.9^26833$	$.9^26928$	$.9^27020$	$.9^27110$	$.9^27197$	$.9^27282$	$.9^27365$
2.8	$.9^27445$	$.9^27523$	$.9^27599$	$.9^27673$	$.9^27744$	$.9^27814$	$.9^27882$	$.9^27948$	$.9^28012$	$.9^28074$
2.9	$.9^28134$	$.9^28193$	$.9^28250$	$.9^28305$	$.9^28359$	$.9^28411$	$.9^28462$	$.9^28511$	$.9^28559$	$.9^28605$
3.0	$.9^28650$	$.9^28694$	$.9^28736$	$.9^28777$	$.9^28817$	$.9^28856$	$.9^28893$	$.9^28930$	$.9^28965$	$.9^28999$

Note: $.0^21350 = .001350$ $.9^28650 = .998650$

Entry $= t_{\nu;p}$ where $\Pr(t_\nu < t_{\nu;p}) = p$ $t_{\nu;1-p} = -t_{\nu;p}$

ν \ P	.60	.70	.80	.90	.95	.975	.990	.995	.999	.9995
1	.325	.727	1.376	3.078	6.314	12.71	31.82	63.66	318.3	636.6
2	.289	.617	1.061	1.886	2.920	4.303	6.965	9.925	22.33	31.60
3	.277	.584	.978	1.638	2.353	3.182	4.541	5.841	10.22	12.94
4	.271	.569	.941	1.533	2.132	2.776	3.747	4.604	7.173	8.610
5	.267	.559	.920	1.476	2.015	2.571	3.365	4.032	5.893	6.859
6	.265	.553	.906	1.440	1.943	2.447	3.143	3.707	5.208	5.959
7	.263	.549	.896	1.415	1.895	2.365	2.998	3.499	4.785	5.405
8	.262	.546	.889	1.397	1.860	2.306	2.896	3.355	4.501	5.041
9	.261	.543	.883	1.383	1.833	2.262	2.821	3.250	4.297	4.781
10	.260	.542	.879	1.372	1.812	2.228	2.764	3.169	4.144	4.587
11	.260	.540	.876	1.363	1.796	2.201	2.718	3.106	4.025	4.437
12	.259	.539	.873	1.356	1.782	2.179	2.681	3.055	3.930	4.318
13	.259	.538	.870	1.350	1.771	2.160	2.650	3.012	3.852	4.221
14	.258	.537	.868	1.345	1.761	2.145	2.624	2.977	3.787	4.140
15	.258	.536	.866	1.341	1.753	2.131	2.602	2.947	3.733	4.073
16	.258	.535	.865	1.337	1.746	2.120	2.583	2.921	3.686	4.015
17	.257	.534	.863	1.333	1.740	2.110	2.567	2.898	3.646	3.965
18	.257	.534	.862	1.330	1.734	2.101	2.552	2.878	3.611	3.922
19	.257	.533	.861	1.328	1.729	2.093	2.539	2.861	3.579	3.883
20	.257	.533	.860	1.325	1.725	2.086	2.528	2.845	3.552	3.850
21	.257	.532	.859	1.323	1.721	2.080	2.518	2.831	3.527	3.819
22	.256	.532	.858	1.321	1.717	2.074	2.508	2.819	3.505	3.792
23	.256	.532	.858	1.319	1.714	2.069	2.500	2.807	3.485	3.767
24	.256	.531	.857	1.318	1.711	2.064	2.492	2.797	3.467	3.745
25	.256	.531	.856	1.316	1.708	2.060	2.485	2.787	3.450	3.725
26	.256	.531	.856	1.315	1.706	2.056	2.479	2.779	3.435	3.707
27	.256	.531	.855	1.314	1.703	2.052	2.473	2.771	3.421	3.690
28	.256	.530	.855	1.313	1.701	2.048	2.467	2.763	3.408	3.674
29	.256	.530	.854	1.311	1.699	2.045	2.462	2.756	3.396	3.659
30	.256	.530	.854	1.310	1.697	2.042	2.457	2.750	3.385	3.646
40	.255	.529	.851	1.303	1.684	2.021	2.423	2.704	3.307	3.551
50	.255	.528	.849	1.298	1.676	2.009	2.403	2.678	3.262	3.495
60	.254	.527	.848	1.296	1.671	2.000	2.390	2.660	3.232	3.460
80	.254	.527	.846	1.292	1.664	1.990	2.374	2.639	3.195	3.415
100	.254	.526	.845	1.290	1.660	1.984	2.365	2.626	3.174	3.389
200	.254	.525	.843	1.286	1.653	1.972	2.345	2.601	3.131	3.339
500	.253	.525	.842	1.283	1.648	1.965	2.334	2.586	3.106	3.310
∞	.253	.524	.842	1.282	1.645	1.960	2.326	2.576	3.090	3.291

† Reprinted by permission from A. Hald, "Statistical Tables and Formulas" (John Wiley & Sons, Inc., New York, 1952). The majority of the entries are from Table III of R. A. Fisher and F. Yates, "Statistical Tables" (Oliver and Boyd, Edinburgh), and are reprinted by permission of the authors and publishers.

Appendix D-7 The chi-square distribution†

Entry $= \chi^2_{\nu;p}$ where $\Pr(\chi^2_\nu < \chi^2_{\nu;p}) = p$

ν \ p	.005	.010	.025	.050	.100	.900	.950	.975	.990	.995
1	0.0⁴393	0.0³157	0.0³982	0.0²393	0.0158	2.71	3.84	5.02	6.63	7.88
2	0.0100	0.0201	0.0506	0.103	0.211	4.61	5.99	7.38	9.21	10.60
3	0.072	0.115	0.216	0.352	0.584	6.25	7.81	9.35	11.34	12.84
4	0.207	0.297	0.484	0.711	1.064	7.78	9.49	11.14	13.28	14.86
5	0.412	0.554	0.831	1.145	1.61	9.24	11.07	12.83	15.09	16.75
6	0.676	0.872	1.24	1.64	2.20	10.64	12.59	14.45	16.81	18.55
7	0.989	1.24	1.69	2.17	2.83	12.02	14.07	16.01	18.48	20.28
8	1.34	1.65	2.18	2.73	3.49	13.36	15.51	17.53	20.09	21.96
9	1.73	2.09	2.70	3.33	4.17	14.68	16.92	19.02	21.67	23.59
10	2.16	2.56	3.25	3.94	4.87	15.99	18.31	20.48	23.21	25.19
11	2.60	3.05	3.82	4.57	5.58	17.28	19.68	21.92	24.72	26.76
12	3.07	3.57	4.40	5.23	6.30	18.55	21.03	23.34	26.22	28.30
13	3.57	4.11	5.01	5.89	7.04	19.81	22.36	24.74	27.69	29.82
14	4.07	4.66	5.63	6.57	7.79	21.06	23.68	26.12	29.14	31.32
15	4.60	5.23	6.26	7.26	8.55	22.31	25.00	27.49	30.58	32.80
16	5.14	5.81	6.91	7.96	9.31	23.54	26.30	28.85	32.00	34.27
17	5.70	6.41	7.56	8.67	10.09	24.77	27.59	30.19	33.41	35.72
18	6.26	7.01	8.23	9.39	10.86	25.99	28.87	31.53	34.81	37.16
19	6.84	7.63	8.91	10.12	11.65	27.20	30.14	32.85	36.19	38.58
20	7.43	8.26	8.59	10.85	12.44	28.41	31.41	34.17	37.57	40.00
21	8.03	8.90	10.28	11.59	13.24	29.62	32.67	35.48	38.93	41.40
22	8.64	9.54	10.98	12.34	14.04	30.81	33.92	36.78	40.29	42.80
23	9.26	10.20	11.69	13.09	14.85	32.01	35.17	38.08	41.64	44.18
24	9.89	10.86	12.40	13.85	15.66	33.20	36.42	39.36	42.98	45.56
25	10.52	11.52	13.12	14.61	16.47	34.38	37.65	40.65	44.31	46.93
26	11.16	12.20	13.84	15.38	17.29	35.56	38.89	41.92	45.64	48.29
27	11.81	12.88	14.57	16.15	18.11	36.74	40.11	43.19	46.96	49.64
28	12.46	13.56	15.31	16.93	18.94	37.92	41.34	44.46	48.28	50.99
29	13.21	14.26	16.05	17.71	19.77	39.09	42.56	45.72	49.59	52.34
30	13.79	14.95	16.79	18.49	20.60	40.26	43.77	46.98	50.89	53.67
40	20.71	22.16	24.43	26.51	29.05	51.80	55.76	59.34	63.69	66.77
50	27.99	29.71	32.36	34.76	37.69	63.17	67.50	71.42	76.15	79.49
60	35.53	37.48	40.48	43.19	46.46	74.40	79.08	83.30	88.38	91.95
70	43.28	45.44	48.76	51.74	55.33	85.53	90.53	95.02	100.4	104.2
80	51.17	53.54	57.15	60.39	64.28	96.58	101.9	106.6	112.3	116.3
90	59.20	61.75	65.65	69.13	73.29	107.6	113.1	118.1	124.1	128.3
100	67.33	70.06	74.22	77.93	82.36	118.5	124.3	129.6	135.8	140.2

† Extracted with permission from H. L. Harter, A New Table of Percentage Points of the Chi-square Distribution, *Biometrika*, June, 1964.

Appendix D-8 Chi-square divided by degrees of freedom†

Entry $= \chi^2_{\nu;p}/\nu$ where $\Pr(\chi^2_\nu/\nu < \chi^2_{\nu;p}/\nu) = p$

ν \ p	.0005	.001	.005	.01	.025	.05	.10	.20	.30	.40	.50	.60	.70	.80	.90	.95	.975	.99	.995	.999	.9995
1	$.0^639$	$.0^5157$	$.0^439$	$.0^316$	$.0^398$	$.0^239$	.016	.064	.148	.275	.455	.708	1.07	1.64	2.71	3.84	5.02	6.64	7.88	10.83	12.12
2	.001	.001	.005	.010	.025	.052	.106	.223	.356	.511	.693	.916	1.20	1.61	2.30	3.00	3.69	4.61	5.30	6.91	7.60
3	.005	.008	.024	.038	.072	.117	.195	.335	.475	.623	.789	.982	1.22	1.55	2.08	2.60	3.12	3.78	4.28	5.42	5.91
4	.016	.023	.052	.074	.121	.178	.266	.412	.549	.688	.839	1.011	1.22	1.50	1.94	2.37	2.79	3.32	3.72	4.62	5.00
5	.032	.042	.082	.111	.166	.229	.322	.469	.600	.731	.870	1.03	1.21	1.46	1.85	2.21	2.57	3.02	3.35	4.10	4.42
6	.050	.064	.113	.145	.206	.272	.367	.512	.638	.762	.891	1.04	1.21	1.43	1.77	2.10	2.41	2.80	3.09	3.74	4.02
7	.069	.085	.141	.177	.241	.310	.405	.546	.667	.785	.907	1.04	1.20	1.40	1.72	2.01	2.29	2.64	2.90	3.47	3.72
8	.089	.107	.168	.206	.272	.342	.436	.574	.691	.803	.918	1.04	1.19	1.38	1.67	1.94	2.19	2.51	2.74	3.27	3.48
9	.108	.128	.193	.232	.300	.369	.463	.598	.710	.817	.927	1.05	1.18	1.36	1.63	1.88	2.11	2.41	2.62	3.10	3.30
10	.126	.148	.216	.256	.325	.394	.487	.618	.727	.830	.934	1.05	1.18	1.34	1.60	1.83	2.05	2.32	2.52	2.96	3.14
11	.144	.167	.237	.278	.347	.416	.507	.635	.741	.840	.940	1.05	1.17	1.33	1.57	1.79	1.99	2.25	2.43	2.84	3.01
12	.161	.184	.256	.298	.367	.436	.525	.651	.753	.848	.945	1.05	1.17	1.32	1.55	1.75	1.94	2.18	2.36	2.74	2.90
13	.177	.201	.274	.316	.385	.453	.542	.664	.764	.856	.949	1.05	1.16	1.31	1.52	1.72	1.90	2.13	2.29	2.66	2.81
14	.193	.217	.291	.333	.402	.469	.556	.676	.773	.863	.953	1.05	1.16	1.30	1.50	1.69	1.87	2.08	2.24	2.58	2.72
15	.207	.232	.307	.349	.418	.484	.570	.687	.781	.869	.956	1.05	1.15	1.29	1.49	1.67	1.83	2.04	2.19	2.51	2.65
16	.221	.246	.321	.363	.432	.498	.582	.697	.789	.874	.959	1.05	1.15	1.28	1.47	1.64	1.80	2.00	2.14	2.45	2.58
17	.234	.260	.335	.377	.445	.510	.593	.706	.796	.879	.961	1.05	1.15	1.27	1.46	1.62	1.78	1.97	2.10	2.40	2.52
18	.247	.272	.348	.390	.457	.522	.604	.714	.802	.883	.963	1.05	1.14	1.26	1.44	1.60	1.75	1.95	2.06	2.35	2.47
19	.258	.285	.360	.402	.469	.532	.613	.722	.808	.887	.965	1.05	1.14	1.26	1.43	1.59	1.73	1.90	2.03	2.31	2.42
20	.270	.296	.372	.413	.480	.543	.622	.729	.813	.890	.967	1.05	1.14	1.25	1.42	1.57	1.71	1.88	2.00	2.27	2.37
22	.291	.317	.393	.434	.499	.561	.638	.742	.823	.897	.970	1.05	1.13	1.24	1.40	1.54	1.67	1.83	1.95	2.19	2.30
24	.310	.337	.412	.452	.517	.577	.652	.753	.831	.902	.972	1.05	1.13	1.23	1.38	1.52	1.64	1.79	1.90	2.13	2.23
26	.328	.355	.429	.469	.532	.592	.665	.762	.838	.907	.974	1.05	1.12	1.22	1.37	1.50	1.61	1.76	1.86	2.08	2.17
28	.345	.371	.445	.484	.547	.605	.676	.771	.845	.911	.976	1.04	1.12	1.22	1.35	1.48	1.59	1.73	1.82	2.03	2.12
30	.360	.386	.460	.498	.560	.616	.687	.779	.850	.915	.978	1.04	1.12	1.21	1.34	1.46	1.57	1.70	1.79	1.99	2.07

Appendix D-8 (Continued)

ν\p	.0005	.001	.005	.01	.025	.05	.10	.20	.30	.40	.50	.60	.70	.80	.90	.95	.975	.99	.995	.999	.9995
35	.394	.420	.491	.529	.588	.642	.708	.795	.862	.922	.981	1.04	1.11	1.19	1.32	1.42	1.52	1.64	1.72	1.90	1.98
40	.423	.448	.518	.554	.611	.663	.726	.809	.872	.928	.983	1.04	1.10	1.18	1.30	1.39	1.48	1.59	1.67	1.84	1.90
45	.448	.472	.540	.576	.630	.680	.741	.820	.880	.933	.985	1.04	1.10	1.17	1.28	1.37	1.45	1.55	1.63	1.78	1.84
50	.469	.494	.560	.594	.647	.695	.754	.829	.886	.937	.987	1.04	1.09	1.16	1.26	1.35	1.43	1.52	1.59	1.73	1.79
55	.488	.512	.577	.610	.662	.708	.765	.837	.892	.941	.988	1.04	1.09	1.16	1.25	1.33	1.41	1.50	1.56	1.69	1.75
60	.506	.529	.592	.625	.675	.720	.774	.844	.897	.944	.989	1.04	1.09	1.15	1.24	1.32	1.39	1.47	1.53	1.66	1.71
70	.535	.558	.618	.649	.697	.739	.790	.856	.905	.949	.990	1.03	1.08	1.14	1.22	1.29	1.36	1.43	1.49	1.60	1.65
80	.560	.582	.640	.669	.714	.755	.803	.865	.911	.952	.992	1.03	1.08	1.13	1.21	1.27	1.33	1.40	1.45	1.56	1.60
90	.581	.602	.658	.686	.729	.768	.814	.873	.917	.955	.993	1.03	1.07	1.12	1.20	1.26	1.31	1.38	1.43	1.52	1.56
100	.599	.619	.673	.701	.742	.779	.824	.879	.921	.958	.993	1.03	1.07	1.12	1.18	1.24	1.30	1.36	1.40	1.49	1.53
120	.629	.648	.699	.724	.763	.798	.839	.890	.929	.962	.994	1.03	1.06	1.11	1.17	1.22	1.27	1.32	1.36	1.45	1.48
140	.653	.671	.719	.743	.780	.812	.850	.898	.934	.965	.995	1.03	1.06	1.10	1.16	1.20	1.25	1.30	1.33	1.41	1.44
160	.673	.690	.736	.758	.793	.824	.860	.905	.939	.968	.996	1.02	1.06	1.09	1.15	1.19	1.23	1.28	1.31	1.38	1.41
180	.689	.706	.749	.771	.804	.833	.868	.910	.942	.970	.996	1.02	1.05	1.09	1.14	1.18	1.22	1.26	1.29	1.36	1.38
200	.703	.719	.761	.782	.814	.841	.874	.915	.945	.972	.997	1.02	1.05	1.08	1.13	1.17	1.21	1.25	1.28	1.34	1.36
250	.732	.746	.785	.804	.332	.858	.887	.924	.951	.975	.997	1.02	1.04	1.07	1.12	1.15	1.18	1.22	1.25	1.30	1.32
300	.753	.767	.802	.820	.846	.870	.897	.931	.956	.977	.998	1.02	1.04	1.07	1.11	1.14	1.17	1.20	1.22	1.27	1.29
350	.770	.783	.816	.833	.857	.879	.904	.936	.959	.979	.998	1.02	1.04	1.06	1.10	1.13	1.15	1.18	1.21	1.25	1.27
400	.784	.796	.827	.843	.866	.887	.911	.940	.962	.981	.998	1.02	1.04	1.06	1.09	1.12	1.14	1.17	1.19	1.24	1.25
450	.795	.807	.837	.852	.874	.893	.916	.944	.964	.982	.999	1.02	1.03	1.06	1.09	1.11	1.13	1.16	1.28	1.22	1.23
500	.805	.816	.845	.859	.880	.898	.920	.946	.966	.983	.999	1.01	1.03	1.05	1.08	1.11	1.13	1.15	1.17	1.21	1.22
750	.839	.848	.872	.884	.901	.917	.934	.956	.972	.986	.999	1.01	1.03	1.04	1.07	1.09	1.10	1.12	1.14	1.17	1.18
1000	.859	.868	.889	.899	.914	.928	.943	.962	.976	.988	.999	1.01	1.02	1.04	1.06	1.07	1.09	1.11	1.12	1.14	1.15
5000	.936	.939	.949	.954	.961	.967	.974	.983	.989	.995	1.00	1.00	1.01	1.02	1.02	1.03	1.04	1.05	1.05	1.06	1.07
∞	1	1	1	1	1	1	1	1	1	1	1.00	1	1	1	1	1	1	1	1	1	1

† Reprinted with permission from W. J. Dixon and F. J. Massey, Jr., "Introduction to Statistical Analysis," 2d ed., McGraw-Hill Book Company, New York, 1957.

Appendix D-9 The F distribution†

Entry $= F_{\nu_1,\nu_2;p}$ where $\Pr(F_{\nu_1,\nu_2} < F_{\nu_1,\nu_2;p}) = p$

ν_2	p	1	2	3	4	5	6	7	8	9	10	11	12	p
1	.0005	$.0^662$	$.0^350$	$.0^238$	$.0^294$	.016	.022	.027	.032	.036	.039	.042	.045	.0005
	.001	$.0^525$	$.0^210$	$.0^260$	.013	.021	.028	.034	.039	.044	.048	.051	.054	.001
	.005	$.0^462$	$.0^251$	.018	.032	.041	.054	.062	.068	.073	.078	.082	.085	.005
	.010	$.0^325$	.010	.029	.047	.062	.073	.082	.089	.095	.100	.104	.107	.010
	.025	$.0^315$	.026	.057	.082	.100	.113	.124	.132	.139	.144	.149	.153	.025
	.05	$.0^262$	.054	.099	.130	.151	.167	.179	.188	.195	.201	.207	.211	.05
	.10	.025	.117	.181	.220	.246	.265	.279	.289	.298	.304	.310	.315	.10
	.25	.172	.389	.494	.553	.591	.617	.637	.650	.661	.670	.680	.684	.25
	.50	1.00	1.50	1.71	1.82	1.89	1.94	1.98	2.00	2.03	2.04	2.05	2.07	.50
	.75	5.83	7.50	8.20	8.58	8.82	8.98	9.10	9.19	9.26	9.32	9.36	9.41	.75
	.90	39.9	49.5	53.6	55.8	57.2	58.2	58.9	59.4	59.9	60.2	60.5	60.7	.90
	.95	161	200	216	225	230	234	237	239	241	242	243	244	.95
	.975	648	800	864	900	922	937	948	957	963	969	973	977	.975
	.99	405^1	500^1	540^1	562^1	576^1	586^1	593^1	598^1	602^1	606^1	608^1	611^1	.99
	.995	162^2	200^2	216^2	225^2	231^2	234^2	237^2	239^2	241^2	242^2	243^2	244^2	.995
	.999	406^3	500^3	540^3	562^3	576^3	586^3	593^3	598^3	602^3	606^3	609^3	611^3	.999
	.9995	162^4	200^4	216^4	225^4	231^4	234^4	237^4	239^4	241^4	242^4	243^4	244^4	.9995
2	.0005	$.0^650$	$.0^350$	$.0^242$	.011	.020	.029	.037	.044	.050	.056	.061	.065	.0005
	.001	$.0^520$	$.0^210$	$.0^268$	.016	.027	.037	.046	.054	.061	.067	.072	.077	.001
	.005	$.0^450$	$.0^250$	.020	.038	.055	.069	.081	.091	.099	.106	.112	.118	.005
	.01	$.0^320$	.010	.032	.056	.075	.092	.105	.116	.125	.132	.139	.144	.01
	.025	$.0^313$	.026	.062	.094	.119	.138	.153	.165	.175	.183	.190	.196	.025
	.05	$.0^250$	.053	.105	.144	.173	.194	.211	.224	.235	.244	.251	.257	.05
	.10	.020	.111	.183	.231	.265	.289	.307	.321	.333	.342	.350	.356	.10
	.25	.133	.333	.439	.500	.540	.568	.588	.604	.616	.626	.633	.641	.25
	.50	.667	1.00	1.13	1.21	1.25	1.28	1.30	1.32	1.33	1.34	1.35	1.36	.50
	.75	2.57	3.00	3.15	3.23	3.28	3.31	3.34	3.35	3.37	3.38	3.39	3.39	.75
	.90	8.53	9.00	9.16	9.24	9.29	9.33	9.35	9.37	9.38	9.39	9.40	9.41	.90
	.95	18.5	19.0	19.2	19.2	19.3	19.3	19.4	19.4	19.4	19.4	19.4	19.4	.95
	.975	38.5	39.0	39.2	39.2	39.3	39.3	39.4	39.4	39.4	39.4	39.4	39.4	.975
	.99	98.5	99.0	99.2	99.2	99.3	99.3	99.4	99.4	99.4	99.4	99.4	99.4	.99
	.995	198	199	199	199	199	199	199	199	199	199	199	199	.995
	.999	998	999	999	999	999	999	999	999	999	999	999	999	.999
	.9995	200^1	200^1	200^1	200^1	200^1	200^1	200^1	200^1	200^1	200^1	200^1	200^1	.9995
3	.0005	$.0^646$	$.0^350$	$.0^244$	.012	.023	.033	.043	.052	.060	.067	.074	.079	.0005
	.0001	$.0^519$	$.0^210$	$.0^271$	.018	.030	.042	.053	.063	.072	.079	.086	.093	.001
	.005	$.0^446$	$.0^250$	.021	.041	.060	.077	.092	.104	.115	.124	.132	.138	.005
	.01	$.0^319$	.010	.034	.060	.083	.102	.118	.132	.143	.153	.161	.168	.01
	.025	$.0^212$	.026	.065	.100	.129	.152	.170	.185	.197	.207	.216	.224	.025
	.05	$.0^246$	.052	.108	.152	.185	.210	.230	.246	.259	.270	.279	.287	.05
	.10	.019	.109	.185	.239	.276	.304	.325	.342	.356	.367	.376	.384	.10
	.25	.122	.317	.424	.489	.531	.561	.582	.600	.613	.624	.633	.641	.25
	.50	.585	.881	1.00	1.06	1.10	1.13	1.15	1.16	1.17	1.18	1.19	1.20	.50
	.75	2.02	2.28	2.36	2.39	2.41	2.42	2.43	2.44	2.44	2.44	2.45	2.45	.75
	.90	5.54	5.46	5.39	5.34	5.31	5.28	5.27	5.25	5.24	5.23	5.22	5.22	.90
	.95	10.1	9.55	9.28	9.12	9.01	8.94	8.89	8.85	8.81	8.79	8.76	8.74	.95
	.975	17.4	16.0	15.4	15.1	14.9	14.7	14.6	14.5	14.5	14.4	14.4	14.3	.975
	.99	34.1	30.8	29.5	28.7	28.2	27.9	27.7	27.5	27.3	27.2	27.1	27.1	.99
	.995	55.6	49.8	47.5	46.2	45.4	44.8	44.4	44.1	43.9	43.7	43.5	43.4	.995
	.999	167	149	141	137	135	133	132	131	130	129	129	128	.999
	.9995	266	237	225	218	214	211	209	208	207	206	204	204	.9995

Read $.0^356$ as .00056, 200^1 as 2000, 162^4 as 1620000, etc.

ν_1 / p	15	20	24	30	40	50	60	100	120	200	500	∞	p	ν_2
.0005	.051	.058	.062	.066	.069	.072	.074	.077	.078	.080	.081	.083	.0005	1
.001	.060	.067	.071	.075	.079	.082	.084	.087	.088	.089	.091	.092	.001	
.005	.093	.101	.105	.109	.113	.116	.118	.121	.122	.124	.126	.127	.005	
.01	.115	.124	.128	.132	.137	.139	.141	.145	.146	.148	.150	.151	.01	
.025	.161	.170	.175	.180	.184	.187	.189	.193	.194	.196	.198	.199	.025	
.05	.220	.230	.235	.240	.245	.248	.250	.254	.255	.257	.259	.261	.05	
.10	.325	.336	.342	.347	.353	.356	.358	.362	.364	.366	.368	.370	.10	
.25	.698	.712	.719	.727	.734	.738	.741	.747	.749	.752	.754	.756	.25	
.50	2.09	2.12	2.13	2.15	2.16	2.17	2.17	2.18	2.18	2.19	2.19	2.20	.50	
.75	9.49	9.58	9.63	9.67	9.71	9.74	9.76	9.78	9.80	9.82	9.84	9.85	.75	
.90	61.2	61.7	62.0	62.3	62.5	62.7	62.8	63.0	63.1	63.2	63.3	63.3	.90	
.95	246	248	249	250	251	252	252	253	253	254	254	254	.95	
.975	985	993	997	100^1	101^1	101^1	101^1	101^1	101^1	102^1	102^1	102^1	.975	
.99	616^1	621^1	623^1	626^1	629^1	630^1	631^1	633^1	634^1	635^1	636^1	637^1	.99	
.995	246^2	248^2	249^2	250^2	251^2	252^2	253^2	253^2	254^2	254^2	254^2	255^2	.995	
.999	616^3	621^3	623^3	626^3	629^3	630^3	631^3	633^3	634^3	635^3	636^3	637^3	.999	
.9995	246^4	248^4	249^4	250^4	251^4	252^4	252^4	253^4	253^4	253^4	254^4	254^4	.9995	
.0005	.076	.088	.094	.101	.108	.113	.116	.122	.124	.127	.130	.132	.0005	2
.001	.088	.100	.107	.114	.121	.126	.129	.135	.137	.140	.143	.145	.001	
.005	.130	.143	.150	.157	.165	.169	.173	.179	.181	.184	.187	.189	.005	
.01	.157	.171	.178	.186	.193	.198	.201	.207	.209	.212	.215	.217	.01	
.025	.210	.224	.232	.239	.247	.251	.255	.261	.263	.266	.269	.271	.025	
.05	.272	.286	.294	.302	.309	.314	.317	.324	.326	.329	.332	.334	.05	
.10	.371	.386	.394	.402	.410	.415	.418	.424	.426	.429	.433	.434	.10	
.25	.657	.672	.680	.689	.697	.702	.705	.711	.713	.716	.719	.721	.25	
.50	1.38	1.39	1.40	1.41	1.42	1.42	1.43	1.43	1.43	1.44	1.44	1.44	.50	
.75	3.41	3.43	3.43	3.44	3.45	3.45	3.46	3.47	3.47	3.48	3.48	3.48	.75	
.90	9.42	9.44	9.45	9.46	9.47	9.47	9.47	9.48	9.48	9.49	9.49	9.49	.90	
.95	19.4	19.4	19.5	19.5	19.5	19.5	19.5	19.5	19.5	19.5	19.5	19.5	.95	
.975	39.4	39.4	39.5	39.5	39.5	39.5	39.5	39.5	39.5	39.5	39.5	39.5	.975	
.99	99.4	99.4	99.5	99.5	99.5	99.5	99.5	99.5	99.5	99.5	99.5	99.5	.99	
.995	199	199	199	199	199	199	199	199	199	199	199	200	.995	
.999	999	999	999	999	999	999	999	999	999	999	999	999	.999	
.9995	200^1	200^1	200^1	200^1	200^1	200^1	200^1	200^1	200^1	200^1	200^1	200^1	.9995	
.0005	.093	.109	.117	.127	.136	.143	.147	.156	.158	.162	.166	.169	.0005	3
.001	.107	.123	.132	.142	.152	.158	.162	.171	.173	.177	.181	.184	.001	
.005	.154	.172	.181	.191	.201	.207	.211	.220	.222	.227	.231	.234	.005	
.01	.185	.203	.212	.222	.232	.238	.242	.251	.253	.258	.262	.264	.01	
.025	.241	.259	.269	.279	.280	.295	.299	.308	.310	.314	.318	.321	.025	
.05	.304	.323	.332	.342	.352	.358	.363	.370	.373	.377	.382	.384	.05	
.10	.402	.420	.430	.439	.449	.455	.459	.467	.469	.474	.476	.480	.10	
.25 `	.658	.675	.684	.693	.702	.708	.711	.719	.721	.724	.728	.730	.25	
.50	1.21	1.23	1.23	1.24	1.25	1.25	1.25	1.26	1.26	1.26	1.27	1.27	.50	
.75	2.46	2.46	2.46	2.47	2.47	2.47	2.47	2.47	2.47	2.47	2.47	2.47	.75	
.90	5.20	5.18	5.18	5.17	5.16	5.15	5.15	5.14	5.14	5.14	5.14	5.13	.90	
.95	8.70	8.66	8.63	8.62	8.59	8.58	8.57	8.55	8.55	8.54	8.53	8.53	.95	
.975	14.3	14.2	14.1	14.1	14.0	14.0	14.0	14.0	13.9	13.9	13.9	13.9	.975	
.99	26.9	26.7	26.6	26.5	26.4	26.4	26.3	26.2	26.2	26.2	26.1	26.1	.99	
.995	43.1	42.8	42.6	42.5	42.3	42.2	42.1	42.0	42.0	41.9	41.9	41.8	.995	
.999	127	126	126	125	125	125	124	124	124	124	124	123	.999	
.9995	203	201	200	199	199	198	198	197	197	197	196	196	.9995	

Appendix D-9 (Continued)

ν_2	ν_1 / p	1	2	3	4	5	6	7	8	9	10	11	12	p
4	.0005	$.0^6 44$	$.0^3 50$	$.0^2 46$	.013	.024	.036	.047	.057	.066	.075	.082	.089	.0005
	.001	$.0^5 18$	$.0^2 10$	$.0^2 73$	.019	.032	.046	.058	.069	.079	.089	.097	.104	.001
	.005	$.0^4 44$	$.0^2 50$	.022	.043	.064	.083	.100	.114	.126	.137	.145	.153	.005
	.01	$.0^3 18$	.010	.035	.063	.088	.109	.127	.143	.156	.167	.176	.185	.01
	.025	$.0^2 11$	.026	.066	.104	.135	.161	.181	.198	.212	.224	.234	.243	.025
	.05	$.0^2 44$	.052	.110	.157	.193	.221	.243	.261	.275	.288	.298	.307	.05
	.10	.018	.108	.187	.243	.284	.314	.338	.356	.371	.384	.394	.403	.10
	.25	.117	.309	.418	.484	.528	.560	.583	.601	.615	.627	.637	.645	.25
	.50	.549	.828	.941	1.00	1.04	1.06	1.08	1.09	1.10	1.11	1.12	1.13	.50
	.75	1.81	2.00	2.05	2.06	2.07	2.08	2.08	2.08	2.08	2.08	2.08	2.08	.75
	.90	4.54	4.32	4.19	4.11	4.05	4.01	3.98	3.95	3.94	3.92	3.91	3.90	.90
	.95	7.71	6.94	6.59	6.39	6.26	6.16	6.09	6.04	6.00	5.96	5.94	5.91	.95
	.975	12.2	10.6	9.98	9.60	9.36	9.20	9.07	8.98	8.90	8.84	8.79	8.75	.975
	.99	21.2	18.0	16.7	16.0	15.5	15.2	15.0	14.8	14.7	14.5	14.4	14.4	.99
	.995	31.3	26.3	24.3	23.2	22.5	22.0	21.6	21.4	21.1	21.0	20.8	20.7	.995
	.999	74.1	61.2	56.2	53.4	51.7	50.5	49.7	49.0	48.5	48.0	47.7	47.4	.999
	.9995	106	87.4	80.1	76.1	73.6	71.9	70.6	69.7	68.9	68.3	67.8	67.4	.9995
5	.0005	$.0^6 43$	$.0^3 50$	$.0^2 47$	.014	.025	.038	.050	.061	.070	.081	.089	.096	.0005
	.001	$.0^5 17$	$.0^2 10$	$.0^2 75$	.019	.034	.048	.062	.074	.085	.095	.104	.112	.001
	.005	$.0^4 43$	$.0^2 50$	.022	.045	.067	.087	.105	.120	.134	.146	.156	.165	.005
	.01	$.0^3 17$	.010	.035	.064	.091	.114	.134	.151	.165	.177	.188	.197	.01
	.025	$.0^2 11$	.025	.067	.107	.140	.167	.189	.208	.223	.236	.248	.257	.025
	.05	$.0^2 43$	.052	.111	.160	.198	.228	.252	.271	.287	.301	.313	.322	.05
	.10	.017	.108	.188	.247	.290	.322	.347	.367	.383	.397	.408	.418	.10
	.25	.113	.305	.415	.483	.528	.560	.584	.604	.618	.631	.641	.650	.25
	.50	.528	.799	.907	.965	1.00	1.02	1.04	1.05	1.06	1.07	1.08	1.09	.50
	.75	1.69	1.85	1.88	1.89	1.89	1.89	1.89	1.89	1.89	1.89	1.89	1.89	.75
	.90	4.06	3.78	3.62	3.52	3.45	3.40	3.37	3.34	3.32	3.30	3.28	3.27	.90
	.95	6.61	5.79	5.41	5.19	5.05	4.95	4.88	4.82	4.77	4.74	4.71	4.68	.95
	.975	10.0	8.43	7.76	7.39	7.15	6.98	6.85	6.76	6.68	6.62	6.57	6.52	.975
	.99	16.3	13.3	12.1	11.4	11.0	10.7	10.5	10.3	10.2	10.1	9.96	9.89	.99
	.995	22.8	18.3	16.5	15.6	14.9	14.5	14.2	14.0	13.8	13.6	13.5	13.4	.995
	.999	47.2	37.1	33.2	31.1	29.7	28.8	28.2	27.6	27.2	26.9	26.6	26.4	.999
	.9995	63.6	49.8	44.4	41.5	39.7	38.5	37.6	36.9	36.4	35.9	35.6	35.2	.9995
6	.0005	$.0^6 43$	$.0^3 50$	$.0^2 47$	.014	.026	.039	.052	.064	.075	.085	.094	.103	.0005
	.001	$.0^5 17$	$.0^2 10$	$.0^2 75$	.020	.035	.050	.064	.078	.090	.101	.111	.119	.001
	.005	$.0^4 43$	$.0^2 50$	.022	.045	.069	.090	.109	.126	.140	.153	.164	.174	.005
	.01	$.0^3 17$	.010	.036	.066	.094	.118	.139	.157	.172	.186	.197	.207	.01
	.025	$.0^2 11$	.025	.068	.109	.143	.172	.195	.215	.231	.246	.258	.268	.025
	.05	$.0^2 43$	.052	.112	.162	.202	.233	.259	.279	.296	.311	.324	.334	.05
	.10	.017	.107	.189	.249	.294	.327	.354	.375	.392	.406	.418	.429	.10
	.25	.111	.302	.413	.481	.524	.561	.586	.606	.622	.635	.645	.654	.25
	.50	.515	.780	.886	.942	.977	1.00	1.02	1.03	1.04	1.05	1.05	1.06	.50
	.75	1.62	1.76	1.78	1.79	1.79	1.78	1.78	1.78	1.77	1.77	1.77	1.77	.75
	.90	3.78	3.46	3.29	3.18	3.11	3.05	3.01	2.98	2.96	2.94	2.92	2.90	.90
	.95	5.99	5.14	4.76	4.53	4.39	4.28	4.21	4.15	4.10	4.06	4.03	4.00	.95
	.975	8.81	7.26	6.60	6.23	5.99	5.82	5.70	5.60	5.52	5.46	5.41	5.37	.975
	.99	13.7	10.9	9.78	9.15	8.75	8.47	8.26	8.10	7.98	7.87	7.79	7.72	.99
	.995	18.6	14.5	12.9	12.0	11.5	11.1	10.8	10.6	10.4	10.2	10.1	10.0	.995
	.999	35.5	27.0	23.7	21.9	20.8	20.0	19.5	19.0	18.7	18.4	18.2	18.0	.999
	.9995	46.1	34.8	30.4	28.1	26.6	25.6	24.9	24.3	23.9	23.5	23.2	23.0	.9995

p \ ν₁	15	20	24	30	40	50	60	100	120	200	500	∞	p	ν₂
.0005	.105	.125	.135	.147	.159	.166	.172	.183	.186	.191	.196	.200	.0005	4
.001	.121	.141	.152	.163	.176	.183	.188	.200	.202	.208	.213	.217	.001	
.005	.172	.193	.204	.216	.229	.237	.242	.253	.255	.260	.266	.269	.005	
.01	.204	.226	.237	.249	.261	.269	.274	.285	.287	.293	.298	.301	.01	
.025	.263	.284	.296	.308	.320	.327	.332	.342	.346	.351	.356	.359	.025	
.05	.327	.349	.360	.372	.384	.391	.396	.407	.409	.413	.418	.422	.05	
.10	.424	.445	.456	.467	.478	.485	.490	.500	.502	.508	.510	.514	.10	
.25	.664	.683	.692	.702	.712	.718	.722	.731	.733	.737	.740	.743	.25	
.50	1.14	1.15	1.16	1.16	1.17	1.18	1.18	1.18	1.18	1.19	1.19	1.19	.50	
.75	2.08	2.08	2.08	2.08	2.08	2.08	2.08	2.08	2.08	2.08	2.08	2.08	.75	
.90	3.87	3.84	3.83	3.82	3.80	3.80	3.79	3.78	3.78	3.77	3.76	3.76	.90	
.95	5.86	5.80	5.77	5.75	5.72	5.70	5.69	5.66	5.66	5.65	5.64	5.63	.95	
.975	8.66	8.56	8.51	8.46	8.41	8.38	8.36	8.32	8.31	8.29	8.27	8.26	.975	
.99	14.2	14.0	13.9	13.8	13.7	13.7	13.6	13.6	13.6	13.5	13.5	13.5	.99	
.995	20.4	20.2	20.0	19.9	19.8	19.7	19.6	19.5	19.5	19.4	19.4	19.3	.995	
.999	46.8	46.1	45.8	45.4	45.1	44.9	44.7	44.5	44.4	44.3	44.1	44.0	.999	
.9995	66.5	65.5	65.1	64.6	64.1	63.8	63.6	63.2	63.1	62.9	62.7	62.6	.9995	
.0005	.115	.137	.150	.163	.177	.186	.192	.205	.209	.216	.222	.226	.0005	5
.001	.132	.155	.167	.181	.195	.204	.210	.223	.227	.233	.239	.244	.001	
.005	.186	.210	.223	.237	.251	.260	.266	.279	.282	.288	.294	.299	.005	
.01	.219	.244	.257	.270	.285	.293	.299	.312	.315	.322	.328	.331	.01	
.025	.280	.304	.317	.330	.344	.353	.359	.370	.374	.380	.386	.390	.025	
.05	.345	.369	.382	.395	.408	.417	.422	.432	.437	.442	.448	.452	.05	
.10	.440	.463	.476	.488	.501	.508	.514	.524	.527	.532	.538	.541	.10	
.25	.669	.690	.700	.711	.722	.728	.732	.741	.743	.748	.752	.755	.25	
.50	1.10	1.11	1.11	1.12	1.13	1.13	1.14	1.14	1.14	1.15	1.15	1.15	.50	
.75	1.89	1.88	1.88	1.88	1.88	1.88	1.87	1.87	1.87	1.87	1.87	1.87	.75	
.90	3.24	3.21	3.19	3.17	3.16	3.15	3.14	3.13	3.12	3.12	3.11	3.10	.90	
.95	4.62	4.56	4.53	4.50	4.46	4.44	4.43	4.41	4.40	4.39	4.37	4.36	.95	
.975	6.43	6.33	6.28	6.23	6.18	6.14	6.12	6.08	6.07	6.05	6.03	6.02	.975	
.99	9.72	9.55	9.47	9.38	9.29	9.24	9.20	9.13	9.11	9.08	9.04	9.02	.99	
.995	13.1	12.9	12.8	12.7	12.5	12.5	12.4	12.3	12.3	12.2	12.2	12.1	.995	
.999	25.9	25.4	25.1	24.9	24.6	24.4	24.3	24.1	24.1	23.9	23.8	23.8	.999	
.9995	34.6	33.9	33.5	33.1	32.7	32.5	32.3	32.1	32.0	31.8	31.7	31.6	.9995	
.0005	.123	.148	.162	.177	.193	.203	.210	.225	.229	.236	.244	.249	.0005	6
.001	.141	.166	.180	.195	.211	.222	.229	.243	.247	.255	.262	.267	.001	
.005	.197	.224	.238	.253	.269	.279	.286	.301	.304	.312	.318	.324	.005	
.01	.232	.258	.273	.288	.304	.313	.321	.334	.338	.346	.352	.357	.01	
.025	.293	.320	.334	.349	.364	.375	.381	.394	.398	.405	.412	.415	.025	
.05	.358	.385	.399	.413	.428	.437	.444	.457	.460	.467	.472	.476	.05	
.10	.453	.478	.491	.505	.519	.526	.533	.546	.548	.556	.559	.564	.10	
.25	.675	.696	.707	.718	.729	.736	.741	.751	.753	.758	.762	.765	.25	
.50	1.07	1.08	1.09	1.10	1.10	1.11	1.11	1.11	1.12	1.12	1.12	1.12	.50	
.75	1.76	1.76	1.75	1.75	1.75	1.75	1.74	1.74	1.74	1.74	1.74	1.74	.75	
.90	2.87	2.84	2.82	2.80	2.78	2.77	2.76	2.75	2.74	2.73	2.73	2.72	.90	
.95	3.94	3.87	3.84	3.81	3.77	3.75	3.74	3.71	3.70	3.69	3.68	3.67	.95	
.975	5.27	5.17	5.12	5.07	5.01	4.98	4.96	4.92	4.90	4.88	4.86	4.85	.975	
.99	7.56	7.40	7.31	7.23	7.14	7.09	7.06	6.99	6.97	6.93	6.90	6.88	.99	
.995	9.81	9.59	9.47	9.36	9.24	9.17	9.12	9.03	9.00	8.95	8.91	8.88	.995	
.999	17.6	17.1	16.9	16.7	16.4	16.3	16.2	16.0	16.0	15.9	15.8	15.7	.999	
.9995	22.4	21.9	21.7	21.4	21.1	20.9	20.7	20.5	20.4	20.3	20.2	20.1	.9995	

ν_2 \ ν_1	1	2	3	4	5	6	7	8	9	10	11	12	p
7 .0005	$.0^642$	$.0^350$	$.0^248$	.014	.027	.040	.053	.066	.078	.088	.099	.108	.0005
.001	$.0^517$	$.0^210$	$.0^276$	.020	.035	.051	.067	.081	.093	.105	.115	.125	.001
.005	$.0^442$	$.0^250$	.023	.046	.070	.093	.113	.130	.145	.159	.171	.181	.005
.01	$.0^317$	.010	.036	.067	.096	.121	.143	.162	.178	.192	.205	.216	.01
.025	$.0^210$	.025	.068	.110	.146	.176	.200	.221	.238	.253	.266	.277	.025
.05	$.0^242$	.052	.113	.164	.205	.238	.264	.286	.304	.319	.332	.343	.05
.10	.017	.107	.190	.251	.297	.332	.359	.381	.399	.414	.427	.438	.10
.25	.110	.300	.412	.481	.528	.562	.588	.608	.624	.637	.649	.658	.25
.50	.506	.767	.871	.926	.960	.983	1.00	1.01	1.02	1.03	1.04	1.04	.50
.75	1.57	1.70	1.72	1.72	1.71	1.71	1.70	1.70	1.69	1.69	1.69	1.68	.75
.90	3.59	3.26	3.07	2.96	2.88	2.83	2.78	2.75	2.72	2.70	2.68	2.67	.90
.95	5.59	4.74	4.35	4.12	3.97	3.87	3.79	3.73	3.68	3.64	3.60	3.57	.95
.975	8.07	6.54	5.89	5.52	5.29	5.12	4.99	4.90	4.82	4.76	4.71	4.67	.975
.99	12.2	9.55	8.45	7.85	7.46	7.19	6.99	6.84	6.72	6.62	6.54	6.47	.99
.995	16.2	12.4	10.9	10.0	9.52	9.16	8.89	8.68	8.51	8.38	8.27	8.18	.995
.999	29.2	21.7	18.8	17.2	16.2	15.5	15.0	14.6	14.3	14.1	13.9	13.7	.999
.9995	37.0	27.2	23.5	21.4	20.2	19.3	18.7	18.2	17.8	17.5	17.2	17.0	.9995
8 .0005	$.0^642$	$.0^350$	$.0^248$	.014	.027	.041	.055	.068	.081	.092	.102	.112	.0005
.001	$.0^517$	$.0^210$	$.0^276$	.020	.036	.053	.068	.083	.096	.109	.120	.130	.001
.005	$.0^442$	$.0^250$	.027	.047	.072	.095	.115	.133	.149	.164	.176	.187	.005
.01	$.0^317$	.010	.036	.068	.097	.123	.146	.166	.183	.198	.211	.222	.01
.025	$.0^210$	.025	.069	.111	.148	.179	.204	.226	.244	.259	.273	.285	.025
.05	$.0^242$	.052	.113	.166	.208	.241	.268	.291	.310	.326	.339	.351	.05
.10	.017	.107	.190	.253	.299	.335	.363	.386	.405	.421	.435	.445	.10
.25	.109	.298	.411	.481	.529	.563	.589	.610	.627	.640	.654	.661	.25
.50	.499	.757	.860	.915	.948	.971	.988	1.00	1.01	1.02	1.02	1.03	.50
.75	1.54	1.66	1.67	1.66	1.66	1.65	1.64	1.64	1.64	1.63	1.63	1.62	.75
.90	3.46	3.11	2.92	2.81	2.73	2.67	2.62	2.59	2.56	2.54	2.52	2.50	.90
.95	5.32	4.46	4.07	3.84	3.69	3.58	3.50	3.44	3.39	3.35	3.31	3.28	.95
.975	7.57	6.06	5.42	5.05	4.82	4.65	4.53	4.43	4.36	4.30	4.24	4.20	.975
.99	11.3	8.65	7.59	7.01	6.63	6.37	6.18	6.03	5.91	5.81	5.73	5.67	.99
.995	14.7	11.0	9.60	8.81	8.30	7.95	7.69	7.50	7.34	7.21	7.10	7.01	.995
.999	25.4	18.5	15.8	14.4	13.5	12.9	12.4	12.0	11.8	11.5	11.4	11.2	.999
.9995	31.6	22.8	19.4	17.6	16.4	15.7	15.1	14.6	14.3	14.0	13.8	13.6	.9995
9 .0005	$.0^641$	$.0^350$	$.0^248$	.015	.027	.042	.056	.070	.083	.094	.105	.115	.0005
.001	$.0^517$	$.0^210$	$.0^277$	.021	.037	.054	.070	.085	.099	.112	.123	.134	.001
.005	$.0^442$	$.0^250$	.023	.047	.073	.096	.117	.136	.153	.168	.181	.192	.005
.01	$.0^317$	.010	.037	.068	.098	.125	.149	.169	.187	.202	.216	.228	.01
.025	$.0^210$	.025	.069	.112	.150	.181	.207	.230	.248	.265	.279	.291	.025
.05	$.0^240$	.052	.113	.167	.210	.244	.272	.296	.315	.331	.345	.358	.05
.10	.017	.107	.191	.254	.302	.338	.367	.390	.410	.426	.441	.452	.10
.25	.108	.297	.410	.480	.529	.564	.591	.612	.629	.643	.654	.664	.25
.50	.494	.749	.852	.906	.939	.962	.978	.990	1.00	1.01	1.01	1.02	.50
.75	1.51	1.62	1.63	1.63	1.62	1.61	1.60	1.60	1.59	1.59	1.58	1.58	.75
.90	3.36	3.01	2.81	2.69	2.61	2.55	2.51	2.47	2.44	2.42	2.40	2.38	.90
.95	5.12	4.26	3.86	3.63	3.48	3.37	3.29	3.23	3.18	3.14	3.10	3.07	.95
.975	7.21	5.71	5.08	4.72	4.48	4.32	4.20	4.10	4.03	3.96	3.91	3.87	.975
.99	10.6	8.02	6.99	6.42	6.06	5.80	5.61	5.47	5.35	5.26	5.18	5.11	.99
.995	13.6	10.1	8.72	7.96	7.47	7.13	6.88	6.69	6.54	6.42	6.31	6.23	.995
.999	22.9	16.4	13.9	12.6	11.7	11.1	10.7	10.4	10.1	9.89	9.71	9.57	.999
.9995	28.0	19.9	16.8	15.1	14.1	13.3	12.8	12.4	12.1	11.8	11.6	11.4	.9995

ν₁ p	15	20	24	30	40	50	60	100	120	200	500	∞	p	ν₂
.0005	.130	.157	.172	.188	.206	.217	.225	.242	.246	.255	.263	.268	.0005	7
.001	.148	.176	.191	.208	.225	.237	.245	.261	.266	.274	.282	.288	.001	
.005	.206	.235	.251	.267	.285	.296	.304	.319	.324	.332	.340	.345	.005	
.01	.241	.270	.286	.303	.320	.331	.339	.355	.358	.366	.373	.379	.01	
.025	.304	.333	.348	.364	.381	.392	.399	.413	.418	.426	.433	.437	.025	
.05	.369	.398	.413	.428	.445	.455	.461	.476	.479	.485	.493	.498	.05	
.10	.463	.491	.504	.519	.534	.543	.550	.562	.566	.571	.578	.582	.10	
.25	.679	.702	.713	.725	.737	.745	.749	.760	.762	.767	.772	.775	.25	
.50	1.05	1.07	1.07	1.08	1.08	1.09	1.09	1.10	1.10	1.10	1.10	1.10	.50	
.75	1.68	1.67	1.67	1.66	1.66	1.66	1.65	1.65	1.65	1.65	1.65	1.65	.75	
.90	2.63	2.59	2.58	2.56	2.54	2.52	2.51	2.50	2.49	2.48	2.48	2.47	.90	
.95	3.51	3.44	3.41	3.38	3.34	3.32	3.30	3.27	3.27	3.25	3.24	3.23	.95	
.975	4.57	4.47	4.42	4.36	4.31	4.28	4.25	4.21	4.20	4.18	4.16	4.14	.975	
.99	6.31	6.16	6.07	5.99	5.91	5.86	5.82	5.75	5.74	5.70	5.67	5.65	.99	
.995	7.97	7.75	7.65	7.53	7.42	7.35	7.31	7.22	7.19	7.15	7.10	7.08	.995	
.999	13.3	12.9	12.7	12.5	12.3	12.2	12.1	11.9	11.9	11.8	11.7	11.7	.999	
.9995	16.5	16.0	15.7	15.5	15.2	15.1	15.0	14.7	14.7	14.6	14.5	14.4	.9995	
.0005	.136	.164	.181	.198	.218	.230	.239	.257	.262	.271	.281	.287	.0005	8
.001	.155	.184	.200	.218	.238	.250	.259	.277	.282	.292	.300	.306	.001	
.005	.214	.244	.261	.279	.299	.311	.319	.337	.341	.351	.358	.364	.005	
.01	.250	.281	.297	.315	.334	.346	.354	.372	.376	.385	.392	.398	.01	
.025	.313	.343	.360	.377	.395	.407	.415	.431	.435	.442	.450	.456	.025	
.05	.379	.409	.425	.441	.459	.469	.477	.493	.496	.505	.510	.516	.05	
.10	.472	.500	.515	.531	.547	.556	.563	.578	.581	.588	.595	.599	.10	
.25	.684	.707	.718	.730	.743	.751	.756	.767	.769	.775	.780	.783	.25	
.50	1.04	1.05	1.06	1.07	1.07	1.07	1.08	1.08	1.08	1.09	1.09	1.09	.50	
.75	1.62	1.61	1.60	1.60	1.59	1.59	1.59	1.58	1.58	1.58	1.58	1.58	.75	
.90	2.46	2.42	2.40	2.38	2.36	2.35	2.34	2.32	2.32	2.31	2.30	2.29	.90	
.95	3.22	3.15	3.12	3.08	3.04	3.02	3.01	2.97	2.97	2.95	2.94	2.93	.95	
.975	4.10	4.00	3.95	3.89	3.84	3.81	3.78	3.74	3.73	3.70	3.68	3.67	.975	
.99	5.52	5.36	5.28	5.20	5.12	5.07	5.03	4.96	4.95	4.91	4.88	4.86	.99	
.995	6.81	6.61	6.50	6.40	6.29	6.22	6.18	6.09	6.06	6.02	5.98	5.95	.995	
.999	10.8	10.5	10.3	10.1	9.92	9.80	9.73	9.57	9.54	9.46	9.39	9.34	.999	
.9995	13.1	12.7	12.5	12.2	12.0	11.8	11.8	11.6	11.5	11.4	11.4	11.3	.9995	
.0005	.141	.171	.188	.207	.228	.242	.251	.270	.276	.287	.297	.303	.0005	9
.001	.160	.191	.208	.228	.249	.262	.271	.291	.296	.307	.316	.323	.001	
.005	.220	.253	.271	.290	.310	.324	.332	.351	.356	366	.376	.382	.005	
.01	.257	.289	.307	.326	.346	.358	.368	.386	.391	.400	.410	.415	.01	
.025	.320	.352	.370	.388	.408	.420	.428	.446	.450	.459	.467	.473	.025	
.05	.386	.418	.435	.452	.471	.483	.490	.508	.510	.518	.526	.532	.05	
.10	.479	.509	.525	.541	.558	.568	.575	.588	.594	.602	.610	.613	.10	
.25	.687	.711	.723	.736	.749	.757	.762	.773	.776	.782	.787	.791	.25	
.50	1.03	1.04	1.05	1.05	1.06	1.06	1.07	1.07	1.07	1.08	1.08	1.08	.50	
.75	1.57	1.56	1.56	1.55	1.55	1.54	1.54	1.53	1.53	1.53	1.53	1.53	.75	
.90	2.34	2.30	2.28	2.25	2.23	2.22	2.21	2.19	2.18	2.17	2.17	2.16	.90	
.95	3.01	2.94	2.90	2.86	2.83	2.80	2.79	2.76	2.75	2.73	2.72	2.71	.95	
.975	3.77	3.67	3.61	3.56	3.51	3.47	3.45	3.40	3.39	3.37	3.35	3.33	.975	
.99	4.96	4.81	4.73	4.65	4.57	4.52	4.48	4.42	4.40	4.36	4.33	4.31	.99	
.995	6.03	5.83	5.73	5.62	5.52	5.45	5.41	5.32	5.30	5.26	5.21	5.19	.995	
.999	9.24	8.90	8.72	8.55	8.37	8.26	8.19	8.04	8.00	7.93	7.86	7.81	.999	
.9995	11.0	10.6	10.4	10.2	9.94	9.80	9.71	9.53	9.49	9.40	9.32	9.26	.9995	

ν_2	ν_1 / p	1	2	3	4	5	6	7	8	9	10	11	12	p
10	.0005	$.0^{6}41$	$.0^{3}50$	$.0^{2}49$	.015	.028	.043	.057	.071	.085	.097	.108	.119	.0005
	.001	$.0^{5}17$	$.0^{2}10$	$.0^{2}77$	.021	.037	.054	.071	.087	.101	.114	.126	.137	.001
	.005	$.0^{4}41$	$.0^{2}50$	.023	.048	.073	.098	.119	.139	.156	.171	.185	.197	.005
	.01	$.0^{3}17$	.010	.037	.069	.100	.127	.151	.172	.190	.206	.220	.233	.01
	.025	$.0^{2}10$	.025	.069	.113	.151	.183	.210	.233	.252	.269	.283	.296	.025
	.05	$.0^{2}41$	.052	.114	.168	.211	.246	.275	.299	.319	.336	.351	.363	.05
	.10	.017	.106	.191	.255	.303	.340	.370	.394	.414	.430	.444	.457	.10
	.25	.107	.296	.409	.480	.529	.565	.592	.613	.631	.645	.657	.667	.25
	.50	.490	.743	.845	.899	.932	.954	.971	.983	.992	1.00	1.01	1.01	.50
	.75	1.49	1.60	1.60	1.59	1.59	1.58	1.57	1.56	1.56	1.55	1.55	1.54	.75
	.90	3.28	2.92	2.73	2.61	2.52	2.46	2.41	2.38	2.35	2.32	2.30	2.28	.90
	.95	4.96	4.10	3.71	3.48	3.33	3.22	3.14	3.07	3.02	2.98	2.94	2.91	.95
	.975	6.94	5.46	4.83	4.47	4.24	4.07	3.95	3.85	3.78	3.72	3.66	3.62	.975
	.99	10.0	7.56	6.55	5.99	5.64	5.39	5.20	5.06	4.94	4.85	4.77	4.71	.99
	.995	12.8	9.43	8.08	7.34	6.87	6.54	6.30	6.12	5.97	5.85	5.75	5.66	.995
	.999	21.0	14.9	12.6	11.3	10.5	9.92	9.52	9.20	8.96	8.75	8.58	8.44	.999
	.9995	25.5	17.9	15.0	13.4	12.4	11.8	11.3	10.9	10.6	10.3	10.1	9.93	.9995
11	.0005	$.0^{6}41$	$.0^{3}50$	$.0^{2}49$	.015	.028	.043	.058	.072	.086	.099	.111	.121	.0005
	.001	$.0^{5}16$	$.0^{2}10$	$.0^{2}78$	.021	.038	.055	.072	.088	.103	.116	.129	.140	.001
	.005	$.0^{4}40$	$.0^{2}50$	.023	.048	.074	.099	.121	.141	.158	.174	.188	.200	.005
	.01	$.0^{3}16$	.010	.037	.069	.100	.128	.153	.175	.193	.210	.224	.237	.01
	.025	$.0^{2}10$	.025	.069	.114	.152	.185	.212	.236	.256	.273	.288	.301	.025
	.05	$.0^{2}41$	.052	.114	.168	.212	.248	.278	.302	.323	.340	.355	.368	.05
	.10	.017	.106	.192	.256	.305	.342	.373	.397	.417	.435	.448	.461	.10
	.25	.107	.295	.408	.481	.529	.565	.592	.614	.633	.645	.658	.667	.25
	.50	.486	.739	.840	.893	.926	.948	.964	.977	.986	.994	1.00	1.01	.50
	.75	1.47	1.58	1.58	1.57	1.56	1.55	1.54	1.53	1.53	1.52	1.52	1.51	.75
	.90	3.23	2.86	2.66	2.54	2.45	2.39	2.34	2.30	2.27	2.25	2.23	2.21	.90
	.95	4.84	3.98	3.59	3.36	3.20	3.09	3.01	2.95	2.90	2.85	2.82	2.79	.95
	.975	6.72	5.26	4.63	4.28	4.04	3.88	3.76	3.66	3.59	3.53	3.47	3.43	.975
	.99	9.65	7.21	6.22	5.67	5.32	5.07	4.89	4.74	4.63	4.54	4.46	4.40	.99
	.995	12.2	8.91	7.60	6.88	6.42	6.10	5.86	5.68	5.54	5.42	5.32	5.24	.995
	.999	19.7	13.8	11.6	10.3	9.58	9.05	8.66	8.35	8.12	7.92	7.76	7.62	.999
	.9995	23.6	16.4	13.6	12.2	11.2	10.6	10.1	9.76	9.48	9.24	9.04	8.88	.9995
12	.0005	$.0^{6}41$	$.0^{3}50$	$.0^{2}49$	.015	.028	.044	.058	.073	.087	.101	.113	.124	.0005
	.001	$.0^{5}16$	$.0^{2}10$	$.0^{2}78$	.021	.038	.056	.073	.089	.104	.118	.131	.143	.001
	.005	$.0^{4}39$	$.0^{2}50$	.023	.048	.075	.100	.122	.143	.161	.177	.191	.204	.005
	.01	$.0^{3}16$	.010	.037	.070	.101	.130	.155	.176	.196	.212	.227	.241	.01
	.025	$.0^{2}10$	.025	.070	.114	.153	.186	.214	.238	.259	.276	.292	.305	.025
	.05	$.0^{2}41$	.052	.114	.169	.214	.250	.280	.305	.325	.343	.358	.372	.05
	.10	.016	.106	.192	.257	.306	.344	.375	.400	.420	.438	.452	.466	.10
	.25	.106	.295	.408	.480	.530	.566	.594	.616	.633	.649	.662	.671	.25
	.50	.484	.735	.835	.888	.921	.943	.959	.972	.981	.989	.995	1.00	.50
	.75	1.46	1.56	1.56	1.55	1.54	1.53	1.52	1.51	1.51	1.50	1.50	1.49	.75
	.90	3.18	2.81	2.61	2.48	2.39	2.33	2.28	2.24	2.21	2.19	2.17	2.15	.90
	.95	4.75	3.89	3.49	3.26	3.11	3.00	2.91	2.85	2.80	2.75	2.72	2.69	.95
	.975	6.55	5.10	4.47	4.12	3.89	3.73	3.61	3.51	3.44	3.37	3.32	3.28	.975
	.99	9.33	6.93	5.95	5.41	5.06	4.82	4.64	4.50	4.39	4.30	4.22	4.16	.99
	.995	11.8	8.51	7.23	6.52	6.07	5.76	5.52	5.35	5.20	5.09	4.99	4.91	.995
	.999	18.6	13.0	10.8	9.63	8.89	8.38	8.00	7.71	7.48	7.29	7.14	7.01	.999
	.9995	22.2	15.3	12.7	11.2	10.4	9.74	9.28	8.94	8.66	8.43	8.24	8.08	.9995

p \ ν_1	15	20	24	30	40	50	60	100	120	200	500	∞	p	ν_2
.0005	.145	.177	.195	.215	.238	.251	.262	.282	.288	.299	.311	.319	.0005	10
.001	.164	.197	.216	.236	.258	.272	.282	.303	.309	.321	.331	.338	.001	
.005	.226	.260	.279	.299	.321	.334	.344	.365	.370	.380	.391	.397	.005	
.01	.263	.297	.316	.336	.357	.370	.380	.400	.405	.415	.424	.431	.01	
.025	.327	.360	.379	.398	.419	.431	.441	.459	.464	.474	.483	.488	.025	
.05	.393	.426	.444	.462	.481	.493	.502	.518	.523	.532	.541	.546	.05	
.10	.486	.516	.532	.549	.567	.578	.586	.602	.605	.614	.621	.625	.10	
.25	.691	.714	.727	.740	.754	.762	.767	.779	.782	.788	.793	.797	.25	
.50	1.02	1.03	1.04	1.05	1.05	1.06	1.06	1.06	1.06	1.07	1.07	1.07	.50	
.75	1.53	1.52	1.52	1.51	1.51	1.50	1.50	1.49	1.49	1.49	1.48	1.48	.75	
.90	2.24	2.20	2.18	2.16	2.13	2.12	2.11	2.09	2.08	2.07	2.06	2.06	.90	
.95	2.85	2.77	2.74	2.70	2.66	2.64	2.62	2.59	2.58	2.56	2.55	2.54	.95	
.975	3.52	3.42	3.37	3.31	3.26	3.22	3.20	3.15	3.14	3.12	3.09	3.08	.975	
.99	4.56	4.41	4.33	4.25	4.17	4.12	4.08	4.01	4.00	3.96	3.93	3.91	.99	
.995	5.47	5.27	5.17	5.07	4.97	4.90	4.86	4.77	4.75	4.71	4.67	4.64	.995	
.999	8.13	7.80	7.64	7.47	7.30	7.19	7.12	6.98	6.94	6.87	6.81	6.76	.999	
.9995	9.56	9.16	8.96	8.75	8.54	8.42	8.33	8.16	8.12	8.04	7.96	7.90	.9995	
.0005	.148	.182	.201	.222	.246	.261	.271	.293	.299	.312	.324	.331	.0005	11
.001	.168	.202	.222	.243	.266	.282	.292	.313	.320	.332	.343	.353	.001	
.005	.231	.266	.286	.308	.330	.345	.355	.376	.382	.394	.403	.412	.005	
.01	.268	.304	.324	.344	.366	.380	.391	.412	.417	.427	.439	.444	.01	
.025	.332	.368	.386	.407	.429	.442	.450	.472	.476	.485	.495	.503	.025	
.05	.398	.433	.452	.469	.490	.503	.513	.529	.535	.543	.552	.559	.05	
.10	.490	.524	.541	.559	.578	.588	.595	.614	.617	.625	.633	.637	.10	
.25	.694	.719	.730	.744	.758	.767	.773	.780	.788	.794	.799	.803	.25	
.50	1.02	1.02	1.03	1.04	1.05	1.05	1.05	1.06	1.06	1.06	1.06	1.06	.50	
.75	1.50	1.49	1.49	1.48	1.47	1.47	1.47	1.46	1.46	1.46	1.45	1.45	.75	
.90	2.17	2.12	2.10	2.08	2.05	2.04	2.03	2.00	2.00	1.99	1.98	1.97	.90	
.95	2.72	2.65	2.61	2.57	2.53	2.51	2.49	2.46	2.45	2.43	2.42	2.40	.95	
.975	3.33	3.23	3.17	3.12	3.06	3.03	3.00	2.96	2.94	2.92	2.90	2.88	.975	
.99	4.25	4.10	4.02	3.94	3.86	3.81	3.78	3.71	3.69	3.66	3.62	3.60	.99	
.995	5.05	4.86	4.76	4.65	4.55	4.49	4.45	4.36	4.34	4.29	4.25	4.23	.995	
.999	7.32	7.01	6.85	6.68	6.52	6.41	6.35	6.21	6.17	6.10	6.04	6.00	.999	
.9995	8.52	8.14	7.94	7.75	7.55	7.43	7.35	7.18	7.14	7.06	6.98	6.93	.9995	
.0005	.152	.186	.206	.228	.253	.269	.280	.305	.311	.323	.337	.345	.0005	12
.001	.172	.207	.228	.250	.275	.291	.302	.326	.332	.344	.357	.365	.001	
.005	.235	.272	.292	.315	.339	.355	.365	.388	.393	.405	.417	.424	.005	
.01	.273	.310	.330	.352	.375	.391	.401	.422	.428	.441	.450	.458	.01	
.025	.337	.374	.394	.416	.437	.450	.461	.481	.487	.498	.508	.514	.025	
.05	.404	.439	.458	.478	.499	.513	.522	.541	.545	.556	.565	.571	.05	
.10	.496	.528	.546	.564	.583	.595	.604	.621	.625	.633	.641	.647	.10	
.25	.695	.721	.734	.748	.762	.771	.777	.789	.792	.799	.804	.808	.25	
.50	1.01	1.02	1.03	1.03	1.04	1.04	1.05	1.05	1.05	1.05	1.06	1.06	.50	
.75	1.48	1.47	1.46	1.45	1.45	1.44	1.44	1.43	1.43	1.43	1.42	1.42	.75	
.90	2.11	2.06	2.04	2.01	1.99	1.97	1.96	1.94	1.93	1.92	1.91	1.90	.90	
.95	2.62	2.54	2.51	2.47	2.43	2.40	2.38	2.35	2.34	2.32	2.31	2.30	.95	
.975	3.18	3.07	3.02	2.96	2.91	2.87	2.85	2.80	2.79	2.76	2.74	2.72	.975	
.99	4.01	3.86	3.78	3.70	3.62	3.57	3.54	3.47	3.45	3.41	3.38	3.36	.99	
.995	4.72	4.53	4.43	4.33	4.23	4.17	4.12	4.04	4.01	3.97	3.93	3.90	.995	
.999	6.71	6.40	6.25	6.09	5.93	5.83	5.76	5.63	5.59	5.52	5.46	5.42	.999	
.9995	7.74	7.37	7.18	7.00	6.80	6.68	6.61	6.45	6.41	6.33	6.25	6.20	.9995	

ν_2	ν_1 / p	1	2	3	4	5	6	7	8	9	10	11	12	p
15	.0005	$.0^641$	$.0^350$	$.0^249$	.015	.029	.045	.061	.076	.091	.105	.117	.129	.0005
	.001	$.0^516$	$.0^210$	$.0^279$	.021	.039	.057	.075	.092	.108	.123	.137	.149	.001
	.005	$.0^439$	$.0^250$	.023	.049	.076	.102	.125	.147	.166	.183	.198	.212	.005
	.01	$.0^316$	.010	.037	.070	.103	.132	.158	.181	.202	.219	.235	.249	.01
	.025	$.0^210$	.025	.070	.116	.156	.190	.219	.244	.265	.284	.300	.315	.025
	.05	$.0^241$	.051	.115	.170	.216	.254	.285	.311	.333	.351	.368	.382	.05
	.10	.016	.106	.192	.258	.309	.348	.380	.406	.427	.446	.461	.475	.10
	.25	.105	.293	.407	.480	.531	.568	.596	.618	.637	.652	.667	.676	.25
	.50	.478	.726	.826	.878	.911	.933	.948	.960	.970	.977	.984	.989	.50
	.75	1.43	1.52	1.52	1.51	1.49	1.48	1.47	1.46	1.46	1.45	1.44	1.44	.75
	.90	3.07	2.70	2.49	2.36	2.27	2.21	2.16	2.12	2.09	2.06	2.04	2.02	.90
	.95	4.54	3.68	3.29	3.06	2.90	2.79	2.71	2.64	2.59	2.54	2.51	2.48	.95
	.975	6.20	4.76	4.15	3.80	3.58	3.41	3.29	3.20	3.12	3.06	3.01	2.96	.975
	.99	8.68	6.36	5.42	4.89	4.56	4.32	4.14	4.00	3.89	3.80	3.73	3.67	.99
	.995	10.8	7.70	6.48	5.80	5.37	5.07	4.85	4.67	4.54	4.42	4.33	4.25	.995
	.999	16.6	11.3	9.34	8.25	7.57	7.09	6.74	6.47	6.26	6.08	5.93	5.81	.999
	.9995	19.5	13.2	10.8	9.48	8.66	8.10	7.68	7.36	7.11	6.91	6.75	6.60	.9995
20	.0005	$.0^640$	$.0^350$	$.0^250$	.015	.029	.046	.063	.079	.094	.109	.123	.136	.0005
	.001	$.0^516$	$.0^210$	$.0^279$	.022	.039	.058	.077	.095	.112	.128	.143	.156	.001
	.005	$.0^439$	$.0^250$	.023	.050	.077	.104	.129	.151	.171	.190	.206	.221	.005
	.01	$.0^316$	.010	.037	.071	.105	.135	.162	.187	.208	.227	.244	.259	.01
	.025	$.0^210$	.025	.071	.117	.158	.193	.224	.250	.273	.292	.310	.325	.025
	.05	$.0^240$	.051	.115	.172	.219	.258	.290	.318	.340	.360	.377	.393	.05
	.10	.016	.106	.193	.260	.312	.353	.385	.412	.435	.454	.472	.485	.10
	.25	.104	.292	.407	.480	.531	.569	.598	.622	.641	.656	.671	.681	.25
	.50	.472	.718	.816	.868	.900	.922	.938	.950	.959	.966	.972	.977	.50
	.75	1.40	1.49	1.48	1.47	1.45	1.44	1.43	1.42	1.41	1.40	1.39	1.39	.75
	.90	2.97	2.59	2.38	2.25	2.16	2.09	2.04	2.00	1.96	1.94	1.91	1.89	.90
	.95	4.35	3.49	3.10	2.87	2.71	2.60	2.51	2.45	2.39	2.35	2.31	2.28	.95
	.975	5.87	4.46	3.86	3.51	3.29	3.13	3.01	2.91	2.84	2.77	2.72	2.68	.975
	.99	8.10	5.85	4.94	4.43	4.10	3.87	3.70	3.56	3.46	3.37	3.29	3.23	.99
	.995	9.94	6.99	5.82	5.17	4.76	4.47	4.26	4.09	3.96	3.85	3.76	3.68	.995
	.999	14.8	9.95	8.10	7.10	6.46	6.02	5.69	5.44	5.24	5.08	4.94	4.82	.999
	.9995	17.2	11.4	9.20	8.02	7.28	6.76	6.38	6.08	5.85	5.66	5.51	5.38	.9995
24	.0005	$.0^640$	$.0^350$	$.0^250$	.015	.030	.046	.064	.080	.096	.112	.126	.139	.0005
	.001	$.0^516$	$.0^210$	$.0^279$	.022	.040	.059	.079	.097	.115	.131	.146	.160	.001
	.005	$.0^440$	$.0^250$	.023	.050	.078	.106	.131	.154	.175	.193	.210	.226	.005
	.01	$.0^316$	.010	.038	.072	.106	.137	.165	.189	.211	.231	.249	.264	.01
	.025	$.0^210$	.025	.071	.117	.159	.195	.227	.253	.277	.297	.315	.331	.025
	.05	$.0^240$	.051	.116	.173	.221	.260	.293	.321	.345	.365	.383	.399	.05
	.10	.016	.106	.193	.261	.313	.355	.388	.416	.439	.459	.476	.491	.10
	.25	.104	.291	.406	.480	.532	.570	.600	.623	.643	.659	.671	.684	.25
	.50	.469	.714	.812	.863	.895	.917	.932	.944	.953	.961	.967	.972	.50
	.75	1.39	1.47	1.46	1.44	1.43	1.41	.140	1.39	1.38	1.38	1.37	1.36	.75
	.90	2.93	2.54	2.33	2.19	2.10	2.04	1.98	1.94	1.91	1.88	1.85	1.83	.90
	.95	4.26	3.40	3.01	2.78	2.62	2.51	2.42	2.36	2.30	2.25	2.21	2.18	.95
	.975	5.72	4.32	3.72	3.38	3.15	2.99	2.87	2.78	2.70	2.64	2.59	2.54	.975
	.99	7.82	5.61	4.72	4.22	3.90	3.67	3.50	3.36	3.26	3.17	3.09	3.03	.99
	.995	9.55	6.66	5.52	4.89	4.49	4.20	3.99	3.83	3.69	3.59	3.50	3.42	.995
	.999	14.0	9.34	7.55	6.59	5.98	5.55	5.23	4.99	4.80	4.64	4.50	4.39	.999
	.9995	16.2	10.6	8.52	7.39	6.68	6.18	5.82	5.54	5.31	5.13	4.98	4.85	.9995

p	15	20	24	30	40	50	60	100	120	200	500	∞	p	ν_2
.0005	.159	.197	.220	.244	.272	.290	.303	.330	.339	.353	.368	.377	.0005	15
.001	.181	.219	.242	.266	.294	.313	.325	.352	.360	.375	.388	.398	.001	
.005	.246	.286	.308	.333	.360	.377	.389	.415	.422	.435	.448	.457	.005	
.01	.284	.324	.346	.370	.397	.413	.425	.450	.456	.469	.483	.490	.01	
.025	.349	.389	.410	.433	.458	.474	.485	.508	.514	.526	.538	.546	.025	
.05	.416	.454	.474	.496	.519	.535	.545	.565	.571	.581	.592	.600	.05	
.10	.507	.542	.561	.581	.602	.614	.624	.641	.647	.658	.667	.672	.10	
.25	.701	.728	.742	.757	.772	.782	.788	.802	.805	.812	.818	.822	.25	
.50	1.00	1.01	1.02	1.02	1.03	1.03	1.03	1.04	1.04	1.04	1.04	1.05	.50	
.75	1.43	1.41	1.41	1.40	1.39	1.39	1.38	1.38	1.37	1.37	1.36	1.36	.75	
.90	1.97	1.92	1.90	1.87	1.85	1.83	1.82	1.79	1.79	1.77	1.76	1.76	.90	
.95	2.40	2.33	2.39	2.25	2.20	2.18	2.16	2.12	2.11	2.10	2.08	2.07	.95	
.975	2.86	2.76	2.70	2.64	2.59	2.55	2.52	2.47	2.46	2.44	2.41	2.40	.975	
.99	3.52	3.37	3.29	3.21	3.13	3.08	3.05	2.98	2.96	2.92	2.89	2.87	.99	
.995	4.07	3.88	3.79	3.69	3.59	3.52	3.48	3.39	3.37	3.33	3.29	3.26	.995	
.999	5.54	5.25	5.10	4.95	4.80	4.70	4.64	4.51	4.47	4.41	4.35	4.31	.999	
.9995	6.27	5.93	5.75	5.58	5.40	5.29	5.21	5.06	5.02	4.94	4.87	4.83	.9995	
.0005	.169	.211	.235	.263	.295	.316	.331	.364	.375	.391	.408	.422	.0005	20
.001	.191	.233	.258	.286	.318	.339	.354	.386	.395	.413	.429	.441	.001	
.005	.258	.301	.327	.354	.385	.405	.419	.448	.457	.474	.490	.500	.005	
.01	.297	.340	.365	.392	.422	.441	.455	.483	.491	.508	.521	.532	.01	
.025	.363	.406	.430	.456	.484	.503	.514	.541	.548	.562	.575	.585	.025	
.05	.430	.471	.493	.518	.544	.562	.572	.595	.603	.617	.629	.637	.05	
.10	.520	.557	.578	.600	.623	.637	.648	.671	.675	.685	.694	.704	.10	
.25	.708	.736	.751	.767	.784	.794	.801	.816	.820	.827	.835	.840	.25	
.50	.989	1.00	1.01	1.01	1.02	1.02	1.02	1.03	1.03	1.03	1.03	1.03	.50	
.75	1.37	1.36	1.35	1.34	1.33	1.33	1.32	1.31	1.31	1.30	1.30	1.29	.75	
.90	1.84	1.79	1.77	1.74	1.71	1.69	1.68	1.65	1.64	1.63	1.62	1.61	.90	
.95	2.20	2.12	2.08	2.04	1.99	1.97	1.95	1.91	1.90	1.88	1.86	1.84	.95	
.975	2.57	2.46	2.41	2.35	2.29	2.25	2.22	2.17	2.16	2.13	2.10	2.09	.975	
.99	3.09	2.94	2.86	2.78	2.69	2.64	2.61	2.54	2.52	2.48	2.44	2.42	.99	
.995	3.50	3.32	3.22	3.12	3.02	2.96	2.92	2.83	2.81	2.76	2.72	2.69	.995	
.999	4.56	4.29	4.15	4.01	3.86	3.77	3.70	3.58	3.54	3.48	3.42	3.38	.999	
.9995	5.07	4.75	4.58	4.42	4.24	4.15	4.07	3.93	3.90	3.82	3.75	3.70	.9995	
.0005	.174	.218	.244	.274	.309	.331	.349	.384	.395	.416	.434	.449	.0005	24
.0001	.196	.241	.268	.298	.332	.354	.371	.405	.417	.437	.455	.469	.001	
.005	.264	.310	.337	.367	.400	.422	.437	.469	.479	.498	.515	.527	.005	
.01	.304	.350	.376	.405	.437	.459	.473	.505	.513	.529	.546	.558	.01	
.025	.370	.415	.441	.468	.498	.518	.531	.562	.568	.585	.599	.610	.025	
.05	.437	.480	.504	.530	.558	.575	.588	.613	.622	.637	.649	.659	.05	
.10	.527	.566	.588	.611	.635	.651	.662	.685	.691	.704	.715	.723	.10	
.25	.712	.741	.757	.773	.791	.802	.809	.825	.829	.837	.844	.850	.25	
.50	.983	.994	1.00	1.01	1.01	1.02	1.02	1.02	1.02	1.02	1.03	1.03	.50	
.75	1.35	1.33	1.32	1.31	1.30	1.29	1.29	1.28	1.28	1.27	1.27	1.26	.75	
.90	1.78	1.73	1.70	1.67	1.64	1.62	1.61	1.58	1.57	1.56	1.54	1.53	.90	
.95	2.11	2.03	1.98	1.94	1.89	1.86	1.84	1.80	1.79	1.77	1.75	1.73	.95	
.975	2.44	2.33	2.27	2.21	2.15	2.11	2.08	2.02	2.01	1.98	1.95	1.94	.975	
.99	2.89	2.74	2.66	2.58	2.49	2.44	2.40	2.33	2.31	2.27	2.24	2.21	.99	
.995	3.25	3.06	2.97	2.87	2.77	2.70	2.66	2.57	2.55	2.50	2.46	2.43	.995	
.999	4.14	3.87	3.74	3.59	3.45	3.35	3.29	3.16	3.14	3.07	3.01	2.97	.999	
.9995	4.55	4.25	4.09	3.93	3.76	3.66	3.59	3.44	3.41	3.33	3.27	3.22	.9995	

Appendix D-9 (Continued)

ν_2	p	1	2	3	4	5	6	7	8	9	10	11	12	p
30	.0005	$.0^640$	$.0^350$	$.0^250$	.015	.030	.047	.065	.082	.098	.114	.129	.143	.0005
	.001	$.0^516$	$.0^210$	$.0^280$	.022	.040	.060	.080	.099	.117	.134	.150	.164	.001
	.005	$.0^440$	$.0^250$	.024	.050	.079	.107	.133	.156	.178	.197	.215	.231	.005
	.01	$.0^316$	.010	.038	.072	.107	.138	.167	.192	.215	.235	.254	.270	.01
	.025	$.0^210$	.025	.071	.118	.161	.197	.229	.257	.281	.302	.321	.337	.025
	.05	$.0^240$	.051	.116	.174	.222	.263	.296	.325	.349	.370	.389	.406	.05
	.10	.016	.106	.193	.262	.315	.357	.391	.420	.443	.464	.481	.497	.10
	.25	.103	.290	.406	.480	.532	.571	.601	.625	.645	.661	.676	.688	.25
	.50	.466	.709	.807	.858	.890	.912	.927	.939	.948	.955	.961	.966	.50
	.75	1.38	1.45	1.44	1.42	1.41	1.39	1.38	1.37	1.36	1.35	1.35	1.34	.75
	.90	2.88	2.49	2.28	2.14	2.05	1.98	1.93	1.88	1.85	1.82	1.79	1.77	.90
	.95	4.17	3.32	2.92	2.69	2.53	2.42	2.33	2.27	2.21	2.16	2.13	2.09	.95
	.975	5.57	4.18	3.59	3.25	3.03	2.87	2.75	2.65	2.57	2.51	2.46	2.41	.975
	.99	7.56	5.39	4.51	4.02	3.70	3.47	3.30	3.17	3.07	2.98	2.91	2.84	.99
	.995	9.18	6.35	5.24	4.62	4.23	3.95	3.74	3.58	3.45	3.34	3.25	3.18	.995
	.999	13.3	8.77	7.05	6.12	5.53	5.12	4.82	4.58	4.39	4.24	4.11	4.00	.999
	.9995	15.2	9.90	7.90	6.82	6.14	5.66	5.31	5.04	4.82	4.65	4.51	4.38	.9995
40	.0005	$.0^640$	$.0^350$	$.0^250$	.016	.030	.048	.066	.084	.100	.117	.132	.147	.0005
	.001	$.0^516$	$.0^210$	$.0^280$	.022	.042	.061	.081	.101	.119	.137	.153	.169	.001
	.005	$.0^440$	$.0^250$	.024	.051	.080	.108	.135	.159	.181	.201	.220	.237	.005
	.01	$.0^316$	.010	.038	.073	.108	.140	.169	.195	.219	.240	.259	.276	.01
	.025	$.0^399$	.025	.071	.119	.162	.199	.232	.260	.285	.307	.327	.344	.025
	.05	$.0^240$	.051	.116	.175	.224	.265	.299	.329	.354	.376	.395	.412	.05
	.10	.016	.106	.194	.263	.317	.360	.394	.424	.448	.469	.488	.504	.10
	.25	.103	.290	.405	.480	.533	.572	.603	.627	.647	.664	.680	.691	.25
	.50	.463	.705	.802	.854	.885	.907	.922	.934	.943	.950	.956	.961	.50
	.75	1.36	1.44	1.42	1.40	1.39	1.37	1.36	1.35	1.34	1.33	1.32	1.31	.75
	.90	2.84	2.44	2.23	2.09	2.00	1.93	1.87	1.83	1.79	1.76	1.73	1.71	.90
	.95	4.08	3.23	2.84	2.61	2.45	2.34	2.25	2.18	2.12	2.08	2.04	2.00	.95
	.975	5.42	4.05	3.46	3.13	2.90	2.74	2.62	2.53	2.45	2.39	2.33	2.29	.975
	.99	7.31	5.18	4.31	3.83	3.51	3.29	3.12	2.99	2.89	2.80	2.73	2.66	.99
	.995	8.83	6.07	4.98	4.37	3.99	3.71	3.51	3.35	3.22	3.12	3.03	2.95	.995
	.999	12.6	8.25	6.60	5.70	5.13	4.73	4.44	4.21	4.02	3.87	3.75	3.64	.999
	.9995	14.4	9.25	7.33	6.30	5.64	5.19	4.85	4.59	4.38	4.21	4.07	3.95	.9995
60	.0005	$.0^640$	$.0^350$	$.0^251$	.016	.031	.048	.067	.085	.103	.120	.136	.152	.0005
	.001	$.0^516$	$.0^210$	$.0^280$	.022	.041	.062	.083	.103	.122	.140	.157	.174	.001
	.005	$.0^440$	$.0^250$	.024	.051	.081	.110	.137	.162	.185	.206	.225	.243	.005
	.01	$.0^316$	.010	.038	.073	.109	.142	.172	.199	.223	.245	.265	.283	.01
	.025	$.0^399$	.025	.071	.120	.163	.202	.235	.264	.290	.313	.333	.351	.025
	.05	$.0^240$	.051	.116	.176	.226	.267	.303	.333	.359	.382	.402	.419	.05
	.10	.016	.106	.194	.264	.318	.362	.398	.428	.453	.475	.493	.510	.10
	.25	.102	.289	.405	.480	.534	.573	.604	.629	.650	.667	.680	.695	.25
	.50	.461	.701	.798	.849	.880	.901	.917	.928	.937	.945	.951	.956	.50
	.75	1.35	1.42	1.41	1.38	1.37	1.35	1.33	1.32	1.31	1.30	1.29	1.29	.75
	.90	2.79	2.39	2.18	2.04	1.95	1.87	1.82	1.77	1.74	1.71	1.68	1.66	.90
	.95	4.00	3.15	2.76	2.53	2.37	2.25	2.17	2.10	2.04	1.99	1.95	1.92	.95
	.975	5.29	3.93	3.34	3.01	2.79	2.63	2.51	2.41	2.33	2.27	2.22	2.17	.975
	.99	7.08	4.98	4.13	3.65	3.34	3.12	2.95	2.82	2.72	2.63	2.56	2.50	.99
	.995	8.49	5.80	4.73	4.14	3.76	3.49	3.29	3.13	3.01	2.90	2.82	2.74	.995
	.999	12.0	7.76	6.17	5.31	4.76	4.37	4.09	3.87	3.69	3.54	3.43	3.31	.999
	.9995	13.6	8.65	6.81	5.82	5.20	4.76	4.44	4.18	3.98	3.82	3.69	3.57	.9995

p	15	20	24	30	40	50	60	100	120	200	500	∞	p	ν₂
.0005	.179	.226	.254	.287	.325	.350	.369	.410	.420	.444	.467	.483	.0005	30
.001	.202	.250	.278	.311	.348	.373	.391	.431	.442	.465	.488	.503	.001	
.005	.271	.320	.349	.381	.416	.441	.457	.495	.504	.524	.543	.559	.005	
.01	.311	.360	.388	.419	.454	.476	.493	.529	.538	.559	.575	.590	.01	
.025	.378	.426	.453	.482	.515	.535	.551	.585	.592	.610	.625	.639	.025	
.05	.445	.490	.516	.543	.573	.592	.606	.637	.644	.658	.676	.685	.05	
.10	.534	.575	.598	.623	.649	.667	.678	.704	.710	.725	.735	.746	.10	
.25	.716	.746	.763	.780	.798	.810	.818	.835	.839	.848	.856	.862	.25	
.50	.978	.989	.994	1.00	1.01	1.01	1.01	1.02	1.02	1.02	1.02	1.02	.50	
.75	1.32	1.30	1.29	1.28	1.27	1.26	1.26	1.25	1.24	1.24	1.23	1.23	.75	
.90	1.72	1.67	1.64	1.61	1.57	1.55	1.54	1.51	1.50	1.48	1.47	1.46	.90	
.95	2.01	1.93	1.89	1.84	1.79	1.76	1.74	1.70	1.68	1.66	1.64	1.62	.95	
.975	2.31	2.20	2.14	2.07	2.01	1.97	1.94	1.88	1.87	1.84	1.81	1.79	.975	
.99	2.70	2.55	2.47	2.39	2.30	2.25	2.21	2.13	2.11	2.07	2.03	2.01	.99	
.995	3.01	2.82	2.73	2.63	2.52	2.46	2.42	2.32	2.30	2.25	2.21	2.18	.995	
.999	3.75	3.49	3.36	3.22	3.07	2.98	2.92	2.79	2.76	2.69	2.63	2.59	.999	
.9995	4.10	3.80	3.65	3.48	3.32	3.22	3.15	3.00	2.97	2.89	2.82	2.78	.9995	
.0005	.185	.236	.266	.301	.343	.373	.393	.441	.453	.480	.504	.525	.0005	40
.001	.209	.259	.290	.326	.367	.396	.415	.461	.473	.500	.524	.545	.001	
.005	.279	.331	.362	.396	.436	.463	.481	.524	.534	.559	.581	.599	.005	
.01	.319	.371	.401	.435	.473	.498	.516	.556	.567	.592	.613	.628	.01	
.025	.387	.437	.466	.498	.533	.556	.573	.610	.620	.641	.662	.674	.025	
.05	.454	.502	.529	.558	.591	.613	.627	.658	.669	.685	.704	.717	.05	
.10	.542	.585	.609	.636	.664	.683	.696	.724	.731	.747	.762	.772	.10	
.25	.720	.752	.769	.787	.806	.819	.828	.846	.851	.861	.870	.877	.25	
.50	.972	.983	.989	.994	1.00	1.00	1.01	1.01	1.01	1.01	1.02	1.02	.50	
.75	1.30	1.28	1.26	1.25	1.24	1.23	1.22	1.21	1.21	1.20	1.19	1.19	.75	
.90	1.66	1.61	1.57	1.54	1.51	1.48	1.47	1.43	1.42	1.41	1.39	1.38	.90	
.95	1.92	1.84	1.79	1.74	1.69	1.66	1.64	1.59	1.58	1.55	1.53	1.51	.95	
.975	2.18	2.07	2.01	1.94	1.88	1.83	1.80	1.74	1.72	1.69	1.66	1.64	.975	
.99	2.52	2.37	2.29	2.20	2.11	2.06	2.02	1.94	1.92	1.87	1.83	1.80	.99	
.995	2.78	2.60	2.50	2.40	2.30	2.23	2.18	2.09	2.06	2.01	1.96	1.93	.995	
.999	3.40	3.15	3.01	2.87	2.73	2.64	2.57	2.44	2.41	2.34	2.28	2.23	.999	
.9995	3.68	3.39	3.24	3.08	2.92	2.82	2.74	2.60	2.57	2.49	2.41	2.37	.9995	
.0005	.192	.246	.278	.318	.365	.398	.421	.478	.493	.527	.561	.585	.0005	60
.001	.216	.270	.304	.343	.389	.421	.444	.497	.512	.545	.579	.602	.001	
.005	.287	.343	.376	.414	.458	.488	.510	.559	.572	.602	.633	.652	.005	
.01	.328	.383	.416	.453	.495	.524	.545	.592	.604	.633	.658	.679	.01	
.025	.396	.450	.481	.515	.555	.581	.600	.641	.654	.680	.704	.720	.025	
.05	.463	.514	.543	.575	.611	.633	.652	.690	.700	.719	.746	.759	.05	
.10	.550	.596	.622	.650	.682	.703	.717	.750	.758	.776	.793	.806	.10	
.25	.725	.758	.776	.796	.816	.830	.840	.860	.865	.877	.888	.896	.25	
.50	.967	.978	.983	.989	.994	.998	1.00	1.00	1.01	1.01	1.01	1.01	.50	
.75	1.27	1.25	1.24	1.22	1.21	1.20	1.19	1.17	1.17	1.16	1.15	1.15	.75	
.90	1.60	1.54	1.51	1.48	1.44	1.41	1.40	1.36	1.35	1.33	1.31	1.29	.90	
.95	1.84	1.75	1.70	1.65	1.59	1.56	1.53	1.48	1.47	1.44	1.41	1.39	.95	
.975	2.06	1.94	1.88	1.82	1.74	1.70	1.67	1.60	1.58	1.54	1.51	1.48	.975	
.99	2.35	2.20	2.12	2.03	1.94	1.88	1.84	1.75	1.73	1.68	1.63	1.60	.99	
.995	2.57	2.39	2.29	2.19	2.08	2.01	1.96	1.86	1.83	1.78	1.73	1.69	.995	
.999	3.08	2.83	2.69	2.56	2.41	2.31	2.25	2.11	2.09	2.01	1.93	1.89	.999	
.9995	3.30	3.02	2.87	2.71	2.55	2.45	2.38	2.23	2.19	2.11	2.03	1.98	.9995	

ν_2	ν_1 / p	1	2	3	4	5	6	7	8	9	10	11	12	p
120	.0005	$.0^640$	$.0^550$	$.0^251$	.016	.031	.049	.067	.087	.105	.123	.140	.156	.0005
	.001	$.0^516$	$.0^210$	$.0^281$	.023	.042	.063	.084	.105	.125	.144	.162	.179	.001
	.005	$.0^439$	$.0^250$	.024	.051	.081	.111	.139	.165	.189	.211	.230	.249	.005
	.01	$.0^316$	.010	.038	.074	.110	.143	.174	.202	.227	.250	.271	.290	.01
	.025	$.0^399$	.025	.072	.120	.165	.204	.238	.268	.295	.318	.340	.359	.025
	.05	$.0^239$	.051	.117	.177	.227	.270	.306	.337	.364	.388	.408	.427	.05
	.10	.016	.105	.194	.265	.320	.365	.401	.432	.458	.480	.500	.518	.10
	.25	.102	.288	.405	.481	.534	.574	.606	.631	.652	.670	.685	.699	.25
	.50	.458	.697	.793	.844	.875	.896	.912	.923	.932	.939	.945	.950	.50
	.75	1.34	1.40	1.39	1.37	1.35	1.33	1.31	1.30	1.29	1.28	1.27	1.26	.75
	.90	2.75	2.35	2.13	1.99	1.90	1.82	1.77	1.72	1.68	1.65	1.62	1.60	.90
	.95	3.92	3.07	2.68	2.45	2.29	2.18	2.09	2.02	1.96	1.91	1.87	1.83	.95
	.975	5.15	3.80	3.23	2.89	2.67	2.52	2.39	2.30	2.22	2.16	2.10	2.05	.975
	.99	6.85	4.79	3.95	3.48	3.17	2.96	2.79	2.66	2.56	2.47	2.40	2.34	.99
	.995	8.18	5.54	4.50	3.92	3.55	3.28	3.09	2.93	2.81	2.71	2.62	2.54	.995
	.999	11.4	7.32	5.79	4.95	4.42	4.04	3.77	3.55	3.38	3.24	3.12	3.02	.999
	.9995	12.8	8.10	6.34	5.39	4.79	4.37	4.07	3.82	3.63	3.47	3.34	3.22	.9995
∞	.0005	$.0^639$	$.0^550$	$.0^251$	.016	.032	.050	.069	.088	.108	.127	.144	.161	.0005
	.001	$.0^516$	$.0^210$	$.0^281$	.023	.042	.063	.085	.107	.128	.148	.167	.185	.001
	.005	$.0^439$	$.0^250$	.024	.052	.082	.113	.141	.168	.193	.216	.236	.256	.005
	.01	$.0^316$	.010	.038	.074	.111	.145	.177	.206	.232	.256	.278	.298	.01
	.025	$.0^398$	.025	.072	.121	.166	.206	.241	.272	.300	.325	.347	.367	.025
	.05	$.0^239$	.051	.117	.178	.229	.273	.310	.342	.369	.394	.417	.436	.05
	.10	.016	.105	.195	.266	.322	.367	.405	.436	.463	.487	.508	.525	.10
	.25	.102	.288	.404	.481	.535	.576	.608	.634	.655	.674	.690	.703	.25
	.50	.455	.693	.789	.839	.870	.891	.907	.918	.927	.934	.939	.945	.50
	.75	1.32	1.39	1.37	1.35	1.33	1.31	1.29	1.28	1.27	1.25	1.24	1.24	.75
	.90	2.71	2.30	2.08	1.94	1.85	1.77	1.72	1.67	1.63	1.60	1.57	1.55	.90
	.95	3.84	3.00	2.60	2.37	2.21	2.10	2.01	1.94	1.88	1.83	1.79	1.75	.95
	.975	5.02	3.69	3.12	2.79	2.57	2.41	2.29	2.19	2.11	2.05	1.99	1.94	.975
	.99	6.63	4.61	3.78	3.32	3.02	2.80	2.64	2.51	2.41	2.32	2.25	2.18	.99
	.995	7.88	5.30	4.28	3.72	3.35	3.09	2.90	2.74	2.62	2.52	2.43	2.36	.995
	.999	10.8	6.91	5.42	4.62	4.10	3.74	3.47	3.27	3.10	2.96	2.84	2.74	.999
	.9995	12.1	7.60	5.91	5.00	4.42	4.02	3.72	3.48	3.30	3.14	3.02	2.90	.9995

p	15	20	24	30	40	50	60	100	120	200	500	∞	p	ν_2
.0005	.199	.256	.293	.338	.390	.429	.458	.524	.543	.578	.614	.676	.0005	120
.001	.223	.282	.319	.363	.415	.453	.480	.542	.568	.595	.631	.691	.001	
.005	.297	.356	.393	.434	.484	.520	.545	.605	.623	.661	.702	.733	.005	
.01	.338	.397	.433	.474	.522	.556	.579	.636	.652	.688	.725	.755	.01	
.025	.406	.464	.498	.536	.580	.611	.633	.684	.698	.729	.762	.789	.025	
.05	.473	.527	.559	.594	.634	.661	.682	.727	.740	.767	.785	.819	.05	
.10	.560	.609	.636	.667	.702	.726	.742	.781	.791	.815	.838	.855	.10	
.25	.730	.765	.784	.805	.828	.843	.853	.877	.884	.897	.911	.923	.25	
.50	.961	.972	.978	.983	.989	.992	.994	1.00	1.00	1.00	1.01	1.01	.50	
.75	1.24	1.22	1.21	1.19	1.18	1.17	1.16	1.14	1.13	1.12	1.11	1.10	.75	
.90	1.55	1.48	1.45	1.41	1.37	1.34	1.32	1.27	1.26	1.24	1.21	1.19	.90	
.95	1.75	1.66	1.61	1.55	1.50	1.46	1.43	1.37	1.35	1.32	1.28	1.25	.95	
.975	1.95	1.82	1.76	1.69	1.61	1.56	1.53	1.45	1.43	1.39	1.34	1.31	.975	
.99	2.19	2.03	1.95	1.86	1.76	1.70	1.66	1.56	1.53	1.48	1.42	1.38	.99	
.995	2.37	2.19	2.09	1.98	1.87	1.80	1.75	1.64	1.61	1.54	1.48	1.43	.995	
.999	2.78	2.53	2.40	2.26	2.11	2.02	1.95	1.82	1.76	1.70	1.62	1.54	.999	
.9995	2.96	2.67	2.53	2.38	2.21	2.11	2.01	1.88	1.84	1.75	1.67	1.60	.9995	
.0005	.207	.270	.311	.360	.422	.469	.505	.599	.624	.704	.804	1.00	.0005	∞
.001	.232	.296	.338	.386	.448	.493	.527	.617	.649	.719	.819	1.00	.001	
.005	.307	.372	.412	.460	.518	.559	.592	.671	.699	.762	.843	1.00	.005	
.01	.349	.413	.452	.499	.554	.595	.625	.699	.724	.782	.858	1.00	.01	
.025	.418	.480	.517	.560	.611	.645	.675	.741	.763	.813	.878	1.00	.025	
.05	.484	.543	.577	.617	.663	.694	.720	.781	.797	.840	.896	1.00	.05	
.10	.570	.622	.652	.687	.726	.752	.774	.826	.838	.877	.919	1.00	.10	
.25	.736	.773	.793	.816	.842	.860	.872	.901	.910	.932	.957	1.00	.25	
.50	.956	.967	.972	.978	.983	.987	.989	.993	.994	.997	.999	1.00	.50	
.75	1.22	1.19	1.18	1.16	1.14	1.13	1.12	1.09	1.08	1.07	1.04	1.00	.75	
.90	1.49	1.42	1.38	1.34	1.30	1.26	1.24	1.18	1.17	1.13	1.08	1.00	.90	
.95	1.67	1.57	1.52	1.46	1.39	1.35	1.32	1.24	1.22	1.17	1.11	1.00	.95	
.975	1.83	1.71	1.64	1.57	1.48	1.43	1.39	1.30	1.27	1.21	1.13	1.00	.975	
.99	2.04	1.88	1.79	1.70	1.59	1.52	1.47	1.36	1.32	1.25	1.15	1.00	.99	
.995	2.19	2.00	1.90	1.79	1.67	1.59	1.53	1.40	1.36	1.28	1.17	1.00	.995	
.999	2.51	2.27	2.13	1.99	1.84	1.73	1.66	1.49	1.45	1.34	1.21	1.00	.999	
.9995	2.65	2.37	2.22	2.07	1.91	1.79	1.71	1.53	1.48	1.36	1.22	1.00	.9995	

† Reprinted with permission from W. J. Dixon and F. J. Massey, Jr., "Introduction to Statistical Analysis," 2d ed., McGraw-Hill Book Company, New York, 1957. Some of the entries in this table were extracted from (1) A. Hald, "Statistical Tables and Formulas," John Wiley & Sons, Inc., New York, 1952; (2) M. Merrington and C. M. Thompson, "Tables of the Percentage Points of the Inverted Beta Distribution," *Biometrika*, vol. 33, p. 73, 1943; (3) C. C. Colcord and L. S. Deming, "The One-tenth Percent Level of Z," *Sankhya*, vol. 2, p. 423, 1936. Permission to reprint the needed entries was granted in each case.

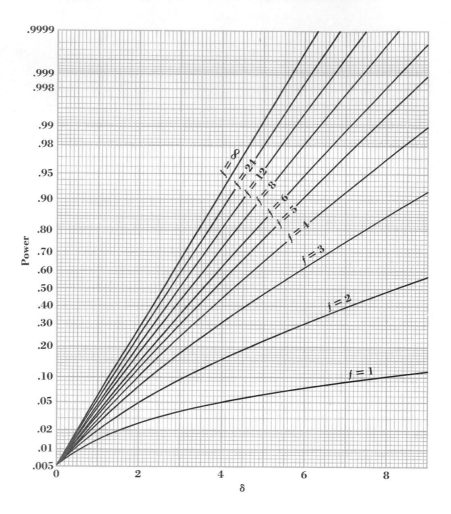

$$\alpha = 0.01 \qquad \delta = |\mu - \mu_0| \sqrt{n}/\sigma; f = \text{degrees of freedom}$$

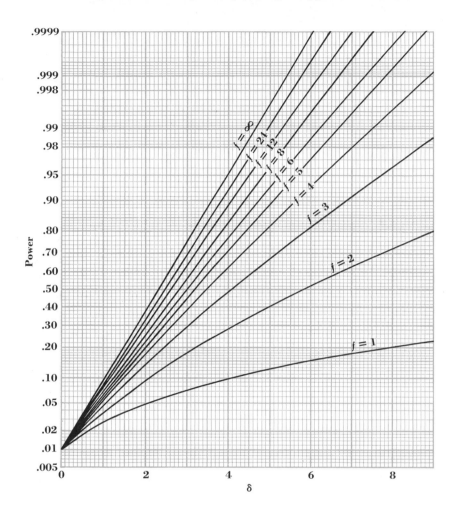

$$\alpha = 0.025 \qquad \delta = |\mu - \mu_0| \sqrt{n}/\sigma; f = \text{degrees of freedom}$$

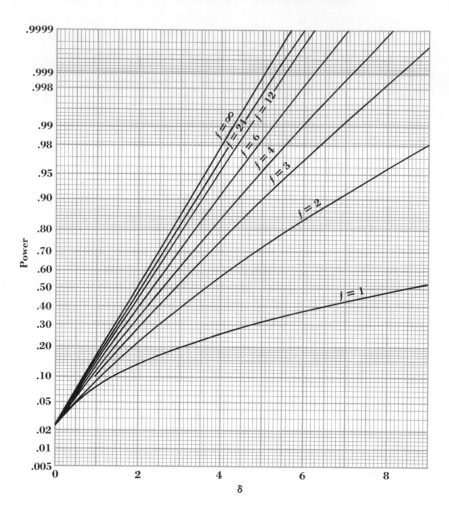

$$\alpha = 0.05 \qquad \delta = |\mu - \mu_0| \sqrt{n}/\sigma; f = \text{degrees of freedom}$$

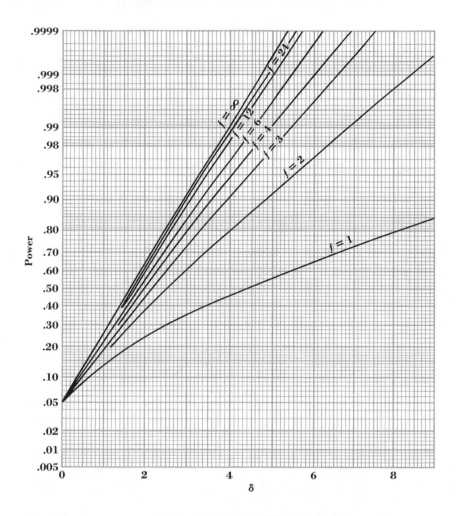

† Reproduced with permission from D. B. Owen, "Handbook of Statistical Tables," Addison-Wesley Publishing Company, Inc., Reading, Mass., 1962.

Appendix D-11 *Graphs of sample sizes required to ensure with a given probability that a confidence interval for the mean with coefficient 1 − α will be shorter than L*

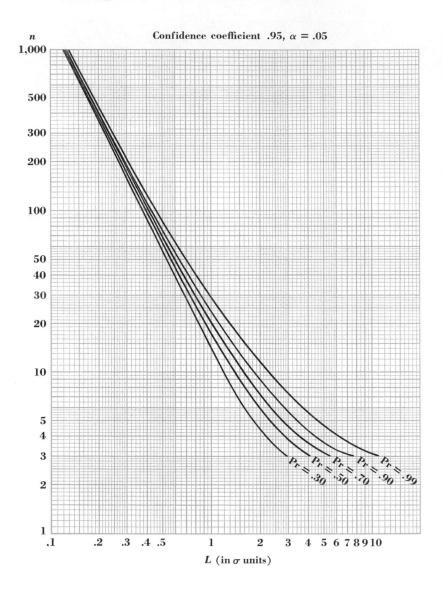

Confidence coefficient .95, α = .05

n

L (in σ units)

$Pr = .30$ $Pr = .50$ $Pr = .70$ $Pr = .90$ $Pr = .99$

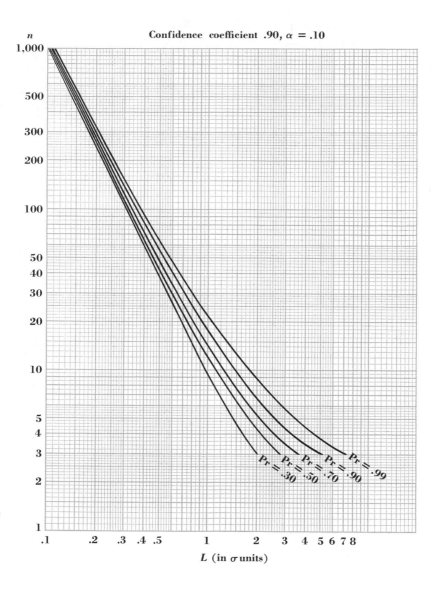

Confidence coefficient .90, $\alpha = .10$

n

L (in σ units)

Appendix D-12 Power curves for testing $H_0: \sigma^2 = \sigma_0^2$ against $H_1: \sigma^2 < \sigma_0^2$

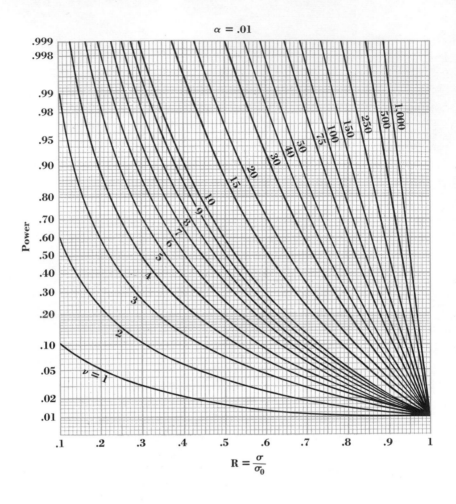

$\alpha = .01$

$$\alpha = .025$$

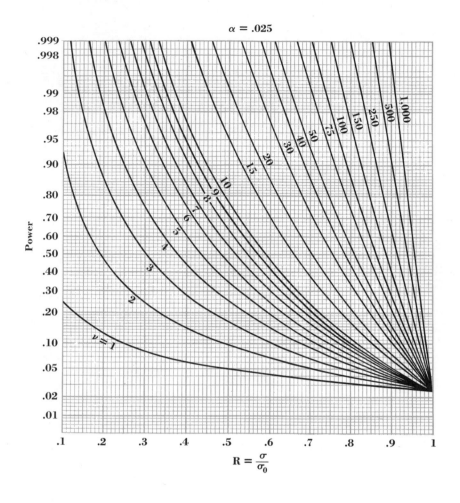

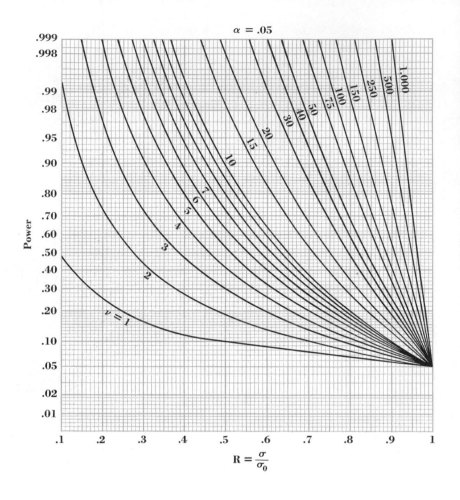

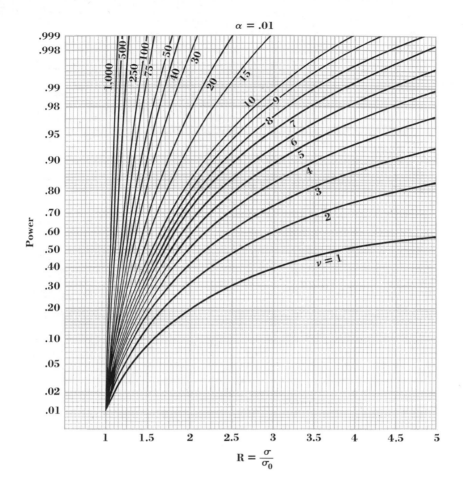

$\alpha = .01$

Power

R $= \dfrac{\sigma}{\sigma_0}$

Appendix D-12   Power curves for testing $H_0: \sigma^2 = \sigma_0^2$ against $H_1: \sigma^2 > \sigma_0^2$

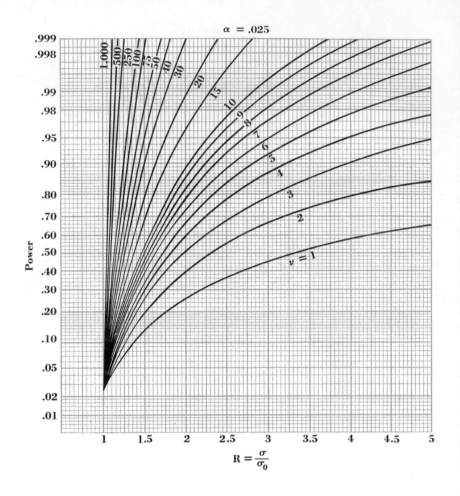

$\alpha = .025$

$$R = \frac{\sigma}{\sigma_0}$$

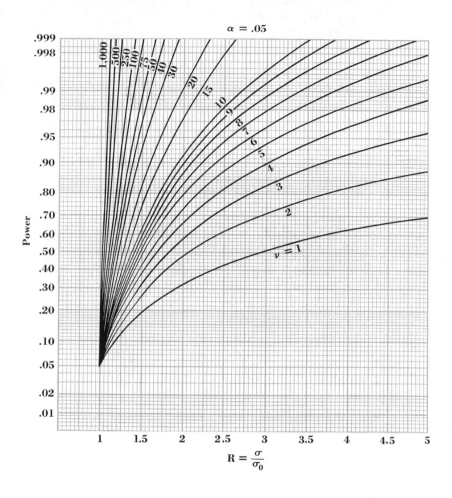

$\alpha = .05$

Power

$$R = \frac{\sigma}{\sigma_0}$$

Graphs of sample sizes required to ensure with a given probability that a confidence interval for the standard deviation with coefficient $1 - \alpha$ will be shorter than L

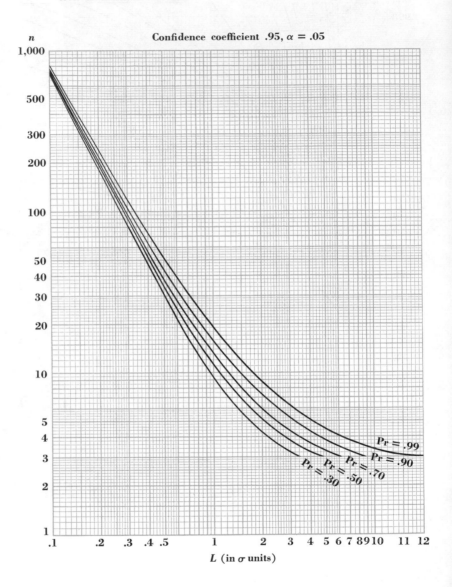

Confidence coefficient .95, $\alpha = .05$

L (in σ units)

Appendix D-13 (*Continued*)

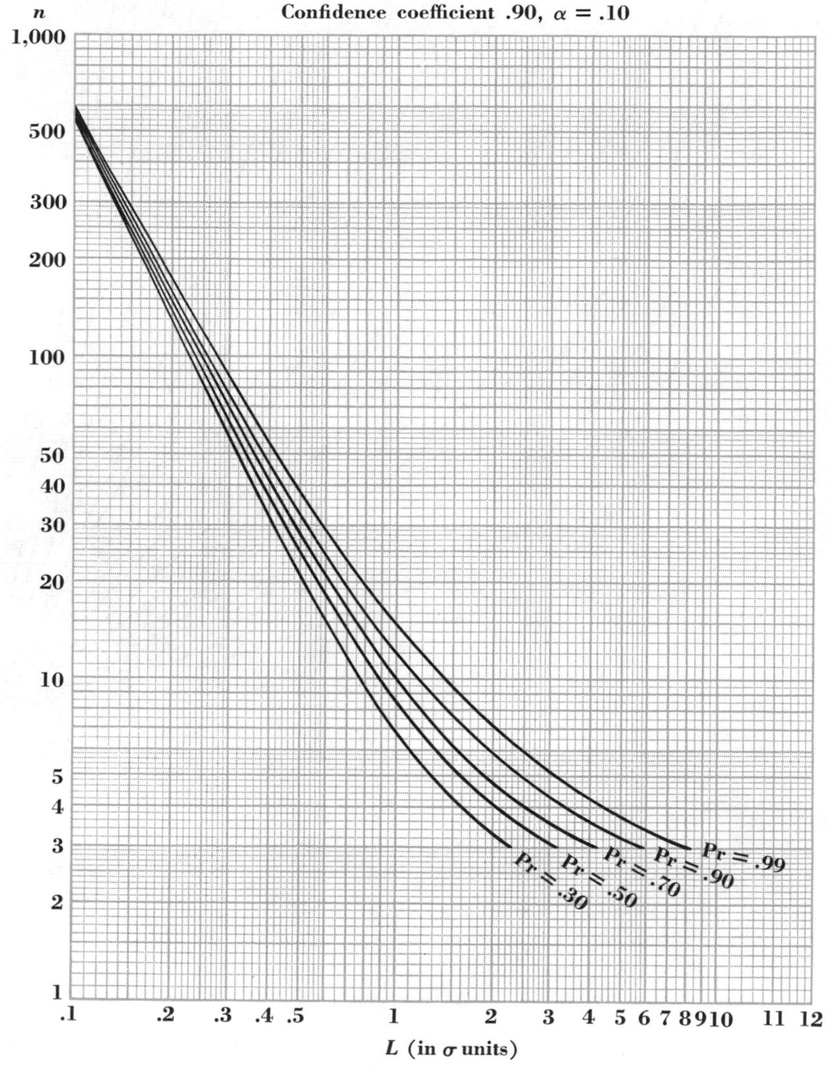

n
Confidence coefficient .90, α = .10
1,000
500
300
200
100
50
40
30
20
10
5
4
3
2
1
.1
.2
.3
.4
.5
1
2
3
4
5
6
7
8
9
10
11
12
L (in σ units)
Pr = .30
Pr = .50
Pr = .70
Pr = .90
Pr = .99

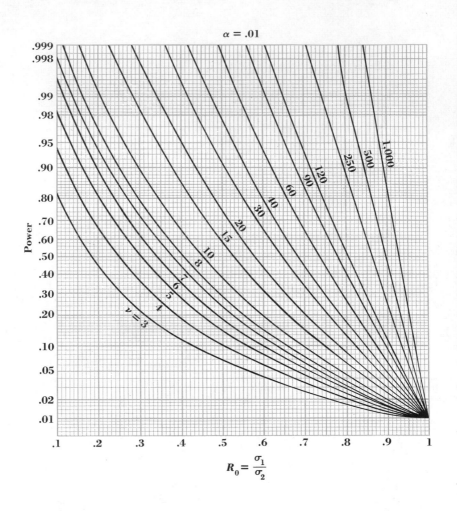

$\alpha = .01$

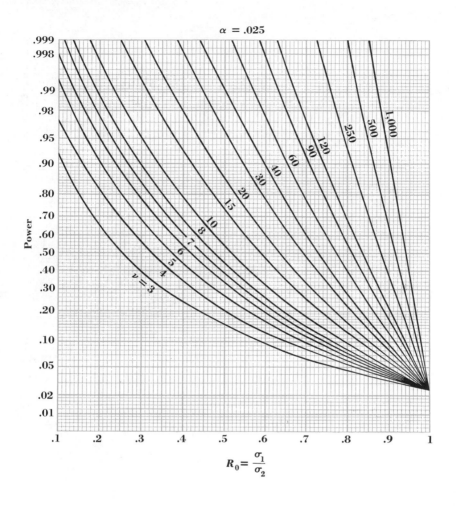

$$\alpha = .025$$

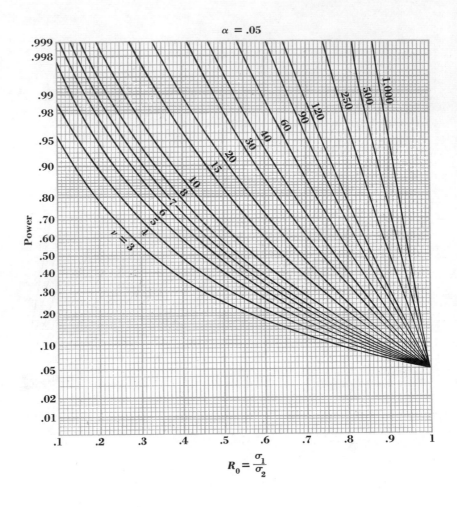

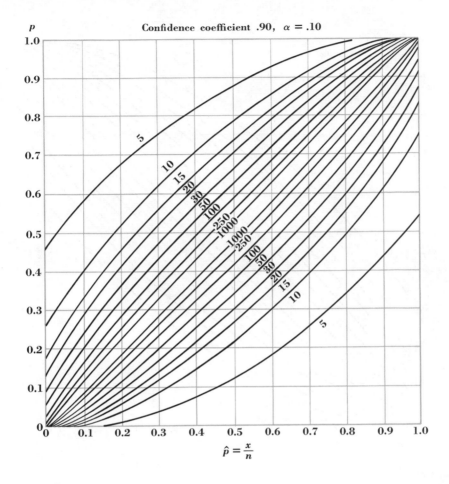

Confidence coefficient .90, $\alpha = .10$

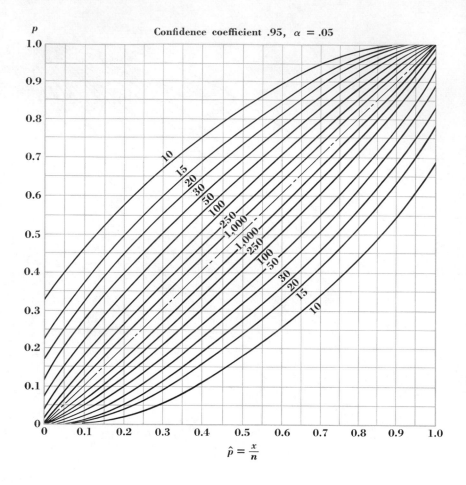

Confidence coefficient .95, $\alpha = .05$

$\hat{p} = \dfrac{x}{n}$

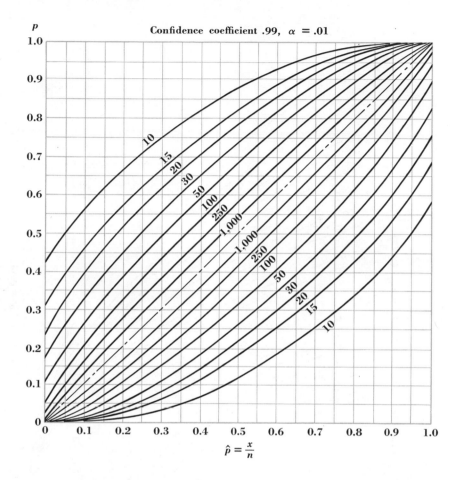

p

Confidence coefficient .99, α = .01

$\hat{p} = \dfrac{x}{n}$

† The graphs for confidence coefficient .95 and .99 are reproduced with permission from E. S. Pearson and C. J. Clopper, The Use of Confidence Intervals or Fiducial Limits Illustrated in the Case of the Binomial, *Biometrika*, vol. 26, p. 404, 1934. The graph for confidence coefficient .90 is reproduced with permission from W. J. Dixon and F. J. Massey, Jr., "Introduction to Statistical Analysis," 2d ed., McGraw-Hill Book Company, New York, 1957.

Appendix D-16   Power curves for the analysis of variance F tests†

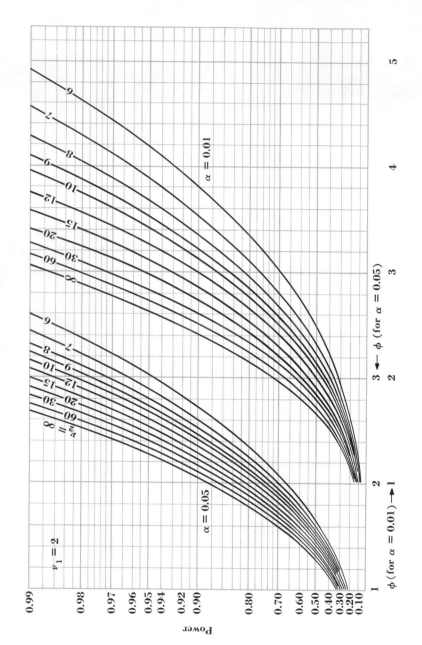

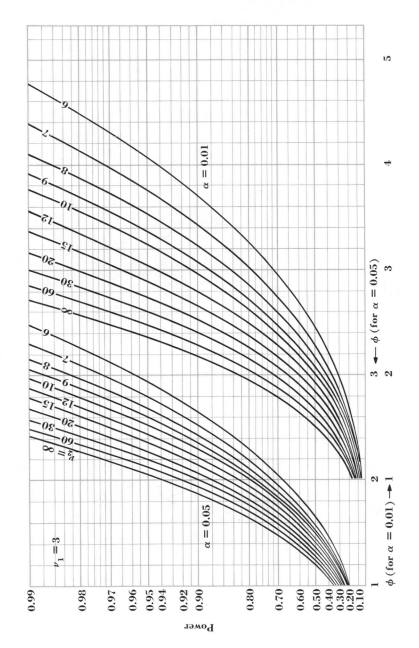

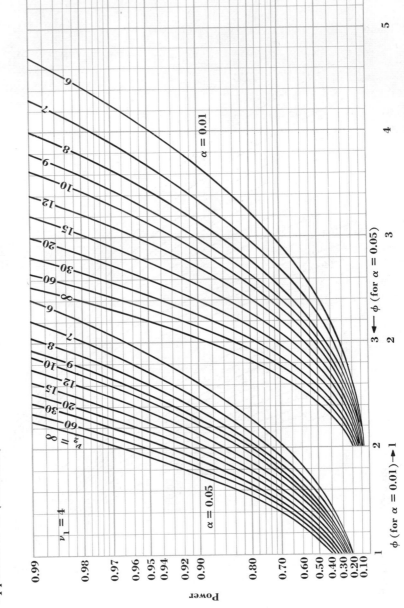

Appendix D-16 (Continued)

334

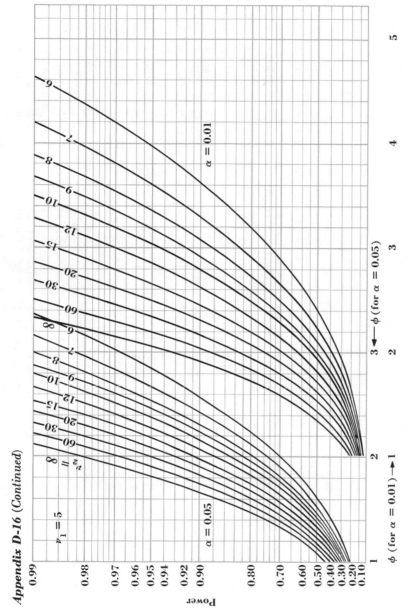

† Reproduced with permission from E. S. Pearson and H. O. Hartley, Charts of the Power Function for Analysis of Variance Tests, Derived from the Non-central *F* Distribution, *Biometrika*, vol. 38, p. 112, 1951.

Appendix D-17 Distribution of Cochran's statistic†

Entry $= R_{n,r;.95}$ where $\Pr(R_{n,r} < R_{n,r;.95}) = .95$

r \ n	2	3	4	5	6	7	8	9	10	11	17	37	145	∞
2	0.9985	0.9750	0.9392	0.9057	0.8772	0.8534	0.8332	0.8159	0.8010	0.7880	0.7341	0.6602	0.5813	0.5000
3	0.9669	0.8709	0.7977	0.7457	0.7071	0.6771	0.6530	0.6333	0.6167	0.6025	0.5466	0.4748	0.4031	0.3333
4	0.9065	0.7679	0.6841	0.6287	0.5895	0.5598	0.5365	0.5175	0.5017	0.4884	0.4366	0.3720	0.3093	0.2500
5	0.8412	0.6838	0.5981	0.5441	0.5065	0.4783	0.4564	0.4387	0.4241	0.4118	0.3645	0.3066	0.2513	0.2000
6	0.7808	0.6161	0.5321	0.4803	0.4447	0.4184	0.3980	0.3817	0.3682	0.3568	0.3135	0.2612	0.2119	0.1667
7	0.7271	0.5612	0.4800	0.4307	0.3974	0.3726	0.3535	0.3384	0.3259	0.3154	0.2756	0.2278	0.1833	0.1429
8	0.6798	0.5157	0.4377	0.3910	0.3595	0.3362	0.3185	0.3043	0.2926	0.2829	0.2462	0.2022	0.1616	0.1250
9	0.6385	0.4775	0.4027	0.3584	0.3286	0.3067	0.2901	0.2768	0.2659	0.2568	0.2226	0.1820	0.1446	0.1111
10	0.6020	0.4450	0.3733	0.3311	0.3029	0.2823	0.2666	0.2541	0.2439	0.2353	0.2032	0.1655	0.1308	0.1000
12	0.5410	0.3924	0.3264	0.2880	0.2624	0.2439	0.2299	0.2187	0.2098	0.2020	0.1737	0.1403	0.1100	0.0833
15	0.4709	0.3346	0.2758	0.2419	0.2195	0.2034	0.1911	0.1815	0.1736	0.1671	0.1429	0.1144	0.0889	0.0667
20	0.3894	0.2705	0.2205	0.1921	0.1735	0.1602	0.1501	0.1422	0.1357	0.1303	0.1108	0.0879	0.0675	0.0500
24	0.3434	0.2354	0.1907	0.1656	0.1493	0.1374	0.1286	0.1216	0.1160	0.1113	0.0942	0.0743	0.0567	0.0417
30	0.2929	0.1980	0.1593	0.1377	0.1237	0.1137	0.1061	0.1002	0.0958	0.0921	0.0771	0.0604	0.0457	0.0333
40	0.2370	0.1576	0.1259	0.1082	0.0968	0.0887	0.0827	0.0780	0.0745	0.0713	0.0595	0.0462	0.0347	0.0250
60	0.1737	0.1131	0.0895	0.0765	0.0682	0.0623	0.0583	0.0552	0.0520	0.0497	0.0411	0.0316	0.0234	0.0167
120	0.0998	0.0632	0.0495	0.0419	0.0371	0.0337	0.0312	0.0292	0.0279	0.0266	0.0218	0.0165	0.0120	0.0083
∞	0	0	0	0	0	0	0	0	0	0	0	0	0	0

Appendix D-17 Distribution of Cochran's statistic†

Entry = $R_{n,r;.99}$ where $\Pr(R_{n,r} < R_{n,r;.99}) = .99$

r \ n	2	3	4	5	6	7	8	9	10	11	17	37	145	∞
2	0.9999	0.9950	0.9794	0.9586	0.9373	0.9172	0.8988	0.8823	0.8674	0.8539	0.7949	0.7067	0.6062	0.5000
3	0.9933	0.9423	0.8831	0.8335	0.7933	0.7606	0.7335	0.7107	0.6912	0.6743	0.6059	0.5153	0.4230	0.3333
4	0.9676	0.8643	0.7814	0.7212	0.6761	0.6410	0.6129	0.5897	0.5702	0.5536	0.4884	0.4057	0.3251	0.2500
5	0.9279	0.7885	0.6957	0.6329	0.5875	0.5531	0.5259	0.5037	0.4854	0.4697	0.4094	0.3351	0.2644	0.2000
6	0.8828	0.7218	0.6258	0.5635	0.5195	0.4866	0.4608	0.4401	0.4229	0.4084	0.3529	0.2858	0.2229	0.1667
7	0.8376	0.6644	0.5685	0.5080	0.4659	0.4347	0.4105	0.3911	0.3751	0.3616	0.3105	0.2494	0.1929	0.1429
8	0.7945	0.6152	0.5209	0.4627	0.4226	0.3932	0.3704	0.3522	0.3373	0.3248	0.2779	0.2214	0.1700	0.1250
9	0.7544	0.5727	0.4810	0.4251	0.3870	0.3592	0.3378	0.3207	0.3067	0.2950	0.2514	0.1992	0.1521	0.1111
10	0.7175	0.5358	0.4469	0.3934	0.3572	0.3308	0.3106	0.2945	0.2813	0.2704	0.2297	0.1811	0.1376	0.1000
12	0.6528	0.4751	0.3919	0.3428	0.3099	0.2861	0.2680	0.2535	0.2419	0.2320	0.1961	0.1535	0.1157	0.0833
15	0.5747	0.4069	0.3317	0.2882	0.2593	0.2386	0.2228	0.2104	0.2002	0.1918	0.1612	0.1251	0.0934	0.0667
20	0.4799	0.3297	0.2654	0.2288	0.2048	0.1877	0.1748	0.1646	0.1567	0.1501	0.1248	0.0960	0.0709	0.0500
24	0.4247	0.2871	0.2295	0.1970	0.1759	0.1608	0.1495	0.1406	0.1338	0.1283	0.1060	0.0810	0.0595	0.0417
30	0.3632	0.2412	0.1913	0.1635	0.1454	0.1327	0.1232	0.1157	0.1100	0.1054	0.0867	0.0658	0.0480	0.0333
40	0.2940	0.1915	0.1508	0.1281	0.1135	0.1033	0.0957	0.0898	0.0853	0.0816	0.0668	0.0503	0.0363	0.0250
60	0.2151	0.1371	0.1069	0.0902	0.0796	0.0722	0.0668	0.0625	0.0594	0.0567	0.0461	0.0344	0.0245	0.0167
120	0.1225	0.0759	0.0585	0.0489	0.0429	0.0387	0.0357	0.0334	0.0316	0.0302	0.0242	0.0178	0.0125	0.0083
∞	0	0	0	0	0	0	0	0	0					

† Reprinted with permission from C. Eisenhart, M. W. Hastay, W. A. Wallis, "Techniques of Statistical Analysis," McGraw-Hill Book Company, New York, 1947.

r or ρ	z_r or z_ρ	r or ρ	z_r or z_ρ	r or ρ	z_r or z_ρ
0.00	0.0000	0.35	0.3654	0.70	0.8673
0.01	0.0100	0.36	0.3769	0.71	0.8872
0.02	0.0200	0.37	0.3884	0.72	0.9076
0.03	0.0300	0.38	0.4001	0.73	0.9287
0.04	0.0400	0.39	0.4118	0.74	0.9505
0.05	0.0500	0.40	0.4236	0.75	0.9730
0.06	0.0601	0.41	0.4356	0.76	0.9962
0.07	0.0701	0.42	0.4477	0.77	1.0203
0.08	0.0802	0.43	0.4599	0.78	1.0454
0.09	0.0902	0.44	0.4722	0.79	1.0714
0.10	0.1003	0.45	0.4847	0.80	1.0986
0.11	0.1104	0.46	0.4973	0.81	1.1270
0.12	0.1206	0.47	0.5101	0.82	1.1568
0.13	0.1307	0.48	0.5230	0.83	1.1881
0.14	0.1409	0.49	0.5361	0.84	1.2212
0.15	0.1511	0.50	0.5493	0.85	1.2562
0.16	0.1614	0.51	0.5627	0.86	1.2933
0.17	0.1717	0.52	0.5763	0.87	1.3331
0.18	0.1820	0.53	0.5901	0.88	1.3758
0.19	0.1923	0.54	0.6042	0.89	1.4219
0.20	0.2027	0.55	0.6184	0.90	1.4722
0.21	0.2132	0.56	0.6328	0.91	1.5275
0.22	0.2237	0.57	0.6475	0.92	1.5890
0.23	0.2342	0.58	0.6625	0.93	1.6584
0.24	0.2448	0.59	0.6777	0.94	1.7380
0.25	0.2554	0.60	0.6931	0.95	1.8318
0.26	0.2661	0.61	0.7089	0.96	1.9459
0.27	0.2769	0.62	0.7250	0.961	1.9588
0.28	0.2877	0.63	0.7414	0.962	1.9721
0.29	0.2986	0.64	0.7582	0.963	1.9857
0.30	0.3095	0.65	0.7753	0.964	1.9996
0.31	0.3205	0.66	0.7928	0.965	2.0139
0.32	0.3316	0.67	0.8107	0.966	2.0287
0.33	0.3428	0.68	0.8291	0.967	2.0439
0.34	0.3541	0.69	0.8480	0.968	2.0595

r or ρ	z_r or z_ρ	r or ρ	z_r or z_ρ	r or ρ	z_r or z_ρ
0.969	2.0756	0.979	2.2729	0.989	2.5987
0.970	2.0923	0.980	2.2976	0.990	2.6467
0.971	2.1095	0.981	2.3235	0.991	2.6996
0.972	2.1273	0.982	2.3507	0.992	2.7587
0.973	2.1457	0.983	2.3796	0.993	2.8257
0.974	2.1649	0.984	2.4101	0.994	2.9031
0.975	2.1847	0.985	2.4427	0.995	2.9945
0.976	2.2054	0.986	2.4774	0.996	3.1063
0.977	2.2269	0.987	2.5147	0.997	3.2504
0.978	2.2494	0.988	2.5550	0.998	3.4534

† Reproduced with permission from D. B. Owen, "Handbook of Statistical Tables," Addison-Wesley Publishing Company, Inc., Reading, Mass., 1962.

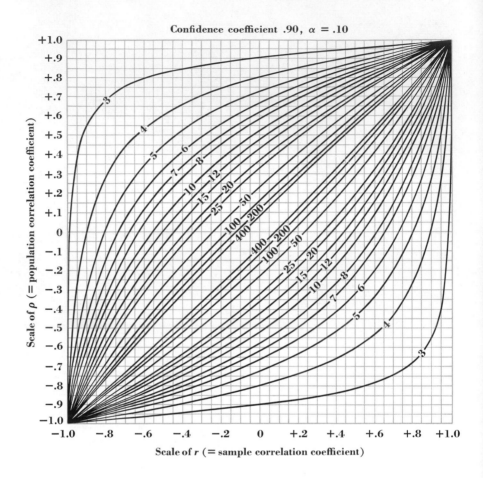

Confidence coefficient .90, $\alpha = .10$

Scale of ρ (= population correlation coefficient)

Scale of r (= sample correlation coefficient)

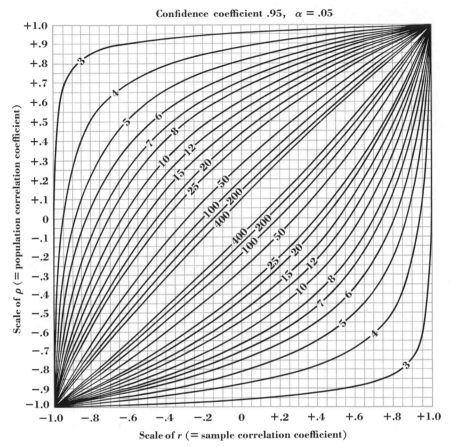

Confidence coefficient .95, $\alpha = .05$

Scale of ρ (= population correlation coefficient)

Scale of r (= sample correlation coefficient)

† Reproduced with permission from F. N. David, "Tables of the Ordinates and Probability Integral of the Distribution of the Correlation Coefficient in Small Samples," *Biometrika*, London, 1938.

ANSWERS TO EXERCISES

1-1 The sample space consists of eight points which can be labeled HHH, HHT, HTH, HTT, THH, THT, TTH, TTT. The weight $\frac{1}{8}$ for each point is reasonable. Three of the points correspond to obtaining two heads. Thus, the probability that two out of three times the result is heads is $\frac{3}{8}$.

1-3 Letting W denote white and R red, we can denote the six points of the sample space by W, W, W, W, R, R. The weight $\frac{1}{6}$ for each point is reasonable. The sum of the weights associated with red balls is $\frac{2}{6}$.

1-5 The sample space consists of 36 points. Letting the first number denote the result of the first throw, the second number the result of the second, we get the pairs appearing in Table 3-3. It is reasonable to assign a weight of $\frac{1}{36}$ to each point. The sum 7 is associated with six points (all lying on one diagonal). Hence, the probability of rolling a seven is $\frac{6}{36}$.

1-7 The three points of the sample space can be designated by A, B, C, the letters corresponding to the sprinters' winning. The best weights we can assign are .60, .30, .10. The probability that A loses is $.30 + .10 = .40$.

1-9 The sample space is W, Y, R, G, B, where the letter denotes the color. The weights are respectively $\frac{8}{20}$, $\frac{5}{20}$, $\frac{3}{20}$, $\frac{3}{20}$, $\frac{1}{20}$. The probability that the selected can is red, white, or blue is $\frac{3}{20} + \frac{8}{20} + \frac{1}{20} = \frac{12}{20}$.

1-11 $\frac{3}{8}$

1-13 $\frac{8}{663}$

1-15 $(\frac{5}{6})^3(\frac{1}{6}) = \frac{125}{1296}$

1-17 $1 - (\frac{1}{2})(\frac{1}{3})(\frac{1}{4}) = \frac{23}{24}$

1-29 Let x = number of heads

1-19 Use of formulas (1-6) yields .70.

1-21 $5! = 120$, $3 \cdot 2 \cdot 3 \cdot 2 \cdot \frac{1}{120} = \frac{3}{10}$

1-23 6720, 56

1-25 1,584

1-27 50,400

x	0	1	2
$f(x)$	$\frac{1}{4}$	$\frac{2}{4}$	$\frac{1}{4}$

$$E(x) = 0(\tfrac{1}{4}) + 1(\tfrac{2}{4}) + 2(\tfrac{1}{4}) = 1$$

1-31

x	2	3	4	5	6	7	8	9	10	11	12
$f(x)$	$\frac{1}{36}$	$\frac{2}{36}$	$\frac{3}{36}$	$\frac{4}{36}$	$\frac{5}{36}$	$\frac{6}{36}$	$\frac{5}{36}$	$\frac{4}{36}$	$\frac{3}{36}$	$\frac{2}{36}$	$\frac{1}{36}$

r	2	3	4	5	6	7	8	9	10	11	12
$F(r)$	$\frac{1}{36}$	$\frac{3}{36}$	$\frac{6}{36}$	$\frac{10}{36}$	$\frac{15}{36}$	$\frac{21}{36}$	$\frac{26}{36}$	$\frac{30}{36}$	$\frac{33}{36}$	$\frac{35}{36}$	1

$E(x) = 7$

1-33 $-\$\frac{1}{18} = -\$.056$

1-35   1.25

1-37   1

2-1   .13230, .16308. Since some players appear to hit in streaks, one might doubt that p remains constant and successive trials are independent.

2-3   .00163. One is apt to doubt the claim.

2-5   .07257, .03268. Perhaps one should improve with practice, so that p may change from trial to trial. In addition, successive trials may not be independent, since a thrower may tend to follow a poor result by another poor result.

2-7   .12560. Since cloudy weather may be associated with fronts lasting several days, there is real doubt that the independence condition is satisfied.

2-9 $\Pr(x \geq 29) = .00004$ if $p = .30$ for the new cure. Consequently, it is reasonable to believe that the new cure is better.

2-11   .92867

2-13   .05095. The probability of a success would change slightly from trial to trial, and successive trials would be dependent. However, with a large group this will not seriously invalidate the negative binomial model. Whether or not one believes the 40 per cent figure depends upon how the probability .05095 is regarded.

2-15   .96875

2-17 $\frac{5!}{1!1!3!}(.5)(.3)(.2)^3 = .024$, .05792. Probabilities associated with the three categories will change slightly from selection to selection, and successive draws will be dependent. However, with a large number of students neither of these objections is serious.

2-19   Begin in column 47 of row 100. Sample consists of items 38, 5, 7, 78, 52, 2, 55, 62, 67, 8 (go to column 49, row 70, for last 7 numbers).

2-21   .476190

2-23 $\sum_{x=7}^{10} \binom{20}{x}\binom{80}{10-x} \Big/ \binom{100}{10}$ Since the probability is so small, one is apt to conclude that the box contains more than 20 frozen oranges.

2-25   .38404

2-27   .00345. With $\mu = 10$, it is quite unlikely that the number of flats will be 20 or more.

2-29   .60653

2-31   (a) 2.326, (b) 1.282, (c) -1.96, (d) -1.645

2-33   .77 (.78 with improved approximation)

2-35   (a) 2.528, (b) -1.753, (c) 0

2-37   (a) 29.71, (b) 76.15

2-39   (a) .100, (b) 5.64, (c) 1.00

3-1 $\bar{x} = 48.4$, $s^2 = 1099.2$, $s = 33.2$, $\tilde{x} = 50$

3-3 $\frac{35}{12} = 2.92$, 1.71

3-5 1, 1

3-7 $\bar{x} = .7, s^2 = .678$

3-9 .9545, .0027

3-11 The sample space consists of the nine pairs (1,1), (1,2), (1,3), (2,1), (2,2), (2,3), (3,1), (3,2), (3,3). The probability distribution of $\bar{x}$ is

$\bar{x}$	1.0	1.5	2.0	2.5	3.0
$f(\bar{x})$	$\frac{1}{9}$	$\frac{2}{9}$	$\frac{3}{9}$	$\frac{2}{9}$	$\frac{1}{9}$

$E(x) = E(\bar{x}) = 2.0, \sigma_x^2 = \frac{2}{3}, \sigma_{\bar{x}}^2 = \frac{1}{3}$.

3-13 The probability is approximately $\Pr(Z < -5)$, or practically zero. It is unlikely that the claim would be accepted.

3-15 The probability distribution of s^2 is

s^2	0	.5	2.0
$f(s^2)$	$\frac{3}{9}$	$\frac{4}{9}$	$\frac{2}{9}$

and $E(s^2) = \frac{2}{3} = \sigma_x^2$.

3-17 (a) x takes on values 1, 2, 3, 4 with probabilities .4, .3, .2, .1 respectively. $E(x) = 1, \sigma^2 = 1$. (b) $\bar{x}$ takes on values 1, 1.5, 2, 2.5, 3, 3.5, 4 with probabilities .16, .24, .25, .20, .10, .04, .01 respectively. (c) s^2 takes on values 0, .5, 2, 4.5 with probabilities .30, .40, .22, .08 respectively.

4-1 .21996, .43890, .65935, .92643, .99268. The power is decreased and β is increased for all $p < .90$.

4-3 .982, .804, .346, .05. The power is increased and β is decreased for all $\mu < 30$.

4-5 .912, .639, .263, .10, .263, .639, .912. The power is increased (except when $\mu = 46$) and β is decreased.

4-7 The critical region is $x \leq 18$ with $\alpha = .00948$. We reject $H_0: p = .90$.

5-1 The observed $Z = -1.7$, and $H_0: \mu = 12$ is accepted when tested against $H_1: \mu \neq 12$.

5-3 Test $H_0: \mu = 67$ against $H_1: \mu \neq 67$, a reasonable choice to make before looking at the results. The observed $Z = 2$. If $\alpha = .05$, the claim is justified. If $\alpha = .01$, it is not. One might question the randomness assumption.

5-5 $\delta = 2$. Since $\alpha = .05$ and the test is two-sided, use graph labeled $\alpha = .025$. Then power = .52. For a power of .99, $\delta = 4.3$ and $n \cong 116$.

5-7 $\delta = 3.2$ and power = .81.

5-9 (66.14,73.86). The interval includes 67, and $H_0: \mu = 67$ is accepted if $\alpha = .01$. $n = 373$.

5-10 The observed value of the statistic is $t_{24} = 2$. Accept $H_0: \mu = 12$.

5-11 $\delta = 2.5$. Entering the graph labeled $\alpha = .025$ yields power = .67. Using $f = \infty$, power = .99 if $\delta = 4.3$. Thus an approximate n is obtained by solving $\sqrt{n}/2 = 4.3$, giving $n = 74$. (The actual value is 76.)

5-12 (11.99,12.49). The test accepts $H_0: \mu = 12$, and the interval includes $\mu = 12$.

5-13 $\Pr(s^2/\sigma^2 < .825) = .29$ (the graphs of Appendix D-11 yield .30). $n = 45$ raises the probability to .99.

344

5-18   Test H_0: $\mu = 30$ against H_1: $\mu \neq 30$, the reasonable choice in the absence of further information. The observed value of the statistic is $t_8 = 2$. Hence, H_0 is accepted.

5-20 $k = (.12228)^2 = .01495$, $n \geq (.01495)(90.2)^2 = 121.63$. Thus $n = 122$. The observed value of the statistic is $t_{19} = 3.68$ and H_0 is rejected.

5-21 $k = (.08372)^2 = .007009$, $n \geq (.007009)(90.2)^2 = 57.02$. Thus $n = 58$. The interval is (960,1010).

5-24   Test H_0: $\sigma^2 \leq .25$ against H_1: $\sigma^2 > .25$. The observed value of the statistic is $\chi_{24}^2 = 34.56$. Accept H_0.

5-25   Use Appendix D-12. We get .40 when $\sigma = .60$, .87 when $\sigma = .75$.

5-26   Use Appendix D-12. $\nu = 34$, $n = 35$.

5-27   (.47,.83)

5-28 $\Pr(s^2/\sigma^2 < 1.32) = .86$. (This can also be approximated from Appendix D-13.) $n = 26$.

5-33   Test H_0: $\sigma_1^2 = \sigma_2^2$ against H_1: $\sigma_1^2 < \sigma_2^2$. The observed value of the statistic is $F_{40,40} = .650$. Accept H_0 and use method 2.

5-34   Approximately .72 using Appendix D-14. When $R_0 = .5$, the power is .996 using either Appendix D-14 or formula (5-58).

5-35   .86 and .987 by using Appendix D-14.

5-36   (.59,1.10)

5-41   Test H_0: $\sigma_1^2 = \sigma_2^2$ against H_1: $\sigma_1^2 \neq \sigma_2^2$. The observed value of the statistic is $F_{60,120} = .444$. Reject H_0 even with $\alpha = .001$.

5-43   Test H_0: $\mu_1 = \mu_2$ against H_1: $\mu_1 \neq \mu_2$. The observed value of the statistic is $t_{62} = -3.6$. Reject H_0 even with $\alpha = .001$.

5-44 $\delta = 4$. Entering the graph of Appendix D-10 labeled $\alpha = .005$ and interpolating between $f = 24$ and $f = \infty$ yields power $= .90$.

5-45 $(-4.7, -.7)$. The interval does not include 0, and H_0: $\mu_1 = \mu_2$ is rejected.

5-49   Test H_0: $\mu_1 = \mu_2$ against H_1: $\mu_1 \neq \mu_2$. $s_p = 9.33$, and the observed value of the statistic is $t_{98} = 2.06$. We reject H_0 and conclude that method 1 produces a higher average.

5-50   Test H_0: $\mu_d = 0$ against H_1: $\mu_d \neq 0$. The observed value of the statistic is $t_7 = 1.46$, and H_0 is accepted.

5-51 $\delta = 2.83$. Enter the graph of Appendix D-10 headed by $\alpha = .025$ with $f = 7$ and read power $= .66$. With $n = 25$, $\delta = 5$ and power is slightly over .997.

5-52 $(-2.72,11.47)$

6-1   Test H_0: $p = .90$ against H_1: $p < .90$, where p is the fraction of seeds which will germinate. With $p = .90$, $\Pr(x \leq 40) = .02454$, $\Pr(x \leq 41) = .05787$. Hence, the critical region is $x \leq 40$ with $\alpha = .02454$. We could also test H_0: $p = .10$ against H_1: $p > .10$ regarding p as the fraction of seeds which will not germinate. With $p = .10$, $\Pr(x \geq 10) = .02454$, $\Pr(x \geq 11) = .05787$, and the critical region is $x \geq 10$ with $\alpha = .02454$. With either formulation accept H_0 and do not reject the company's claim.

6-2   The power is .83632 if $p = .75$ and .99924 if $p = .60$.

6-3   (.71,.93) for the proportion which will germinate or (.07,.29) for the proportion which will not.

6-7   The negative binomial model with $c = 6$ is appropriate. Since $N = 51$, $\dot{p} = \frac{5}{50} = .10$.

6-9   Test H_0: $p = .30$ against H_1: $p > .30$. The critical region is $x \geq 24$ with $\alpha = .00569$. Hence, H_0 is rejected and the new cure is recommended. $\Pr(x \geq 29) = .00004$.

6-10 Test H_0: $\mu = 1$ against H_1: $\mu > 1$. The critical region is $y \geqq 10$. The significance level is $\alpha = \Pr(y \geqq 10) = .03183$ computed with $\mu = 5$. $\Pr(y \geqq 13) = .00202$, so that H_0 is rejected.

6-11 The power is $\Pr(y \geqq 10)$ computed with $\mu = 5(1.6) = 8$. This yields .28338. If the mean is 2, then the same calculation with $\mu = 5(2) = 10$ yields .54207.

6-12 $(1.38, 4.45)$

6-16 The observed value of the statistic is $Z' = -2$. Thus H_0: $p = .90$ is rejected in favor of H_1: $p < .90$.

6-17 The power is $\Pr(Z < .97) = .83$. To raise this to .90, n would have to be approximately 2,070.

6-18 $(.102, .128)$

6-22 As in Exercise 6-10, test H_0: $\mu = 1$ against H_1: $\mu > 1$. The observed value of the statistic is $Z' = 1.8$. Hence, H_0 is rejected.

6-24 $(.98, 1.26)$

6-25 The observed value of the statistic is $\chi_6'^2 = 8.2$, so that the hypothesis is not contradicted.

6-27 The observed value of the statistic is $\chi_3'^2 = 4.44$. The hypothesis is not contradicted at any reasonable significance level.

6-29 $\bar{x} = 2$. The expected frequencies are respectively 33.534, 27.067, 27.067, 18.044, 9.023, 5.265 (for five or more). $\chi_4'^2 = 3.31 + .95 + 4.53 + .00 + 3.69 + .10 = 12.58$. Since $\chi_{4;.95}^2 = 9.49$, reject the hypothesis that the Poisson model is correct.

6-31 We test the hypothesis of homogeneity. The expected numbers are 60 for each cell in the first column, 100 for each cell in the second, 40 for each cell in the third. We get $\chi_6'^2 = 79.0$. Since the probability of obtaining a value of the statistic this large or larger is practically zero, H_0 is rejected.

6-33 We test the hypothesis of independence. The expected frequencies are 80, 160, 120, 40 for the first column, 20, 40, 30, 10 for the second, 60, 120, 90, 30 for the third, and 40, 80, 60, 20 for the fourth. These yield $\chi_9'^2 = .31 + .31 + .53 + .90 + .45 + .40 + .53 + .90 + .27 + .53 + 1.34 + 7.50 + .40 + .31 + 3.75 + 28.80 = 47.23$. We conclude that there is a relationship between smoking and drinking habits, probably because heavy smokers are heavy drinkers.

7-1 $$\sum_{j=1}^{r} \sum_{i=1}^{n_j} (x_{ij} - \bar{x}_{.j})(\bar{x}_{.j} - \bar{x}_{..}) = \sum_{j=1}^{r} (\bar{x}_{.j} - \bar{x}_{..}) \sum_{i=1}^{n_j} (x_{ij} - \bar{x}_{.j})$$

For every j we have $\sum_{i=1}^{n_j} (x_{ij} - \bar{x}_{.j}) = \sum_{i=1}^{n_j} x_{ij} - n_j \bar{x}_{.j}$. Since $\bar{x}_{.j} = \sum_{i=1}^{n_j} x_{ij}/n_j$ by definition, $\sum_{i=1}^{n_j} x_{ij} = n_j \bar{x}_{.j}$. Consequently, for every j $\sum_{i=1}^{n_j} x_{ij} - n_j \bar{x}_{.j} = n_j \bar{x}_{.j} - n_j \bar{x}_{.j} = 0$ and the original double sum is equal to $\sum_{j=1}^{r} (\bar{x}_{.j} - \bar{x}_{..})(0)$ $= 0$.

7-2 $SS_A = 1,877$, $SS_W = 4,753$, and the observed value of the statistic is $F_{2,30} = 5.94^{**}$. Reject H_0.

7-5 $\nu_1 = 2$, $\nu_2 = 30$. Let $\mu_1 = \mu_2$, $\mu_3 = \mu_1 + 1.2\sigma$. Then $\phi = 1.88$ and power $\cong .80$.

7-7 $\nu_1 = 2$, $\nu_2 = 30$, $\phi = 1.62$ yields power $\cong .66$.

7-8 $\bar{x}_{.1} = 100.5$, $\bar{x}_{.2} = 111.4$, $\bar{x}_{.3} = 93.0$, $MS_W = 158.4$, $S = 2.58$.   The intervals are $-24.8 \leqq \mu_1 - \mu_2 \leqq 3.0$, $-6.4 \leqq \mu_1 - \mu_3 \leqq 21.4$, $4.5 \leqq \mu_2 - \mu_3 \leqq 32.3$, $-27.6 \leqq 2\mu_1 - \mu_2 - \mu_3 \leqq 20.8$, $-53.5 \leqq \mu_1 - 2\mu_2 + \mu_3 \leqq -5.1$, $1.7 \leqq \mu_1 + \mu_2 - 2\mu_3 \leqq 50.1$.   Consequently, we conclude (a) the mean of population 2 is higher than the mean for population 3, (b) the mean for population 2 is higher than the average of the means for populations 1 and 3, (c) the mean for population 3 is lower than the average of the means for populations 1 and 2.

7-10 $MS_A = 8,500$, $MS_W = 500$, $S = 3.89$.   The estimate of the contrast comparing averages for A and B is -300 with $\hat{\sigma}^2_{\hat{L}} = 1,500$.   Thus, $S\hat{\sigma}_{\hat{L}} = 150$ and -300 ± 150 does not cover 0.   Hence we conclude that the average for textbook B is higher than the average for textbook A.   To compare professors, obtain the interval for $\mu_2 + \mu_3 - \mu_4 - \mu_5$.   The estimate of the latter contrast is -10 with $\hat{\sigma}^2_{\hat{L}} = 200$.   Thus, $S\hat{\sigma}_{\hat{L}} = 55.1$ and -10 ± 55.1 does cover 0.   Hence the data have failed to demonstrate a difference in the average examination grades associated with the two professors.

7-11   The observed value of the statistic is $R_{8,4} = .527$.   Accept H_0 with either $\alpha = .05$ or $\alpha = .01$.

8-1   (a) $\hat{\mu}_{y|x} = -.5 + x$, (b) 2.5, (c) .16, (d) .40

8-3   The observed value of the statistic is $t_{40} = -4.20$, which is significant even with $\alpha = .0005$.   Thus, it is almost a certainty that the average college grade point is less than 2.0 for those students whose high school average is 2.0.

8-5 $\delta = 3.36$, $f = 40$.   Using $\alpha = .05$, Appendix D-10 gives a power slightly over .95.

8-7 $\delta = 1.96$, $f = 40$.   If $\alpha = .05$, we enter Appendix D-10 with $\alpha = .025$ and find that the power is approximately .49.

8-9   We get $\Pr(t_{40} > .245)$, which is just slightly more than .40.

8-11   The observed value of the statistic is $\chi^2_{40} = 25.6$.   Since this is smaller than $\chi^2_{40;.05} = 26.51$, H_0 is rejected.

8-13   The observed value of the statistic is $t_{16} = 3.52$.   Hence H_0 is rejected not only with $\alpha = .05$ but also with $\alpha = .01$.   Preliminary calculations yield $\sum_{i=1}^{18} x_i = 733$, $\sum_{i=1}^{18} x_i^2 = 31,717$, $\sum_{i=1}^{18} y_i = 776$, $\sum_{i=1}^{18} y_i^2 = 36,190$, $\sum_{i=1}^{18} x_i y_i = 33,084$, $r = .66$.

8-14 $r < -.47$ and $r > .47$.

8-15 $(.27, .85)$.   This interval does not include 0 and the test rejects H_0: $\rho = 0$.

Index